INDUSTRIAL
EFFLUENT TREATMENT

Volume 1

WATER AND SOLID WASTES

INDUSTRIAL EFFLUENT TREATMENT

Volume 1

WATER AND SOLID WASTES

Edited by

J.K. Walters and A. Wint

Department of Chemical Engineering,
University of Nottingham, UK

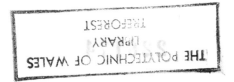

APPLIED SCIENCE PUBLISHERS LTD
LONDON

APPLIED SCIENCE PUBLISHERS LTD
RIPPLE ROAD, BARKING, ESSEX, ENGLAND

British Library Cataloguing in Publication Data

Industrial effluent treatment.
  Vol.1: Water and solid wastes
  1. Factory and trade waste
  I. Walters, J K   II. Wint, A
  628.5'4   TD897

  ISBN 0-85334-891-X

WITH 43 TABLES AND 77 ILLUSTRATIONS
© APPLIED SCIENCE PUBLISHERS LTD 1981

Photoset by Thomson Press (I) Limited, New Delhi
Printed in Great Britain by Galliard (Printers) Ltd. Great Yarmouth

Preface

The proper treatment and disposal of effluents and wastes has become an increasingly important aspect of the design and operation of all industrial plants. As industrial output rises, improvements are necessary in effluent treatment processes if the land, water and atmospheric environments are not to deteriorate. Benefits will accrue from recycling recovered materials and these will partially offset the increased costs associated with meeting tighter specifications on discharges. The costs of discharging waste water to sewers and of supplying fresh water have both risen sharply in recent years. Both were once relatively minor components in the overall costs of many industrial plants, but they have now become significant factors in determining economic success.

Over the past six years the Department of Chemical Engineering in the University of Nottingham has given a series of one-week courses, approved by the Institution of Chemical Engineers, on pollution control for engineers and scientists in positions of responsibility for environmental matters in industry and commerce. The present Volume is based on lectures given during these courses on Water Pollution and Solid Waste treatment. Volume 2 covers the fields of Air Pollution and Industrial Noise Control.

The first half of the book covers the legal constraints within which the process designer must work. Chapters 2 and 3 discuss the approach taken by the water authorities in controlling discharges to sewers and water-courses, while details of the law and the penalties for non-compliance are discussed in the appendix. Chapter 4 considers the role of dissolved oxygen in a watercourse and how it is affected by discharges and Chapter 5 covers the effects on aquatic life of various pollutants. Chapters 6, 7 and 8 discuss physical, chemical and biological processes for the treatment of effluents and they are followed by two Case Studies in Chapter 9. The final two chapters cover the problem of the disposal of toxic materials and the incineration and pyrolysis of wastes.

We would like to thank our co-authors for the time and effort they have put into their chapters. Our thanks are due also to Mrs Jackie Carlin and Miss Sue Close who cheerfully typed our own sections of the manuscript. Any faults, errors and omissions remain the responsibility of the editors.

J.K. WALTERS
A. WINT

Contents

List of Contributors

W.A. ALLEN
Assistant Divisional Scientist, Soar Division, Severn–Trent Water Authority, Leicester Water Centre, Gorse Hill, Anstey, Leicestershire LE7 7GU, UK.

B. J. BORNE
Formerly Head, Industrial Wastes Section, Water Research Centre, Stevenage Laboratory, Elder Way, Stevenage, Hertfordshire SG1 1TH, UK.

J.G. CHILDS
Principal Trade Effluent Officer, Lower Trent Division, Severn–Trent Water Authority, Mapperley Hall, Lucknow Avenue, Nottingham NG3 5BN, UK.

R.W. GRAFTON
Safety and Environment Officer, The Boots Company Ltd, Nottingham NG2 3AA, UK.

J.H. HILLS
Lecturer, Department of Chemical Engineering, University of Nottingham, University Park, Nottingham NG7 2RD, UK.

D.M. HOLDICH
Lecturer, Department of Zoology, University of Nottingham, University Park, Nottingham NG7 2RD, UK.

G.D. KELSEY
Chief Engineer, Process Engineering, NEI International Combustion Ltd, Sinfin Lane, Derby DE2 9GJ, UK.

J.C. MECKLENBURGH
Senior Lecturer, Department of Chemical Engineering, University of Nottingham, University Park, Nottingham NG7 2RD, UK.

P.W.H. MOON
Division Environmental Adviser, ICI Petrochemicals Division, PO Box 90, Wilton, Middlesbrough, Cleveland TS6 8JE, UK.

V.J. SHRUBSALL
Lecturer, Department of Law, University of Nottingham, University Park, Nottingham NG7 2RD, UK.

J.K. WALTERS
   *Senior Lecturer, Department of Chemical Engineering, University of
   Nottingham, University Park, Nottingham NG7 2RD, UK.*
A. WINT
   *Lecturer, Department of Chemical Engineering, University of
   Nottingham, University Park, Nottingham NG7 2RD, UK.*

1

Water Resources: Perspective and Effects

J.K. WALTERS

Senior Lecturer in Chemical Engineering, University of Nottingham, UK

1.1. INTRODUCTION

The aims of the process industries are to produce final products and intermediates from raw materials dug from the earth or taken from water or air. Inevitably there are waste products to be disposed of and if these are of no use they must be returned to the air, water or land environment. Such return should be carried out in such a way as to minimise any adverse effects on the environment[24].

That there are social and political problems as well as the economic and technical ones of pollution control was recognised in the UK in 1970 with the appointment of the Royal Commission on Environmental Pollution and the central government reorganisation to form the Department of the Environment. The Commission has since presented six reports[15 – 20]. In the decade since 1970 both industry and the public generally have become increasingly aware of the need to reduce the quantity and improve the quality of effluent discharges and significant improvements have been made. The three principal forms of pollution are very closely linked and, while it may be possible to reduce (say) an air pollution problem by wet scrubbing of the gases, the resulting aqueous effluent may produce a water pollution problem that is more harmful to the environment than the original air pollution. Unfortunately there is no body with *overall* responsibility for pollution control. At present it is part of the job of the process design engineer to assess the overall effects and produce a design that is least harmful to the environment. It is certainly less costly to consider the full environmental impact at the design stage than to complete the plant and *then* consider cleaning up the waste streams. Of course the uprating of existing plants to meet more stringent emission criteria still has to be done

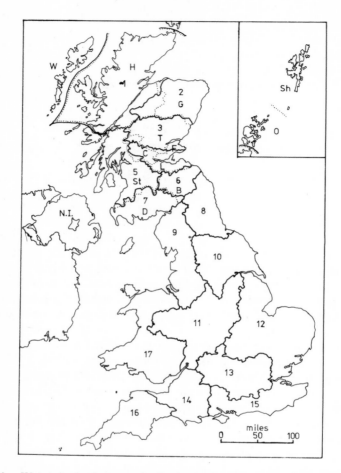

FIG. 1.1—Water Authority areas in England and Wales and River Purification Board areas in Scotland: 1 Highland; 2 North East; 3 Tay; 4 Forth; 5 Clyde; 6 Tweed; 7 Solway; 8 Northumbrian; 9 North West; 10 Yorkshire; 11 Severn–Trent; 12 Anglian; 13 Thames; 14 Wessex; 15 Southern; 16 South West; 17 Welsh Water Authority.

. . . . Regional and Island Authorities in Scotland: B Borders; C Central; D Dumfries and Galloway; F Fife; G Grampian; H Highland; L Lothian; O Orkney; Sh Shetland; St Strathclyde; T Tayside; W Western Isles. Modified from *Water Data* 1975[9].

but there is no longer any excuse for the designer to ignore the waste streams. Control over aqueous emissions to sewers and water courses and the management of water supply is the responsibility of the Water Authorities in England and Wales and the Department of the Environment (Northern Ireland) in Northern Ireland. In Scotland the water supply and sewage treatment are the responsibility of the Regional Authorities and the control of pollution is the responsibility of the River Purification Boards. Figure 1.1 shows these areas in the UK.[9]

1.2. WATER USAGE—THE HYDROLOGICAL CYCLE

Let us first consider the availability of water. The total amount of water on earth has been estimated to be about 10^9 km^3,[25] of which 97% is ocean and only 3%, or 3×10^7 km^3, is fresh water. Of this fresh water[11] three quarters is locked up as ice in the polar regions and in glaciers and a further 14% is groundwater at depths too deep to be readily available. At reasonable depths 11% is groundwater, some of which is withdrawn from boreholes, but only about 0.06% of the fresh water is readily available as lakes and rivers and it is just these waters that receive the majority of the world's wastes in the form of sewage and trade effluents. It is little wonder that ecologists, conservationists and the intelligent public are concerned.

Water vapour present in the atmosphere amounts to about 10 000 km^3 at any one time and with a residence time in the atmosphere of about 50 days, the average daily precipitation over land is about 200 km^3 per day. About 0.2% of this falls on the UK and gives an average precipitation of about 3 mm of rain per day when averaged over the total area of the UK (244 000 km^2). Of that about half comes from transpiration of vegetation and evaporation from the land mass and the other half from evaporation from the sea. The water cycle for the UK is shown in Fig. 1.2 which is based on Downing[10] and the most recent (1975) data available from the Water Data Unit[9]. For comparison the projected utilisation of water for 1980 in the USA is shown in Fig. 1.3 with numerical values based on Dugan[11]. It is interesting to note that the domestic and industrial water abstraction is about the same percentage (8 to 9%) of the total stream flow in the USA as in the UK. The main differences are in the relative amounts of domestic and industrial water—industry is a much greater user in the USA—and in power station cooling where the USA uses a much lower proportion because air cooling can be used in many locations.

The abstraction of 18×10^6 m^3/day in the UK is close to the potential

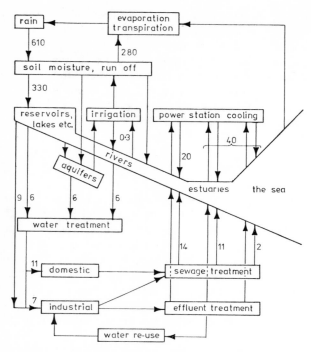

FIG. 1.2. Water usage in the UK in millions of m^3 per day. Modified from Downing[10].

maximum of $20 \times 10^6 \; m^3/day$ that can be handled by existing pumping and treatment plants[9]. It therefore represents almost complete utilisation of the readily available sources and one of the main problems for the future is likely to be the provision of new supplies over the next 20 years to meet the expected doubling of demand by the year 2000 which was predicted in the first report[15] of the Royal Commission on Environmental Pollution. However, a more recent report from the Water Data Unit[9] indicates that there has been very little change in demand in the period 1970–75, so the earlier forecast is likely to be an overestimate, although any prolonged drought will still have a big effect. The 1976 drought caused widespread restrictions on surface water supplies, although ground water supplies were hardly affected. Increased supplies can come from long-term projects to build more reservoirs or in the short term from greater abstractions from rivers. Rivers, of course, receive all the effluents from treated sewage and

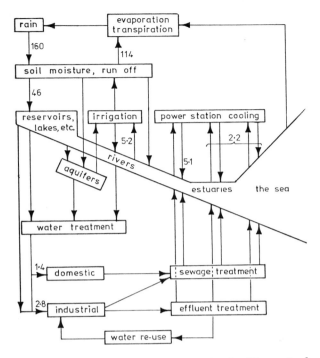

FIG. 1.3. Water usage in the USA in hundreds of millions of m³ per day.

some industrial discharges, so it is necessary to improve the quantity of such discharges to enable increased abstractions to be made.

1.3. WATER POLLUTION AND EFFLUENT QUALITY CRITERIA

Pollution is a relative effect and waters which may be considered polluted by one user may be accepted as quite satisfactory by another. It is thus very difficult to give a precise definition of pollution and the generally accepted approach is to consider the use to which the waters are to be put. Klein[14] quotes Coulson and Forbes' 'The Law of Waters'[2] where pollution is defined as *the addition of something to water which changes its natural qualities so that the riparian proprietor does not get the natural water of the stream transmitted to him.* The addition is not qualified and natural occurrences are not excluded. More recently pollution has been restricted to changes brought about by man's activities. Fish[12] in 1970 included this point in his definition and also spelt out the changes with which we are concerned: *Water resources are said to be polluted when, because of man's actions in adding or causing the addition of matter to the water or in altering its temperature, the physical, chemical or biological characteristics of the water are changed to such an extent that its utility for any reasonable purpose, or its environmental value, is demonstrably depreciated.*

The main point is clearly that, if the water is no longer suitable for the purpose to which it was originally put, then it is polluted. Another point is that there is no *absolute* definition of pollution—it is a *relative* matter. In some places, notably California[14], a distinction is made between 'contamination' and 'pollution'. 'Contamination' is regarded as an impairment of water quality leading to an immediate health hazard, whereas 'pollution' is impairment without an immediate health hazard. Such a distinction is obviously useful, but there is no uniform agreement on such definitions and the two terms are often used interchangeably.

Since the nature of the receiving water is vital in the definition of pollution, it is useful to relate effluent quality to the effects it produces on the receiving stream. The existing discharge standard of 30 mg/litre suspended solids and 20 mg/litre biochemical oxygen demand (BOD)* was set in 1912[21] and has stood the test of time for over 60 years, but more stringent emission criteria may be needed if we are to satisfy the expected increase in demand for water. 'Dilution is the solution to pollution' goes

TABLE 1.1
SUMMARY OF EFFLUENT CATEGORIES. MAXIMUM CONCENTRATIONS IN mg/litre

Category	A	B	C	D
Suspended solids	30	10	2	1
BOD	20	10	2	1
Ammoniacal nitrogen		10	5	1
Soluble organic carbon			5	2
Phosphorus			0.5	0.5
Total toxic heavy metals			0.5	0.1
Nitrate nitrogen				10
Pathogens				0

* BOD is defined in a later chapter but may be considered here as a measure of the biodegradable organic materials present in the discharge.

against all the principles of separation processes and will be disastrous if more abstractions are to be made from rivers. Downing[10] has considered the 30:20 standard mentioned above and has suggested three other categories with more stringent requirements. These four categories are summarised in Table 1.1 and will now be considered in more detail.

1.3.1. Category A. The 30:20 Standard

This is the Royal Commission[21] standard and such effluent would produce offensive conditions only if present in a concentration greater than 1 part in 8 parts of river water. It may produce significant reduction in the dissolved oxygen content of the river and may change the appearance, but should not produce any serious risk to fish, which are sensitive indicators of pollution. Such effluent is normally obtained from conventional sewage works using sedimentation tanks and percolating filters or activated sludge treatment. It may contain nitrates and phosphates which may lead to excessive growths of algae. It is not suitable for direct re-use.

1.3.2. Category B. The 10:10:10 Standard

This imposes tighter limits on suspended solids and BOD and imposes a limit on ammonia in the discharge. This effluent is usually obtained by further treatment of the 30:20 effluent by processes such as sand filtration, lagooning or irrigation on grass plots. It has little effect on a river unless there are other constituents present which are toxic. Nitrates and phosphates would again stimulate algal growth if present. Such effluent would not be suitable for direct re-use but could be used for cooling.

1.3.3. Category C. The 2:2:5:5:0.5:0.5 Standard

This effluent is usually obtained by further treatment of the 10:10:10 effluent by processes used in the treatment of water for public supply, such as coagulation, sterilisation, softening and adsorption on activated carbon. In addition to tighter limits on suspended solids, BOD, and ammonia, limits are imposed on soluble organic carbon, phosphorus and toxic heavy metals. Such effluent would have no significant effect on a river and would be suitable for direct re-use as reclaimed water by many industries. It would not be suitable for potable purposes.

1.3.4. Category D. The 1:1:1:2:0.5:0.1:10:0 Standard

This effluent is reclaimed water possibly of potable quality, although it may still need some form of partial desalination especially if used in a 'closed-loop' system. In addition to tighter limits on the six parameters of Category

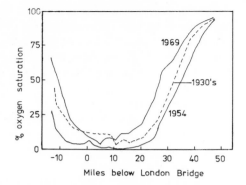

FIG. 1.4. Dissolved oxygen concentrations in the River Thames in London. From the Royal Commission on Environmental Pollution 1st Report[15].

C a limit is imposed on nitrate and the water must be free of pathogens.

At present most sewage works discharges are of Category A standard, but Downing[10] estimates that Category C may become quite a common requirement for discharge to rivers over the next 50 years. Another reason for an improvement in standards is the increasing abstraction from rivers leaving less clean river water available for the dilution of the discharges. As an example we may consider the fresh water lengths of the Thames and its tributaries above Teddington Weir; the discharge of sewage and trade effluent is about 1.1×10^6 m^3/day and the natural dry weather flow is about the same, giving a total flow of about 2.2×10^6 m^3/day. Of this about 1.3×10^6 m^3/day is abstracted to supply two thirds of London's water supply. To obtain this high utilisation of water more than half the effluent discharged to the fresh water reaches of the Thames already conforms to a much better standard than the 30:20 Royal Commission standard referred to above. In spite of heavy discharges the Thames is one of the cleanest rivers, because it is historically the main supply for London. The tidal reaches of the Thames are also showing an improvement since the mid 1950s when there was virtually no dissolved oxygen ten miles below London Bridge as can be seen from Fig. 1.4. This is also a good example of the 'oxygen sag curve' which will be considered in detail in Chapter 4.

1.4. RIVER QUALITY AND DISCHARGES TO RIVERS

The River Pollution Surveys of England and Wales[4−8] and of Scotland[22] define four classes of river quality based on the BOD of the river water and the dissolved oxygen content, ranging from the 'unpolluted' which is class 1, through 'doubtful' and 'poor' to 'polluted' which is class 4. These are summarised in Table 1.2. More recently these classes have been more closely defined with class 1 effectively being divided into 1A and 1B and the definitions of classes 2, 3 and 4 being adjusted to agree with the EEC

TABLE 1.2
SUMMARY OF CHEMICAL CLASSIFICATION OF RIVER QUALITY

Class	Average BOD	Oxygen saturation	Toxic materials	River life
1. Unpolluted	< 3 mg/litre	close to 100%	absent	Trout, salmon diverse invertebrate fauna microorganisms sparse
2. Doubtful	3–8 mg/litre	50–100%	may be present but no effects	Mixed coarse fisheries restricted invertebrate fauna microorganisms in larger numbers
3. Poor	8–12 mg/litre	< 50%	present at times	Moderate to poor fisheries macroscopic fauna restricted microorganisms present
4. Polluted	> 12 mg/litre	< 50%	present	No fish invertebrate fauna absent or nearly so microorganisms abundant

categories for the quality of surface waters intended for abstraction for drinking water. This will be discussed in more detail in Chapter 3. The biological implications will be included in the discussion in Chapter 5.

Streams with flows greater than 4500 m^3/day (1 million gallons/day) were included in the River Pollution Surveys and classified according to length. This could be misleading because an upstream stretch of a given length, having a much lower volumetric flow, carries the same statistical weight as a downstream stretch of the same length with a much higher volumetric flow. The total volume of polluted water cannot therefore be deduced from data on polluted lengths, but with this reservation the

J.K. Walters

TABLE 1.3

MILEAGES BY CHEMICAL CLASSIFICATION, NON-TIDAL RIVERS, ENGLAND AND WALES

Chemical classification	1958 miles	%	1970 miles	%	1972 miles	%	1975 miles	%
1. Unpolluted	14 603	72.9	17 000	76.2	17 279	77.4	17 422	77.6
2. Doubtful	2 865	14.3	3 290	14.7	3 267	14.7	3 392	15.1
3. Poor	1 279	6.4	1 071	4.8	939	4.2	900	4.0
4. Polluted	1 278	6.4	952	4.3	832	3.7	732	3.3
	20 025	100.0	22 313	100.0	22 317	100.0	22 446	100.0

TABLE 1.4

MILEAGES BY CHEMICAL CLASSIFICATION, TIDAL RIVERS, ENGLAND AND WALES

Chemical classification	1958 miles	%	1970 miles	%	1972 miles	%	1975 miles	%
1. Unpolluted	720	40.7	862	48.1	880	49.4	884	49.6
2. Doubtful	580	32.8	419	23.4	414	23.2	447	25.1
3. Poor	250	14.1	301	16.8	253	14.2	263	14.8
4. Polluted	220	12.4	209	11.7	236	13.2	187	10.5
	1 770	100.0	1 791	100.0	1 783	100.0	1 781	100.0

TABLE 1.5

MILEAGES BY CHEMICAL CLASSIFICATION, CANALS, ENGLAND AND WALES

Chemical classification	1958 miles	%	1970 miles	%	1972 miles	%	1975 miles	%
1. Unpolluted	900	58.8	700	45.4	706	45.7	760	50.7
2. Doubtful	380	24.9	601	39.1	614	39.7	575	38.3
3. Poor	130	8.5	136	8.8	147	9.5	110	7.3
4. Polluted	120	7.8	103	6.7	78	5.1	55	3.7
	1 530	100.0	1 540	100.0	1 545	100.0	1 500	100.0

statistics taken from the Surveys[3-8] and shown in Tables 1.3 to 1.6 indicate a general improvement over the last two decades in spite of an increase of approximately 13% in the discharge of treated sewage effluent between 1970 and 1975. The details of discharges of both sewage and industrial effluent in England and Wales are given in Table 1.7 and for Scotland in Table 1.8. Only about 28% by volume of the treated sewage was considered

TABLE 1.6
MILEAGES BY CHEMICAL CLASSIFICATION, SCOTLAND, 1968

Chemical classification	Non-tidal miles	Non-tidal %	Tidal miles	Tidal %
1. Unpolluted	2 394	80.2	124	63.7
2. Doubtful	394	13.2	36	18.5
3. Poor	107	3.6	17	8.7
4. Polluted	91	3.0	18	9.2
	2 986	100.0	195	100.0

TABLE 1.7
DISCHARGES TO WATERCOURSES IN ENGLAND AND WALES ($10^3 m^3$/day)

Discharge		Non-tidal	Tidal	Canals	Total
Treated sewage†	1970	7 160	2 900	83	10 143
	1975	7 817	3 558	57	11 432
Crude sewage†	1970	6	1 194	0	1 200
Industrial effluent					
in treated sewage	1970	1 360	405	25	1 790
	1975	1 440‡	480‡	20‡	1 940
in crude sewage	1970	0	346	0	346
direct discharge	1970	4 850	5 790	137	10 777
	1975	4 605	5 367	144	10 116
Cooling water	1970	21 300	40 000	858	62 158
	1975	18 086	40 586	771	59 443

†DWF—dry weather flows.
‡Estimated breakdown; the total is correct.

TABLE 1.8
DISCHARGES TO RIVERS IN SCOTLAND

Discharge	Non-tidal	Tidal	Canals	Total
Industrial effluent direct discharge ($10^3 m^3$/day)	527	228	—	755
Cooling water and mine and pit water ($10^3 m^3$/day)	2 035	11 140	—	13 175

J.K. Walters

TABLE 1.9

INDUSTRIAL DISCHARGES BY INDUSTRY $(10^3 m^3/day)$

Industry	Industrial effluent excl. cooling water	% Satis- factory	Cooling Water	% Satis- factory
Brewing	17	44	12	100
Brick making	10	98	1	100
Cement making	30	93	13	100
Chemical, etc.	1 869	15	1 153	65
Coal mining	148	69	15	98
Ethanol distillation	0	—	< 1	100
Electricity generation	2 870	99	57 600	98
Engineering	111	43	494	98
Food processing	348	49	414	77
Gas and coke	154	62	148	91
Glass making	8	33	17	86
Glue and gelatine	17	0	24	62
General manufacturing	65	69	30	92
Iron and steel	703	39	403	56
Laundering, dry cleaning	2	38	4	100
Leather tanning	8	0	2	100
Metal smelting	64	57	115	96
Paint making	7	88	1	97
Paper and board making	1 050	13	776	100
Petroleum refining	2 080	99	696	30
Plastics manufacture	2	33	13	88
Plating and metal finishing	30	39	6	83
Pottery making	1	39	< 1	100
Printing ink, etc.	2	100	1	100
Quarrying and mining	610	50	2	100
Rubber processing	21	47	89	99
Soap and detergent	40	8	19	49
Textile, cotton and man made	261	17	78	100
Textile, wool	21	16	7	100
General farming	16	61	< 1	100
Atomic energy establishments	9	100	0	—
Water treatment	182	86	17	100
Disposal tip drainage	21	33	0	—
Mine waters	938	—	—	—
TOTAL	11 715		82 150	

'satisfactory' by the River Authority in whose area the discharge was made in 1970, whereas 62% was considered 'satisfactory' by the Water Authorities in 1975. It is this improvement in sewage treatment that has made the improvement in river quality possible. By 'satisfactory' is meant that the discharge complied with the Consent conditions laid down by the River or Water Authority concerned. In wet weather the sewage discharge rates may be many times the Dry Weather Flow (DWF) and crude sewage may be discharged through storm overflows at treatment plants. Industrial effluents, while being subject to seasonal variations in some industries, are not subject to significant variations in storm conditions.

1.5. TYPES AND SOURCES OF INDUSTRIAL EFFLUENTS

The Confederation of British Industry (CBI) undertook a supplementary survey at the same time as the River Pollution Survey and the results were published in Volume 2 of the Survey in 1972.[3] Details of the discharges from different industries are summarised in Table 1.9. A discharge was considered satisfactory by the River Authority if it met the Consent conditions. Most of the cooling water discharges were satisfactory, but some of the other process effluents were very unsatisfactory. The chief offenders with less than 20% of their effluent in a satisfactory state were chemicals; glue and gelatine; leather tanning; paper and board making; soap and detergents; and textiles. Apart from chemicals, the common factor among these industries is that they process natural products. Their effluents are therefore likely to have very high BODs and thus impose heavy loads on sewage works or receiving waters, although they are not intrinsically difficult to treat nor likely to contain toxic materials. The two industries with the largest discharges are electricity generation and petroleum refining and both have very good records. The remaining industries have small to moderate discharges and are moderately satisfactory.

1.6. DISCHARGES TO ESTUARIES AND COASTAL WATERS

A total of nine estuaries and stretches of coastal water were included in the River Pollution Survey, and details were given in Volume 3 of the Report[6]. Three of those nine, the Humber, the Severn Estuary and Swansea Bay receive the most industrial effluent discharges and crude sewage discharges. The other six receive only small discharges and those are mostly crude

TABLE 1.10
SUMMARY OF ESTUARY AND COASTAL WATERS

Discharge	The Humber	Severn Estuary	Swansea Bay	Other six†	Total
Treated sewage					
No. of discharges	5	2	—	4	11
DWF ($10^3 m^3$/day)	5	2	—	1	8
% DWF satisfactory	83	100	—	39	78
Crude sewage					
No. of discharges	8	10	3	54	75
DWF ($10^3 m^3$/day)	171	213	41	89	514
% DWF satisfactory	32	81	14	27	50
Industrial Effluent (excluding cooling water)					
No. of discharges	12	3	4	4	23
DWF ($10^3 m^3$/day)	165	42	211	8	426
% DWF satisfactory	97	25	1	17	40

†The Wash, the Solent, Bristol Channel (Somerset), Menai Strait, Morecombe Bay and the Solway Firth.

sewage. Details are summarised in Table 1.10. The industrial discharges into the Humber are mostly satisfactory, but those into Swansea Bay are very bad with only 1% of the flow being in a satisfactory state. On the other hand, crude sewage discharges to the Humber are poor, but those to the Severn Estuary are reasonably satisfactory. Treated sewage discharges are small and are not a problem.

1.7 TYPES OF POLLUTION

Pollution arises from the presence of materials that are foreign to the body of water being considered. They may be toxic in themselves or they may be biodegradable and give rise to a high oxygen demand and thus deplete the water of oxygen. Physical effects such as colour or turbidity or the presence of foam are also caused by the presence of foreign materials which may be present in very small amounts although giving rise to very large physical effects. Temperature is the only physical effect not associated with the presence of materials. Eight classes of pollution are discussed briefly in the following sections and comments made on their effects on aquatic life. More detailed discussion will be given in later chapters.

1.7.1. Organic Materials

The presence of organic materials depletes the dissolved oxygen content of water courses and can create unpleasant tastes and odours. Severe organic loading can produce completely anaerobic conditions. The main sources are industries treating natural products such as food processing, canning, slaughterhouses, dairies, tanneries, glue making and the pulp and paper industries. If the water course is well oxygenated, aerobic bacteria will oxidise the organic material in 'self-purification' processes which release carbon dioxide, water and ammonia leaving the remainder as an insoluble 'humus', a dark brown complex organic material containing C, H, O and N, which is very resistant to microbial degradation[14] and which becomes part of the river bed. If the loading is so great that the dissolved oxygen is exhausted, anaerobic bacteria which use combined oxygen from inorganic sources such as nitrates, sulphates and phosphates can break down the organic material. Such breakdown gives rise to putrid odours from organic amines and hydrogen sulphide. Lack of oxygen stifles most aquatic life. There is great variation from species to species, but a dissolved oxygen level of 3 to 4 ppm is desirable to support fish. Many organic substances are toxic to fish and may be present in effluents from chemical plants, plating works and other industries. There are too many compounds to list in detail, but some of the more common ones of concern to the Water Authorities are phenols, cyanides and chlorinated hydrocarbons. A measure of the (non-toxic) organic loading is the BOD and the Royal Commission[21] recommended limit for discharges is 20 mg/litre as mentioned before.

1.7.2. Inorganic Materials

Salts are nearly always present and cause the 'hardness' of water. Hard water can cause deposition of scale in pipes and can affect some industries notably brewing and canning, which have a large water content in their product. The total absence of salt gives tasteless water, so the degree of hardness is important. Chloride is fatal to fresh water fish if present in concentrations greater than about 400 ppm. Iron can produce brown stains of hydroxide precipitate which would affect textile and paper manufacture. Nitrogen and phosphorous induce the growth of algae, which are usually microscopic in fresh water but may be very large in salt water, e.g. seaweed, and in addition phosphates affect coagulation and sedimentation processes. Alkalis, as for example from industries producing soap, textiles, rubber or leather, cause embrittlement of pipes and seriously affect flocculation in water treatment plants. Acids cause corrosion of metals and concrete and can be fatal to fish. A pH of between 4.5 and 9.5 is required for fish to survive. Many inorganic compounds are toxic, some of the commonest being free chlorine, chloramines, ammonia, sulphides and heavy metal ions, such as copper, lead, zinc, nickel, chromium, cadmium and mercury. Any appreciable amounts of these materials will hinder the self-purification of a river. Copper is particularly toxic in quantities as small as 0.1–0.5 ppm and a concentration of 1–2 ppm of copper was quoted by Klein[14] as having completely killed all animal life for over 10 miles with sewage fungus rare and algae extremely rare.

1.7.3. Colour

Colour is produced by the preferential absorption and reflection of different wavelengths of light and is mainly due to organic dyes, some inorganic compounds of chromium and iron, slaughterhouse wastes and pulp and paper wastes. In many cases the coloured material is present in such small quantities that there is insignificant pollutional load. However colour is unsightly and it does affect transmission of sunlight and hence photosynthesis. Colour is measured in Hazen units on the platinum-cobalt standard in which the solution is compared with mixtures of chloroplatinic acid and cobalt chloride. Details may be found in *Approved Methods*[1] and *Standard Methods*[23] and are briefly discussed by Holden.[13]

1.7.4. Turbidity

Turbidity is caused by the presence of colloidal or very finely divided solids which will not settle in sedimentation tanks. Such particles have very large specific surface areas and are electrically charged, usually negatively, and require ions of opposite charge for neutralisation and subsequent coagulation. The degree of turbidity is often closely allied to the intensity of pollution and is often used as an approximate measure of pollution. There is unfortunately no specific definition of turbidity. A number of ways have been suggested for measuring turbidity and they can be classified into four types: comparison with suspensions of known concentration, light extinction, light transmission and light scattering. Comparisons between different instruments remain difficult and largely unresolved.[13]

1.7.5. Temperature

The main sources of heated effluents are cooling water discharges and the main effects are stratification and a lowering of the dissolved oxygen content. The dissolved oxygen content is lower partly because oxygen is less soluble at higher temperatures and partly because bacterial activity is enhanced so the BOD is greater. Fish can normally withstand slow changes of temperature, but are susceptible to rapid changes. There is an upper limit to temperature above which a fish will die. It depends on the species and for trout the lethal limit is 25°C.

1.7.6. Suspended Solids

Suspended matter has a larger particle size than the colloidal material that gives rise to turbidity and can be separated by simple settling in lagoons or sedimentation tanks. If they are allowed to reach a watercourse, the particles will settle on the river bed and increase the benthic BOD or interfere with self-purification by smothering the benthic organisms. Excessive solids can harm fish and seriously interfere with photosynthesis by preventing sunlight being transmitted through the water. Suspended solids were recognised by the Royal Commission in 1912[21] as being important and their recommended limit for a discharge was 30 mg/litre as discussed before.

1.7.7. Floating Material

Foams, oils, greases, etc, that float on the surface reduce sunlight transmission and hence reduce photosynthesis, reaeration and the dissolved oxygen content of the river. In addition they are unsightly and an aesthetic nuisance.

1.7.8. Biological Effects

Viruses are all parasitic. They lack the normal metabolic functions and lie on the border between living organisms and chemical compounds. They are agents of disease and are commonly found in sewage effluents and are difficult to remove because they are so small and so resistant to normal disinfection. Bacteria are single-cell organisms whose vital processes involve oxidising organic material either using dissolved oxygen (aerobic bacteria) or by using combined oxygen (anaerobic bacteria). They are nearly all sensitive to pH, preferring neutral conditions, and to temperature, there being an optimum growth temperature for each type. Fungi are aerobic unicellular or multicellular plants which obtain their energy from breaking down organic molecules. They are present in biological treatment plants and often give rise to tastes and odours. Algae are unicellular or multicellular plants which use sunlight for the photosynthesis of new organic material from carbon dioxide, nitrogen compounds and phosphates. They produce oxygen and so react synergistically with bacteria, fungi and animals which consume oxygen and produce carbon dioxide and nitrogen compounds. Algae have characteristic colours — blue-green,

green, yellow-green—and require phosphorus for growth. They are, however, able to store far more phosphorus than they need for growth and this is returned to the water when the algae die. The phosphorus (mainly from detergents) thus accumulates and contributes to eutrophication, especially in lakes. Animals utilize organic food only and require oxygen. They feed on other animals or plant life. The lowest forms are protozoa which are single cells some 10–100 microns long. They feed mainly on bacteria. The simplest multi-cellular animals are rotifers, worms and larvae, which are important scavengers.

The overall effects of a heavy non-toxic pollution load at an outfall are discussed in detail in Chapter 5. The dissolved oxygen decreases rapidly, but recovers downstream as the BOD diminishes. Bacteria are numerous at the outfall and then gradually decline. Algae decline slightly, increase greatly and then return to their original level. Protozoa appear some distance from the outfall, multiply rapidly and then die away. Higher animals follow the protozoa in like manner further downstream, until eventually the original fresh water fauna return well downstream. Toxic materials would, of course, have a drastic effect on all forms of aquatic life.

REFERENCES

1. *Approved Methods for the Physical and Chemical Examination of Water*, 3rd edition. Inst. of Water Engrs, 1960.
2. Coulson and Forbes, in *The Law of Waters and Land Drainage*, 6th edition. (ed. S.R. Hobday), Sweet and Maxwell, London, 1952.
3. Department of Environment, *Report of a River Pollution Survey of England and Wales*, 1970. HMSO, London, Vol. 1, 1971; Vol. 2, 1972.
4. Department of Environment, *Ibid*, Updated 1972, *River Quality*. HMSO, London, 1972.
5. Department of Environment, *Ibid*, Updated 1972. *Discharges of Sewage and Industrial Effluent*. HMSO, London, 1973.
6. Department of Environment, *Ibid*, 1973, Vol. 3. HMSO, London, 1974.
7. Department of Environment, *Ibid*, Updated 1973. HMSO, London, 1975.
8. Department of Environment, *Ibid*, Updated 1975. HMSO, London, 1978.
9. Department of Environment, *Water Data* 1975, HMSO, London, 1977.
10. Downing, A.L., Chemical Engineering and the Hydrological Cycle, *The Chemical Engineer*, No. 260 (April 1972) 150.
11. Dugan, P.R., *Biochemical Ecology of Water Pollution*. Plenum Press, London, 1972.
12. Fish, H., Water pollution, *Royal Inst. of Chem. Review*, **3** (October 1970) 105.
13. Holden, W.S. (ed.), *Water Treatment and Examination*. J. and A. Churchill, London, 1970.

14. Klein, L., *River Pollution*, Vol. 2. *Causes and Effects*: Butterworths, London, 1962.
15. Royal Commission on Environmental Pollution, 1*st Report*, Cmnd 4585. HMSO, London, 1971.
16. *Ibid*, 2*nd Report*, Cmnd 4894. HMSO, London, 1972.
17. *Ibid*, 3*rd Report*, Cmnd 5054, HMSO, London, 1972.
18. *Ibid*, 4*th Report*, Cmnd 5780. HMSO, London, 1974.
19. *Ibid*, 5*th Report*, Cmnd 6371. HMSO, London, 1976.
20. *Ibid*, 6*th Report*, Cmnd 6618. HMSO, London, 1976.
21. Royal Commission on Sewage Disposal, 1901–1915, 8*th Report*. HMSO, London, 1912.
22. Scottish Development Department, *Towards Cleaner Water — Report of a Rivers Pollution Survey of Scotland*. HMSO, London, 1972.
23. *Standard Methods for the Examination of Water and Wastewater*, 14th edition, Am. Pub. Health Assoc., New York, 1975.
24. Walters, J.K. and Wint, A., Process design and the environment, *The Chemical Engineer.*, No. 315 (Nov/Dec 1976) 751.
25. Wollman, A., *Water Resources*. Publication No. 100-B. National Academy of Sciences, National Research Council, Washington DC, 1962.

2

Discharge of Trade Effluent to Public Sewers

J.G. CHILDS

Principal Trade Effluent Officer, Lower Trent Division, Severn– Trent Water Authority, Nottingham, UK

2.1. INTRODUCTION

When firms, which need to dispose of a trade effluent, are located in urban areas, the usual method of disposal is to discharge the effluent to the public sewerage system. This method of disposal is generally considered to be the best way of dealing with trade effluents, a view endorsed by the Jeger Report *Taken for Granted*.[1] Over the years many effluents which were previously discharged direct to watercourses have been diverted to the public sewerage system as a result of pressure from the various authorities that have in the past been responsible for the control of river pollution.

This option, however, may not be readily available to firms located in rural areas where a public sewerage system has not been provided, or where sufficient capacity, either for conveyance and/or treatment, does not exist. At a small sewage works, trade effluent from just one factory may constitute a substantial increase in the flow and load to that works. It may not be possible to accept such an effluent without incurring heavy expenditure on sewerage and extensions at the treatment works. The financing arrangements for such work may prove difficult and under such circumstances the only practical option may be to discharge the effluent direct to a watercourse or to land (e.g. by a spray irrigation scheme). If a discharge is made to a watercourse then the firm will have to comply with any conditions imposed by the Water Authority, conditions much more stringent than if the effluent were to be accepted into the public sewerage system. To meet such Consent conditions a complete effluent treatment plant may be required.

Industrial effluent discharged to the public sewerage system is treated at the sewage works as a mixture with domestic sewage. There are usually

21

advantages to the trader in disposing of his effluent in this way, for example:

(1) Most firms will only wish to install the minimum of plant for effluent treatment; provision of a complete effluent treatment plant is expensive and expert staff are required to operate it. Industry generally would prefer to carry out only the pretreatment necessary to allow the effluent to be discharged to the public sewerage system, leaving the bulk of the treatment to be performed by the Water Authority at the sewage treatment works.

(2) Large sewage treatment works should have an 'economy of scale' and the treatment costs should be lower than if the trade effluent were treated on its own. To an extent this is lost when charges made for treatment are equalised over a large area, as is done by most Water Authorities. Nevertheless, trade effluent charges made by the Water Authorities should, in most cases, compare favourably with the costs incurred in operating a private effluent treatment plant.

(3) Biological treatment is usually the cheapest method of effluent treatment available, but certain industrial wastes require the addition of nutrients if they are to be treated by such a system. Mixing the waste with domestic sewage will generally provide all the necessary nutrients to allow such treatment to be used. Dilution with domestic sewage may also reduce any inhibitory effects the effluent might possess, possibly allowing the use of a biological system when alternative methods might otherwise be required.

(4) Most traders are reassured to know that a sewage works stands between them and the river. In the event of an accidental discharge or plant failure, the domestic sewage may act as a buffer and after passing through the sewage works the impact on the river should be greatly reduced. There have, however, been instances where such an incident has completely destroyed the biological activity at the sewage works and it has taken some considerable time for the works to recover. During this period the works may continue to discharge an unsatisfactory effluent. It is most important, therefore, that all accidental discharges are reported to the appropriate authority so that action may be taken to minimise any possible effects. It must be stressed that an accidental discharge could result in prosecution by the Water Authority, although there will be less likelihood of such a prosecution if a firm has cooperated fully with the Authority in dealing with the incident.

Prior to the formation of the Water Authorities in England and Wales, the control over discharges to public sewers was exercised by Local Authorities. The larger authorities generally controlled trade discharges effectively and recovered costs through some form of trade effluent charging scheme. There were many authorities, however, which neither controlled nor made any charges. Where charges were made, these varied greatly from one area to another. Whilst the charges made by Water Authorities will obviously vary, the differences encountered in the past will not be as great and the approach adopted in controlling the discharges will be more uniform.

2.2. OBJECTIVES OF TRADE EFFLUENT CONTROL

The objectives of trade effluent control have been outlined in the recommended guidelines issued by a joint CBI/RWA Working Party in February 1976. In summary their objectives are:

(i) to protect the sewerage system, the sewage treatment works and the personnel employed therein,

(ii) to ensure that the mixed sewage can be effectively and economically treated by the processes employed at the sewage treatment works,

(iii) to ensure that the products of that treatment, in the form of effluents or residues, have no unacceptable effects on water resources and the environment,

(iv) to ensure that if, in times of storm, storm sewage reaches a river via a storm overflow, its quality will be acceptable under those conditions,

(v) to provide data upon which the design of future sewage treatment works can be based,

(vi) to ensure that the trader pays a fair charge for the reception, conveyance, treatment and disposal of his effluent.

Although there have been large increases in trade effluent charges following the formation of the Water Authorities, it must be stressed that the recovery of costs via the charging system is not the chief objective of any trade effluent control scheme. The most important aspect is that of preventing problems occurring in the sewerage system and with any of the treatment processes employed.

2.3. SUMMARY OF LEGISLATION

Legislation controlling the discharge of effluents to public sewers has been in force in England and Wales for many years with a progressive tightening of the legislation with successive Acts. The Control of Pollution Act 1974 is the latest of these Acts and this will bring about certain changes which have been thought necessary for a number of years. Similar control exists in Scotland, the most important Act being the Sewerage (Scotland) Act 1968 which came into force on 16th May 1973.

Acts which control or have controlled the discharge of trade effluents to public sewers are:

Public Health Act 1875
Rivers Pollution Prevention Act 1876
Public Health Act 1936
Public Health (Drainage of Trade Premises) Act 1937
Public Health Act 1961
Water Act 1973
Control of Pollution Act 1974
Burgh Police (Scotland) Act 1892
Sewerage (Scotland) Act 1968

Much of the early legislation has now been repealed by the later Acts. Certain of the above Acts apply only in England and Wales whilst others are restricted to Scotland. The summary which follows is one which refers essentially to the effect of the legislation in England and Wales.

The Public Health Act 1875 established the right of any owner or occupier of premises within the district of a Local Authority to 'cause his drains to empty into the sewers of that Authority'. There was no control over the quality or quantity of effluent to be discharged but certain regulations could be enforced and the owner had to give notice of intention. This right to discharge was preserved until the 1936 Act came into force. The 1936 Act prohibited the discharge of effluent from trade premises to public sewers other than domestic sewage or surface or storm water. However, the right to discharge was quickly re-established by the Public Health (Drainage of Trade Premises) Act 1937, which came into force in July 1938.

The 1937 Act re-established the right to discharge subject to a certain procedure being followed involving the serving of a Trade Effluent Notice and obtaining the Consent of the Authority. Only new discharges were required to have a Consent — those firms discharging effluents of a similar nature and no greater volume than discharged on any day within a period of one year ended on 3rd March 1937 were exempt. These discharges were usually referred to as 'prescriptive right discharges'.

The 1937 Act also allowed by-laws to be made, enabling amongst other things, charges to be levied. So far as the writer is aware, no by-laws were made and generally no charges levied, most Local Authorities taking the view that it was unfair to charge for new effluents whilst those with 'prescriptive rights' could not be charged.

This Act also gave exemption to certain other traders. Laundries were exempt as were those traders with agreements made between them and the Local Authority before the passing of the Act and which, in many cases, could not be terminated.

The next change came with the passing of the Public Health Act 1961. Briefly, this allowed a certain amount of control to be exercised over 'prescriptive right discharges', including the making of charges. This was carried out by the issue of a Direction by the Authority. Also, the provision for making the by-laws under the 1937 Act was repealed and the requirements which could be specified in such by-laws were included in the 1961 Act (Section 59) as conditions which could be attached to Consents. The rights enjoyed by firms for discharges made under the terms of pre-1937 agreements were, to the disappointment of many Local Authorities, upheld.

Thus charges could be made for pre- and post-1937 discharges, with the exception of those with old agreements in which no charges were specified. It was after this Act came into force that many Local Authorities began to make charges for trade effluent disposal. The legislation was also extended to allow farms, places used for scientific research and, under certain circumstances, laundries, to be controlled and charged.

The Water Act 1973 established Water Authorities and these took over their duties on 1st April 1974. All the duties and powers of Local Authorities referred to in the above legislation with regard to the discharge of effluents to public sewers are now with these new authorities. This Act also removed the exemption given to laundries and most have now been brought under control.

The latest Act, the Control of Pollution Act 1974, will eventually enable almost all discharges to public sewers to be brought under full control. Firms with 'prescriptive right discharges' and those made under the terms of pre-1937 agreements should have given notice to the Water Authority for their area by 31st January 1975. Those firms which have given notice have now been granted a 'deemed Consent'. The 'appointed day' referred to in Section 43 of the 1974 Act was 19th July 1976. Water Authorities may now give 'actual Consents' to these firms in which appropriate Consent conditions may be specified. Such Consents may therefore remove any 'prescriptive rights' thus allowing full control over the effluents discharged.

A few anomalies will still exist. Agreements made after the commencement of the 1937 Act are not covered by the 1974 Act. Any such agreement made after July 1938 therefore and which does not provide for termination cannot be changed under this legislation.

Section 109(2) of the 1974 Act allows the commencement of the various sections to be phased and this power has been used by the Department of the Environment to introduce the Act in stages.

2.4. OBTAINING A 'CONSENT TO DISCHARGE'

Under existing legislation any trader who wishes to discharge a trade effluent which is new or materially altered since 1937 must obtain the Consent of the Water Authority. To obtain such a Consent a certain procedure must be followed which is described as follows.

A trader wishing to discharge a new or modified effluent must serve a 'Trade Effluent Notice' on the Water Authority. This notice is a requirement of the Public Health (Drainage of Trade Premises) Act 1937, Section 2. The notice must be served two months before any discharge is made and must give the following information in respect of the proposed discharge:

   (i) the nature or composition of the trade effluent,
  (ii) the maximum quantity of trade effluent it is proposed to discharge on any one day,
 (iii) the highest rate at which it is proposed to discharge trade effluent.

Provided that this information is given, the notice can be in the form of a letter to the Authority. However, most Authorities have standard forms available for this purpose and will supply these on request.

Unless the Authority agrees in writing, no discharge may commence until a period of two months has elapsed after the serving of the notice and only then if Consent is given. This period is called the 'initial period' and during this time the Authority must decide which of several courses of action it is to follow; this is discussed in more detail later.

It is obviously in the interests of both trader and Authority that for large or 'difficult' trade effluents, negotiations about acceptance of the waste commence as soon as possible. For large discharges this may be two to four years before discharge is due to commence. Acceptance of large volumes and/or loads may involve the relaying of sewers, provision of pre-treatment plant, extensions to the Sewage Works, etc. The trader will need to know the limits which will be imposed and the charges to be made when deciding how best to dispose of any effluent. Thus there may be many items which require to be resolved before Consent is given, items which may well need more than two months to resolve.

Where firms do not make a direct approach to the Water Authority, potential discharges may be located when planning permission is sought since there is consultation between Planning Authorities and Water Authorities. Generally it is the smaller discharges which are located in this way; firms who propose to make large discharges are usually aware of the need for early discussion.

Those firms that had 'prescriptive rights' and which were previously controlled by a Direction given under Sections 55 and 57 of the 1961 Act should have given notice to the Water Authorities as explained earlier. These firms have now been granted a 'deemed Consent' which will ultimately be replaced with an 'actual Consent.'

2.5. ACTION TAKEN BY WATER AUTHORITY ON RECEIPT OF A TRADE EFFLUENT NOTICE

On receiving a Trade Effluent Notice the Water Authority has a period of two months (the 'initial period') during which it may decide on one of four courses of action:

(i) Consent to discharge may be granted unconditionally.

(ii) Consent to discharge may be granted with certain conditions specified,

(iii) Consent to discharge may be refused,

(iv) A direction may be issued that no trade effluent be discharged until a specified date after the end of the initial period.

Provided traders who wish to dispose of effluents which could be a problem discuss acceptance long before the notice is served, the need to refuse or delay the issue of the Consent can usually be avoided.

If a trader considers that the Consent conditions are unreasonable or Consent has been refused, then the trader has the right of appeal to the Secretary of State for the Environment. If a Water Authority fails to give Consent within the 'initial period,' it cannot be assumed that Consent is deemed approved. An offence is committed in discharging without Consent even if Consent has not been granted because of some failure on the part of the Authority. In such a case the trader again has a right of appeal and if Consent is not forthcoming then the correct course of action would be for the trader to lodge such an appeal. Appeals made against Consent conditions are not restricted to any specific period after the issue of the Consent. However, when Consent conditions are later changed by Notice of Direction, appeal against the new conditions must be made within the period of two months after the giving of the Notice of Direction.

In dealing with the acceptance of a trade effluent to a public sewer, the following will require consideration:

(i) whether or not the receiving Works has sufficient treatment capacity,

(ii) whether the effluent will cause any problems in the sewerage system,

(iii) whether the effluent will contain substances toxic or inhibitory to the purification processes or such as to affect the disposal of sludges on agricultural land,

(iv) whether the effluent will contain intractable substances which will affect the quality of the receiving watercourse (e.g. pesticides).

These points will be considered therefore when deciding whether or not an effluent can be accepted and the conditions to be specified in the Consent.

2.6. CONDITIONS ATTACHED TO CONSENTS TO DISCHARGE

Under Section 2(3) of the Public Health (Drainage of Trade Premises) Act 1937 and Section 59(1) of the Public Health Act 1961 conditions may be attached to Consents with respect to the following:

(i) the sewer or sewers into which the discharge is to be made,

(ii) the nature or composition of the trade effluent,

(iii) the maximum quantity of trade effluent which may be discharged on any one day,

(iv) the highest hourly rate of discharge,

(v) the period or periods of the day during which discharge may be made,

(vi) the elimination or reduction in concentration of any specified constituent (see Section 59(1) (c) of the 1961 Act),

(vii) the temperature of the trade effluent at the time of discharge to the sewer,

(viii) the payment of charges for the reception and treatment of the effluent,

(ix) the provision and maintenance of an inspection chamber to enable samples to be taken,

(x) the provision and maintenance of meters for measuring the volume and rate of discharge,

(xi) the provision and maintenance of apparatus for analysing the effluent,

(xii) the keeping of certain records of meter readings, etc.,

(xiii) the making of returns and giving of information to the Authority concerning the volume, rate of discharge, etc.

Certain conditions are often standard conditions; others will vary according to the nature and volume of the effluent to be discharged, the dilution available, the type of Works receiving the effluent and the quality required in the receiving watercourse.

For administrative ease it would be advantageous to standardise quality conditions and in certain instances this is possible. However, it is the local conditions which dictate the permissible levels of certain constituents. Amongst other things, consideration will be given to the following in setting quality conditions:

(a) the dilution available in the sewerage system,

(b) the atmosphere in the sewers,

(c) the fabric of the sewers,

(d) the type of treatment processes employed at the receiving works,

(e) the fate of the various constituents at the works,

(f) any toxic or inhibitory effects of the constituents,

(g) any build up of toxic materials in sludges, especially where those sludges are disposed of on agricultural land,

(h) any harmful effects caused by residues which pass to the receiving watercourse.

A logical and scientific approach to the setting of quality conditions is given in a Technical Report TR 17 published by the Water Research Centre.[2]

One quality condition which may be specified in the Consent is the oxygen demand of the effluent. This is most important where the effluent constitutes an appreciable proportion of the total load at a Works. The smaller the Works, the more likely it is to be overloaded by a variation in the trade effluent oxygen demand. A typical effluent which can cause this type of problem is that from poultry processing which is usually situated in a rural area and discharges to a small Works. Many effluents discharging to large Works have no limit placed on the oxygen demand.

In certain areas standard oxygen demand conditions have been applied but were often relaxed where circumstances allowed. It is the writer's opinion that where oxygen demand limits are to be imposed then each should be assessed individually according to the local conditions. In some cases oxygen demand may be limited in terms of load rather than concentration. This has the advantage of allowing the trader some flexibility in his effluent parameters. Where this is done, an upper limit for COD in terms of concentration may still be required to prevent slugs of concentrated liquor being discharged. Such slugs could give rise to shock loads on the receiving works and could cause problems. The use of load limits may well have certain advantages in controlling effluents but practical problems can arise from their use, therefore they may be viewed with some caution by Water Authorities. It may also be necessary in some cases to insist on a balanced flow to avoid shock loads. Again, this is usually of more importance when dealing with an effluent which is to be treated at a small Works.

Examples of some quality control conditions which have been specified for effluents passing into public sewers are:

   (i) suspended solids not to exceed 500 mg/litre,
  (ii) cyanide as CN^- not to exceed 5 mg/litre,
 (iii) pH to be not less than 5 nor greater than 10 (range 6–9 is commonly used in some areas),
 (iv) soluble salts of chromium, copper, zinc, cadmium, tin and lead not to exceed a total of 10 mg/litre expressed as the metals,
  (v) total of insoluble and soluble compounds of chromium, copper, nickel, zinc, cadmium, tin and lead not to exceed 30 mg/litre expressed as the metals, (an alternative method used for limiting metal concentration is to limit each metal individually, e.g. chromium as Cr not to exceed 5 mg/litre, etc.),
 (vi) sulphide as S not to exceed 5 mg/litre.

When a trade effluent may contain substances, the effect of which on the sewers, treatment works and/or receiving waters is unknown to the person or persons dealing with the Consent, certain investigations must be carried out. These may involve pilot plant studies, a literature search, use of the information service on toxicity and biodegradability (INSTAB) given by the Water Research Centre, Stevenage Laboratory, etc. A detailed case study is given in the next section.

Acceptance of the majority of effluents usually entails obtaining information on the chemical constituents, the maximum daily and hourly rates of flow, the oxidation and solids loads, etc. A decision may then be made as to whether or not the effluent can be discharged and under what conditions.

Where the effluent will be a significant proportion of the daily flow and load and, as in the case below, may contain a wide range of chemicals, a more detailed investigation may be required before acceptance of the effluent. It must be stressed however that this type of investigation is the exception rather than the rule.

2.7. CASE STUDY: ACCEPTANCE OF A LARGE VOLUME OF CHEMICAL/PHARMACEUTICAL EFFLUENT

A chemical firm wished to discharge $4500 \, m^3/day$ (1 000 000 gallons per day) of effluent to a sewage works treating a dry-weather flow of 150 000 m^3/day (33 000 000 gallons per day). The effluent was derived from the manufacture of a wide range of chemical and pharmaceutical products.

The design dry-weather flow of the treatment works was 159 000 m^3/day 35 000 000 gallons per day) and sufficient treatment capacity would be available to meet the oxygen demand of the effluent and for the treatment of the solids load because another major discharge was about to end. Treatment at the Works was by an activated-sludge plant with heated anaerobic sludge digestion and final disposal of digested sludge to agricultural land. Problems existed in accepting such a large volume into the sewerage system and this was resolved by the firm undertaking to relay a certain length at its own expense.

Samples of the effluent were available and a detailed analysis was carried out. Laboratory-scale activated-sludge plants were set up to treat the effluent as a mixture with settled sewage. The organisms in the activated sludge from these plants were examined to see if adding the effluent caused any changes in the numbers and types of these organisms. The quality of the effluent produced by these plants was also monitored. This investigation showed that the effluent could be treated in admixture with domestic sewage in an activated-sludge plant.

One problem with the effluent was that it had a high soluble sulphate concentration, 40 000 mg/litre being typical. Soluble sulphate at such a concentration will cause rapid corrosion to take place in concrete sewers and a pre-treatment plant on site would be necessary to reduce the sulphate concentration to an acceptable level. The firm engaged consultants to advise on such a pre-treatment plant for removal of sulphate and pH control.

Consent conditions were then drafted. Information had been requested from the Water Pollution Research Laboratory (now the Water Research

Centre, Stevenage Laboratory) as to the possible effects on the treatment processes and the receiving watercourse of certain chemicals likely to be in the effluent. This information assisted in the drafting of the Consent conditions. These conditions were then discussed with the firm. Particular attention was given to the limiting concentrations of various chlorinated hydrocarbons, since these can cause serious inhibition of anaerobic digestion processes, even at low concentrations. It must be stressed that the proposed pre-treatment plant was not to be designed to remove these chemicals; they were to be prevented from being discharged by 'good housekeeping' methods, although in some of the production areas they were removed by steam stripping the waste process waters.

Agreement was reached on the need for the conditions and the limits to be imposed. Work commenced on the building of the pre-treatment plant, basically for treatment with lime and vacuum filtration of the sludges, and other civil engineering works on site. Approximately two months before discharge was due to commence, the trade effluent notice was served and the Consent issued.

It took a period of four years from the initial inquiry to the commissioning of the pre-treatment plant and the commencement of discharge to the public sewer. To date acceptance of the effluent has caused no problems in the sewerage system and has not adversely affected any of the treatment processes or the quality of effluent discharged from the sewage treatment works.

2.8. TRADE EFFLUENT CHARGES

Prior to the formation of the Water Authorities, charges made by Local Authorities in many areas did not cover the cost of treating and conveying trade effluent. In some areas, no charges at all were made, whilst in others the charges had not been revised for several years. Charges, and the basis on which charges were made, varied widely from one area to another. Some Authorities did, however, charge in accordance with a 'Mogden'-type formula. The basis of this formula is credited[3] to Townend and Lockett of the Mogden works. The formula can be expressed as:

$$\text{Charge per unit volume} = R + V + \frac{Ot}{Os}B + \frac{St}{Ss}S \qquad (2.1)$$

where R = one third of the amount determined by the Authority as the average cost to the Authority for the year of charge of receiving into its sewers (other than those used solely for surface water) and conveying $1\,m^3$ of sewage to the Authority's sewage treatment works;

V = the amount determined by the Authority as the average cost for the year of charge of primary treatment and other volumetric treatment costs in the treatment of $1\,m^3$ of sewage at the Authority's sewage treatment works;

Ot = the Chemical Oxygen Demand (COD) of the trade effluent in milligrams per litre after 1 h quiescent settlement;

Os = the estimated average Chemical Oxygen Demand (COD) of settled sewage in milligrams per litre at the Authority's works as determined by the Authority for the purposes of the year of charge;

B = the amount determined by the Authority as the average cost to the Authority for the year of charge of biological treatment of $1\,m^3$ of sewage at the Authority's sewage treatment works;

St = the total Suspended Solids in the trade effluent in milligrams per litre at the pH of the trade effluent if within Consent conditions or otherwise at the minimum pH of the Consent conditions;

Ss = the estimated average amount of Suspended Solids in milligrams per litre, determined on a shaken sample, in sewage received for treatment at the Authority's works as determined by the Authority for the purposes of the year of charge; and

S = the amount determined by the Authority as the average cost to the Authority for the year of charge, of primary sludge treatment and disposal of $1\,m^3$ of sewage at the Authority's sewage treatment works.

Most Water Authorities have adopted this formula for assessing charges, the only significant variation being that used by the Welsh Water Authority.

Oxygen demand was expressed in the original formula as McGowan strength. This is seldom used nowadays, (although the Anglian Water Authority does use a modified version of McGowan strength in its charging scheme), oxygen demand for charging purposes being usually measured in terms of the Chemical Oxygen Demand (Dichromate Value) of the effluent. An alternative measurement of oxygen demand is the biochemical oxygen demand (BOD).

Traders may, and often do, argue that COD is not a measure of the actual oxidation carried out by the treatment works. Whilst this may be true, it can also be argued that the BOD test as performed in the laboratory is not analogous to the situation found on the works. Nevertheless, BOD is a measure of the biological oxidation requirement of the effluent as opposed to a purely chemical assessment. However, the argument is only really of importance to the trader when the $COD:BOD_5$ ratio of trade effluent greatly exceeds that of sewage (say 2.2:1). Some chemical wastes may have ratios of 5 and upwards and on a COD charging basis will no doubt pay more than if charged on a BOD system. Most Water Authorities are willing to make allowance for this by the use of an appropriate factor if approaches are made by the trader. A detailed discussion of the arguments for and against the use of COD for charging purposes is given in a paper by Dart.[4]

At the present time the formula used by the Welsh Water Authority differs significantly from that used by other Authorities. It is:

$$C = \frac{Ot - Os}{Os}B + \frac{St - Ss}{Ss}S \tag{2.2}$$

where C = total rate of charge in pence per cubic metre and the other symbols are essentially the same as those used in eqn. (2.1).

In practice the above formula will result in no charges being levied for effluents below the regional average strength. This charging scheme is currently being reviewed, as in fact are many of the charges levied by the various Water Authorities. Solids may be determined as either Total Suspended Solids or Settleable Solids, the Northumbrian, Thames and Yorkshire Water Authorities currently use Settleable Solids.

The South West Water Authority uses BOD in the charging formula, but most other Authorities express oxidation demand in terms of COD. All Authorities, with the exception of the North West Water Authority, have introduced Regional charging schemes in which the unit costs are the averages for the whole region. However, it is understood that the North West Water Authority intends to proceed to an equalised Regional charge over the next few years. The various charge rates are shown in Table 2.1 To allow an easier comparison of the charge rates, the rates for an effluent with a COD of 600 mg/litre and Suspended Solids concentration of 300 mg/litre are shown at the bottom of the Table. As can be seen, there may still be large differences in charges from one region to another. For the effluent strength chosen, the charges would vary from 2.57 p/m³ to 18.65 p/m³, depending on where the discharge is to be made.

Most Water Authorities have applied some kind of phasing policy to the implementation of full Regional charges and, in some Authorities, these

TABLE 2.1
TRADE EFFLUENT CHARGE RATES—ENGLAND AND WALES 1979/80

	Symbol in STWA Formula	Units	Water authorities									
			Anglian	North West[2]	North-umbrian	Severn-Trent	South West	Southern	Thames	Welsh[4]	Wessex	Yorks
Reception and Conveyance	R	p/m³	3.11	1.182	3.14	1.63	3.50	4.22	1.73	—	1.60	1.18
Volumetric	V	p/m³	1.62	1.623	3.25	2.69	1.93		1.46	—	2.66	2.04
Oxidation	B	p/m³	2.24	2.142	5.26	4.04	3.27	3.48	1.96	6.60	2.66	2.77
Sludge	S	p/m³	2.43	1.372	2.95	2.24	2.34	2.84	2.07	2.70	3.72	1.65
OVERALL RATE		p/m³	9.40	6.319	14.60	10.60	11.04	10.54	7.22	—	10.64	7.64
Regional COD	O_S	mg/litre	572[1]	367	372	379	155[3]	388	292	432	400	523
Regional Suspended Solids	S_S	mg/litre	337	268	164[5]	332	301	365	221[5]	304	350	200[5]
Charge rate for 600 mg/litre COD 300 mg/litre SS		p/m³	10.12	7.843	18.65	12.74	13.51	11.93	9.19	2.57	11.44	8.13

[1] A modified McGowan strength is used by the Anglian Water Authority, the oxidation parameter being $COD + 4.5 \times$ unoxidised nitrogen. The trade effluent used in the charging example has been assumed to have an unoxidised nitrogen value of 50 mg/litre.

[2] Currently the North West Water Authority applies different charge rates in the 12 areas of its region, shown are the regional averages.

[3] In the South West Water Authority's scheme, O_S is the five-day BOD. To calculate the charge rate shown at the bottom of the Table it has been assumed that the trade effluent COD of 600 mg/litre has a $COD : BOD_5$ ratio of 2.2 : 1.

[4] The Welsh Water Authority charging formula differs markedly from the others, see text.

[5] Solids for charging purposes in the Northumbrian, Thames and Yorkshire Water Authorities are determined as Settleable Solids. In the charging example shown, a value of 210 mg/litre Settleable Solids has been used in the calculation instead of 300 mg/litre total Suspended Solids (this assumes that the Settleable Solids are equivalent to 70% of the total Suspended Solids).

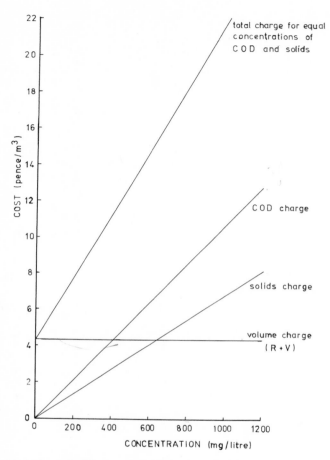

FIG. 2.1. Variation of effluent costs with concentration. (Severn–Trent Water Authority charges 1979/80).

schemes are still in operation. In the Severn–Trent area the increases in charges were phased over a period of five years, full charges being levied for all discharges with effect from April 1979. Examples of the charges made at the 1979/80 Severn–Trent rates for varying parameters are shown in Figs 2.1 and 2.2.

At the present time, the charges made for trade effluent treatment are made under the provisions of the Public Health Act 1961, Section 59(1)(e).

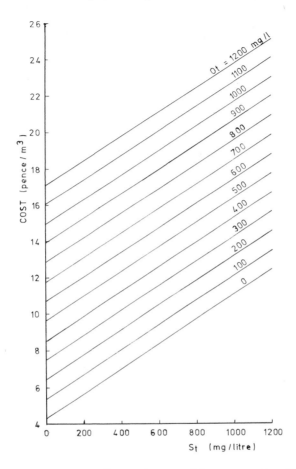

FIG. 2.2. Variation of total effluent charges with concentration (Severn–Trent Water Authority charges 1979/80).

Section 52 of the Control of Pollution Act 1974 allows the Secretary of State to make an order repealing Sections 59(1)(e) and 61(4) of the 1961 Act and to apply the provisions of Sections 30 and 31 of the Water Act 1973 to trade effluent charging schemes. Such an order is expected to be made sometime in 1980.

As a final comment on charging policy Water Authorities may still enter into Agreements with traders for the acceptance of trade effluents. Although the majority of effluents will be controlled by the issue of a Consent, situations may still arise in which it is in the interests of both parties to enter into an Agreement. Where the discharge of a trade effluent would constitute an appreciable proportion of the flow or load received, then this procedure may be preferred, especially if the Works has to be extended in order to accept the waste. The agreement may, for example, cover the financing by the trader of any extensions required at the sewage treatment works in order that his effluent may be accepted. The capital may be provided as a lump sum or as a series of payments over a number of years. In the latter case there is likely to be provision in the agreement for the immediate recovery of any outstanding debt should the trader, for any reason, cease to discharge before the total debt has been repaid. Guarantee bonds may also be required in such cases.

2.9. COST REDUCTION IN TRADE EFFLUENT DISPOSAL

The graph of the Severn–Trent trade effluent charges shown in Fig. 2.1 indicates that for effluents with a COD of less than 405 mg/litre, the volume charge $(R + V)$ is the major component of the overall charging rate. Traders may well be able to reduce their effluent charges, especially where relatively 'weak' effluents are involved, by reducing the volume of water used, even though this may well increase the strength of the effluent.

An effluent with COD and Suspended Solids concentrations of 200 mg/litre each would cost, on this charging rate, 7.80 p/m³ for disposal. Halving the volume and, say, doubling the strength would result in an effluent costing 11.28 p/m³ for disposal. For an annual discharge of, say, 100 000 m³, halving the volume and doubling the strength would result in the following saving:

$$100\ 000\ \text{m}^3 \text{ at } 7.80 \text{ p/m}^3 = \pounds7800$$
$$50\ 000\ \text{m}^3 \text{ at } 11.28 \text{ p/m}^3 = \pounds5640$$

$$\text{Annual saving} \qquad = \pounds2160$$

$$\text{(a saving of 30\% on the}$$
$$\text{original bill)}$$

This type of saving ought to be possible in many industries, but especially so in the metal finishing industry. There the major part of the trade effluent charges, under most charging schemes, will be the volumetric element $(R + V)$. Recirculation schemes, or at least using the water more than once before disposal, should result in considerable saving, not only on effluent charges but also on metered water supply charges.

A reduction in effluent volume will always produce some saving. However, where COD is the major proportion of the effluent charges, as it is for effluents from breweries, chemical works, dairies, abattoirs and certain other industries, then the savings in effluent charges simply from volume reduction may not be as significant as in the case of 'weak' effluents. In such cases, ways of reducing the pollution load should be sought and there are usually several possibilities worthy of consideration.

In seeking COD reduction the trader probably first considers the provision of an effluent pre-treatment plant to remove some of the COD on site. Many plants are commercially available which will carry out this function. It remains for the trader to evaluate the capital and revenue costs associated with such plants and compare these costs with the Water Authority's charges. Most plants, however, produce sludge and it is often the disposal of this, which is the prohibitive factor, because it can be very expensive in certain areas. If there is a cheap outlet for such sludges, such as suitable agricultural land in close proximity, then removal of some COD by an effluent treatment plant may show some savings.

If the increased solids in the effluent arising as a result of COD removal, by say chemical coagulation, are acceptable for discharge to the public sewerage system, then there may be savings in adopting such a method. The COD charge is usually the highest element of charge in most charging formulae and removal of COD at the expense of an increase in Suspended Solids may reduce charges. The discharge must of course remain within Consent conditions. Again, relative costs will have to be assessed by the trader.

Some wastes with relatively high COD values may be suitably disposed of by spray irrigation, e.g. effluents from the manufacture of frozen foods. Whether or not this is feasible will depend upon the availability of land, the effect on water resources, the nature of the land, etc. Pea processing is a seasonal process resulting in a large surge in effluent production for a few weeks of the year. It may be economical to discharge a certain level of effluent to the public sewerage system and to spray irrigate the excess as and when it arises.

A further area for examination, and one which it is considered may well produce the best results in the majority of cases, is how to prevent the discharge of materials with high COD to the sewerage system. An improvement in 'housekeeping' methods and changes in production methods may be required to achieve this. Sweeping up and collecting spilled materials rather than hosing them down the drains is one simple measure which can show savings. The adoption of better production methods in which less material is wasted and the substitution of 'dry' methods where 'wet' methods have traditionally been used in the past are also areas worthy of examination. In seeking such ways to reduce trade effluent charges materials may be recovered which are of value. In addition, other savings may result, such as reduced chemical and raw material costs, a decrease in product loss and savings in energy usage.

2.10. CONCLUSIONS

Powers are available to ensure that all new and most of the existing trade effluents discharged to public sewers are subject to full control. However, the way to control such effluents is not through the powers given by the various pieces of legislation but by co-operation between the trader and the Water Authority. Traders should be aware of the problems their effluents may cause and officers of the Water Authority should try to understand the problems facing the trader.

When trade effluent charges were a relatively small proportion of operating expenditure, little attention was generally given to this subject by most traders. As long as the effluent disappeared from site without adverse comment from the Authority responsible for its treatment, then the service was truly 'taken for granted'. Revision of charges has changed this and without doubt many firms are examining ways of reducing their trade effluent treatment costs.

It will be interesting to see how this affects the demand for water. The population of the United Kingdom appears to have stabilised and this, together with possible economies in the use of water by industry, may well mean that demand forecasts for water usage made only a few years ago are too high. It must surely be in the national interest to conserve our water resources and a new look by industry at its water usage will play a most useful part in preventing the waste of this valuable natural resource.

ACKNOWLEDGEMENT

The author wishes to express his thanks to Mr W.H. Richardson, CEng, MICE, MIMunE, MRTPI, Dip TP, Divisional Manager, Lower Trent

Division, Severn–Trent Water Authority, for permission to publish this chapter.

The views expressed are those of the author and not necessarily those of the Severn–Trent Water Authority.

REFERENCES

1. Ministry of Housing and Local Government, *Taken for Granted, Report of the Working Party on Sewage Disposal.* HMSO, London, 1970.
2. Technical Report TR17, *Emission Standards in Relation to Water Quality Objectives.* Water Research Centre, Medmenham, June, 1976.
3. Griffiths, J. and Kirkbright, A.A., Charges for treatment of trade effluent, *Inst. Sewage Purification J. & Proc.*, Pt. 4 (1959), 505.
4. Dart, M.C., Trade effluent control and charges, *Water Pollution Control*, **76** (2) (1977), 192.

3

Discharges to Watercourses

W.A. ALLEN

Assistant Divisional Scientist, Soar Division, Severn–Trent Water Authority, Anstey, UK

3.1. DEVELOPMENT OF CONTROL

Although local pollution of streams had been known for probably hundreds of years the problem was greatly increased as a result of the Industrial Revolution and the enormous growth in population from the late eighteenth century onwards. Sewage drained to cesspools which were neglected and as a consequence overflowed into the streets, while the increasing use of the water-carriage system of sewage disposal aggravated the situation. The discharge of offensive material to the sewers, which had been constructed and linked to existing watercourses for the removal of rain water, was forbidden but this fact was frequently ignored. Later on, however, connection of private drains to the sewers was made compulsory on public health grounds.

In London the sewage from about 3 000 000 people was discharged directly into the River Thames within the city and there were epidemics of cholera in 1866 and 1872. In other areas of rapid industrial development and population growth increasing volumes of polluting effluents and crude sewage were allowed to pass into watercourses. Rivers became foul in odour and appearance, devoid of fish and other aquatic life and unavailable as sources of drinking water. Two Royal Commissions on Rivers Pollution were set up in 1865 and 1868 and their subsequent reports on the seriousness of the conditions brought legislative action.

The British Government passed the Public Health Act 1875, in which local authorities were given the duty of treating sewage to render it harmless to a receiving stream, but there was insufficient development of sewage purification methods at this time. There had been a Commission on Sewage Disposal appointed in the 1850s which reported on methods of dealing with sewage, but thoughts were centred on the possibility of its utilisation and some commercial undertakings were hoping to profit thereby!

The Rivers Pollution Prevention Act 1876, although admirable in its intent, proved to be of limited practical value. Nevertheless this Act remained as the basis of the law on river pollution for 75 years, augmented by a further Act of 1893 and the various Salmon and Freshwater Fisheries Acts. The 1876 Act prohibited the discharge of solid or liquid sewage matter into a river and also the discharge of poisonous, noxious or polluting industrial effluents. However, an amending clause reduced almost completely the impact on industrialists of the latter prohibition while the duty of enforcing the Act was left to the local councils as sanitary authorities most of whom were themselves amongst the gross polluters.

County Councils also were granted the powers under the Local Government Act of 1888 which provided for additional bodies to be set up to administer the Act of 1876 and by 1893 three such authorities were formed in the areas of the Ribble, the Mersey and Irwell and the West Riding of Yorkshire. The Thames and Lee Conservancy Boards were already in existence and had greater powers than the other authorities in pollution control because of the need to protect the purity of the water abstracted by the Metropolitan Water Board for supply to London and the adjoining areas.

In 1898 another Royal Commission was appointed to report on the treatment and disposal of sewage and trade effluents. Ten reports were published between 1901 and 1915, the last being a summary of recommendations given in the first nine reports. Four of the reports dealt mainly with the purification of sewage, two with discharge of sewage into tidal waters and three with industrial effluents. The Eighth Report (1912) classified rivers according to their biological condition and the biochemical oxygen demand (BOD) of their waters.

The Commissioners, for their Eighth Report, ascertained that a river having a BOD not exceeding 4 mg/litre would normally be free from indications of pollution. From the analyses of a number of streams which were considered by observation to be of average purity the average BOD of 2 mg/litre was obtained. In the Fifth Report it had been stated provisionally that an effluent would be generally satisfactory with no more than 30 mg/litre suspended matter and with a BOD no greater than 20 mg/litre both levels being regarded as attainable in practice.

Dilution of such an effluent with at least eight times its volume of river water of BOD 2 mg/litre would be necessary for the receiving water to remain in a reasonably clean condition. It was recognised that more stringent standards should be prescribed in cases of lower dilution and conversely that a lower standard might be allowed where the dilution was much greater. However the standard of quality recommended by the Royal Commission came to be regarded as a 'norm' for the great majority of fully-treated effluents from inland sewage disposal works.

Eighteen Acts dating from 1861 to 1921 relating to salmon and freshwater fisheries in England and Wales were repealed when the Salmon and Freshwater Fisheries Act 1923 was enacted. The Act gave fishery boards powers to take proceedings against persons poisoning or injuring fish life and required notice to be given of any new work for the discharge of trade effluent into fishery waters.

In 1929 the first report of the Joint Advisory Committee on River Pollution drew attention to the desirability of increasing the number of bodies having the power to administer the Rivers Pollution Prevention Acts, reminding the appropriate Ministers that the formation of River Boards had been recommended by various Committees and Royal Commissions including that on Rivers Pollution, 1868, and that on Sewage Disposal in the Third Report of 1903. The 1898 Commission had in fact suggested in both 1901 and 1903 a 'Supreme Rivers Authority'.

The River Dee Joint Committee and the Lancashire Rivers Board were set up in 1932 and 1938 respectively, but it was not until the River Boards Act of 1948 took effect that boards were established to cover the whole of England and Wales, the functions of the boards covering fisheries and land drainage as well as pollution control. The Rivers (Prevention of Pollution) (Scotland) Act 1951 brought into being the River Purification Boards in Scotland.

For England and Wales the Rivers (Prevention of Pollution) Act 1951 conferred powers on the new river boards to control new discharges to rivers and the Clean Rivers (Estuaries and Tidal Waters) Act 1960 brought extension of these provisions to cover new discharges to tidal waters and to specified parts of the sea.

A further Rivers (Prevention of Pollution) Act in 1961 gave powers to control the continuation of discharges which had existed prior to 1st October 1951, although excluding those to estuaries and tidal waters. There were provisions in the 1951 Acts which enabled a Board to make application for a Ministerial Order to control polluting discharges to such waters.

In 1965, when the Water Resources Act of 1963 became effective, the River Boards were superseded by River Authorities which in turn disappeared under the provisions of the Water Act 1973, their functions and others being carried on by multi-purpose Regional Water Authorities from 1st April 1974.

The 1951 Act for Scotland gave powers to the River Purification Boards to control new discharges to rivers whilst the later Act to control existing discharges appeared in 1965. Ministerial Orders were obtained for the control of pollution in Scottish estuaries. Reorganisation has reduced the number of boards, but they remain as pollution control authorities although prosecutions have to be brought through the Procurator Fiscal.

The depositing on land of poisonous, noxious or polluting waste was controlled under the hastily-produced Deposit of Poisonous Waste Act 1972. Under its provisions the water authorities had a secondary involvement in the protection of water supplies, and not water resources generally, their rôle being only to advise that the deposit of dangerous waste at unapproved sites could lead to prosecution. As a result of the notification procedures which were necessary a large amount of information was collected on the quantity and type of waste which was being disposed of.

The Act is replaced by Part 1 of the Control of Pollution Act 1974, which contains more safeguards for the protection of the quality of water whether on the surface or underground. Part 2 of the 1974 Act replaces most of the water pollution prevention legislation, extending control to the sea within three nautical miles from any point on the coast; other tidal waters; specified underground water and any prescribed lake, loch or pond without discharge to a stream, (referred to collectively as 'relevant waters').

3.2. PRECAUTIONS

When specifying conditions in relation to the acceptance of a trade discharge into a sewer the Water Authority must have regard to the safety of men working in the sewers and at sewage pumping stations; protection of the fabric of the sewers and maintenance of the flow therein and protection of the sewage purification processes at the reclamation works. Accordingly there must be limits, *inter alia*, on temperature, acidity, alkalinity, suspended solids and toxic materials. Discharge of waste steam or liquid with a temperature in excess of 43°C is prohibited as are hazardous materials such as petroleum spirit and calcium carbide and excessive amounts of cyanides and sulphides.

An industrialist may well have to pre-treat an effluent for discharge to a sewer in order to meet the requirements of the Water Authority, but he would no doubt need more extensive and costly purification plant in order to satisfy the conditions for discharge to a watercourse. These conditions which a Water Authority attach to a Consent to discharge an effluent to a watercourse will be more stringent than those related to discharges to sewers, bearing in mind the susceptibility of stream life to polluting material and the need to incorporate a factor of safety.

In considering proposed discharges to underground strata the Water Authority must obviously have regard to the proximity of wells and other underground water supplies. In connection with the deposit of waste materials on land the Authority must study the possible effects of run-off or leaching on surface and underground water resources.

Geologists have assessed the risks to underground water which were likely to result from the deposit of poisonous waste on tips and the tips have been classified in relation to the type of waste which it is considered may safely be tipped. Some tips were found to be safe for inert materials only while some other tips may be regarded, from the standpoint of water pollution control, as suitable for the reception of any materials. It was necessary for many tips to receive further investigation before their classification could be ascertained. Monitoring the effects of tipping will need to continue beyond this requirement because any resulting pollution may not manifest itself immediately.

3.3. DISCHARGE CONDITIONS

Appendix 3.1 gives details of Consent conditions typical of those normally applied to effluents for discharge to streams. It will be apparent that the foundation for these conditions is the Royal Commission recommendation of 1912, although the indication is given that a more stringent standard may well be imposed. There could be variations according to local circumstances and the merits of any particular case. The list of conditions is not exhaustive and others could be added where the need arises.

The formulae A and B referred to in the conditions and quoted at the end thereof were devised by the Technical Committee on Storm Overflows and the Disposal of Storm Sewage whose final report was issued in 1970. The formulae revised the criteria on which was based the treatment of storm water, as it had been called previously, and which provided for full treatment to sewage flows up to three times 'dry-weather flow' and sedimentation to additional flows up to a total six times 'dry-weather flow' with any excess flow above six times being allowed to overflow direct to a watercourse.

The Committee began its studies and investigations in 1955 and in the final report concluded that there was no justification, generally, for a radical improvement but there was a need for a 'modest improvement' on traditional practice. It regarded its recommendations as fulfilling this need.

For a river to remain in a healthy condition so that aquatic life can be sustained it is most important that the content of dissolved oxygen should be maintained at a satisfactory level. Game fish require oxygen at a level no lower, ideally, than 75% of the saturation value (at normal temperatures), although coarse fish are able to survive a reduction to 30%, but shortage of oxygen can render fish more susceptible to any toxic substances present. Anything which removes oxygen from the water may be regarded as polluting that water and the limit for the biochemical oxygen demand of any such material being discharged to a stream is normally 20 mg/litre.

The limit of 30 mg/litre Suspended Solids applies to matter which may or may not have an oxygen demand. The effects of the discharge of solid matter, as with many other materials, will vary according to the type of river receiving the discharge. The solids may be carried away immediately or somewhat later if the stream is flashy. If the solids settle and remain, there will be an accumulation which may continue to absorb oxygen and, whether active or inert, will blanket the river bed and cover plant life and the spawning grounds, spawn and food of fish. Solids in suspension can affect the gill action and turbidity will restrict the vision of fish. Beneficial photosynthesis can also be limited by restriction of the passage of sunlight through the water.

In 1912 no recommendation was made by the Royal Commission with regard to the ammonia content of an effluent. At that time a satisfactory effluent from treatment by percolating filters was well nitrified and it was only the introduction in 1914 of the activated-sludge process that made possible an unnitrified effluent of Royal Commission standard. It is necessary to maintain at a low level the ammonia content of a river from which water is abstracted for public supply because of the use of chlorine for disinfection. Ammonia and chlorine produce chloramines which although bactericidal do not have the power or speed of action of so-called 'free' chlorine.

Ammonia is toxic to fish especially at high pH values, 20 mg/litre (as N) being lethal. A river is unlikely to recover as a fishery if the level remains above 5 mg/litre. Nitrification occurs in streams, more noticeably in those that are well aerated, and the oxidation of the ammonia will present another demand on the dissolved oxygen content. It is sometimes considered necessary to impose a more stringent limit on the content of ammoniacal nitrogen in an effluent during the 'summer' period, allowing that the available dilution is likely to be lower and, on account of higher temperatures, the rate of oxygen consumption is greater.

For these reasons there may well be more stringent conditions for some of the other parameters. The most suitable period for the more restrictive conditions is probably from May to October inclusive, because a reclamation works may take until the end of April to recover from winter conditions. This is also the most likely period for the lower 'summer' flows in the receiving watercourse.

Heavy metal salts in solution are a serious form of pollution, being stable and having deleterious effects on the performance of fishes' gills, thereby causing asphyxiation. The salts are fatal to fish at very low concentrations, especially in soft water, at levels below 0.1 mg/litre for cadmium and copper. Additionally there are extremely low limits to the concentration of heavy metals permitted in water for public supply.

Cyanides are often associated with metals in industry, being used in electroplating and case-hardening. The effect of hydrogen cyanide on fish is to reduce their ability to utilise oxygen. Levels of 1 mg/litre and less of cyanides have been quoted as lethal. Hydrogen sulphide and soluble sulphides are similar to cyanides in their inhibition of the use of oxygen by fish, although the lethal concentrations are not as low.

Similarly phenolic substances, whose lethal levels are not as low as those of cyanides, are capable of tainting the flesh of fish at sub-lethal concentrations. A strict limit of 0.001 mg/litre is given for phenol in water for public supply as the taste of chlorophenol produced on chlorination of phenol, even as dilute as 0.002 mg/litre, can be readily detected.

Values of pH outside the range given in the Consent conditions have a direct effect on organisms. In water having a pH value below 5 the activity of the gills of fish is likely to be adversely affected with asphyxiation as the result. The toxicity of pollutants such as ammonia and cyanides is likely to vary at different pH levels, ammonia, for instance, being more toxic in alkaline waters.

The extent to which many of the polluting discharges exhibit toxicity will depend also on the hardness of the receiving water, the temperature and the amount of pollution already present. The effect of the discharge of a pollutant to a stream will be greater if the stream is already carrying a degree of pollutional load. Higher temperatures will make bacteria and micro-organisms more active and increase the rate of oxidation of organic matter and, as the solubility of oxygen is lower in warmer water, the pollution can more readily deoxygenate a stretch of water under such conditions. In summer it is possible for severe deoxygenation to occur naturally by the overnight absorption of oxygen by aquatic plants.

The effect of temperature on fish will vary with the species and the degree of acclimatisation. A rapid change in temperature may result in death. Game fish thrive best in cool water (about 13–19°C) while coarse fish can survive much higher temperatures. However, temperatures quoted as lethal are 30°C for pike, 28°C for roach and rainbow trout and 25°C (the Consent condition) for perch and brown trout. An increase in temperature will increase the toxicity and lower the lethal dose of many fish poisons.

The Report of 1969 from the Committee on Fish Toxicity Tests standardised a test which could be used in conditions of Consent to discharge. The test enables the toxicity of an effluent to be determined without identifying the individual components contributing to the total toxicity and is of value in cases where the constituents of an effluent are not known in detail and analysis for the offending materials would be difficult.

3.4. POLLUTION BY OIL

Oil is frequently a contaminant of sewage and industrial effluents, for which a discharge Consent limit of 5 mg/litre may be applied, but all too often it enters a stream as a spasmodic emission from a surface water sewer or a drain of a highway authority as the result of an accident. Accidental spillages do occur, but there is also a great deal of carelessness in the handling of oil equipment and the extent of this can be reduced by following the precautions detailed in a code for the Storage and Piped Distribution of Heating Oil published by the Institute of Petroleum in 1967.

Heavy fuel oil causes unsightly fouling of stream verges, emergent aquatic plants, boats and tackle, while diesel and lubricating oils cause similar problems. It is possible to contain any of these oils by placing a boom at a suitable point and subsequently removing them manually or by means of skimming devices. Details of these and oil dispersants and absorbent materials may be found in advertisements in the technical press. As much oil as possible should be removed before resorting to the use of a dispersant, which should be of low toxicity, but dispersed oil will remain a hazard to water intakes.

These oils may come from barges, tankers or boats on rivers or canals, but it is an offence to make a discharge of oil under the Oil in Navigable Waters Act 1955. Industry uses other oils such as vegetable oils as well as emulsified oils for degreasing and as coolants and lubricants for high-speed tools. The latter 'soluble' oils contain toxic ingredients and form stable milky emulsions with water.

Oil in only small amounts can spread over a large area. One gallon of oil can give an ll-millionths-of-an-inch film over four acres of water. An oil film will prevent the uptake by the water of oxygen from the atmosphere and will itself have a BOD. The film will also lessen the sunlight penetration into the water and thereby the amount of photosynthesis. Re-oxygenation will thus be retarded in two ways.

Oil can kill stream flora and fauna at the surface and below if it becomes attached to particles of material which can settle on the river bed. The gills of fish can be fouled and the flesh can be tainted by oil while fish eggs and fry may be directly damaged.

3.5. CLASSIFICATION OF RIVERS

In the 1970 River Pollution Survey of England and Wales chemical and biological classifications of the rivers were used, the chemical classification being as follows:

Class 1 — Rivers unpolluted and recovered from pollution.
Class 2 — Rivers of doubtful quality and needing improvement.
Class 3 — Rivers of poor quality requiring improvement as a matter of some urgency.
Class 4 — Grossly polluted rivers.

In a consultation paper published in 1977 the National Water Council suggested a classification of river quality which was an extension of the above and is given in Appendix 3.2. Class 1 was sub-divided and it is considered that Class 2 which covers a wide range of quality should also be divided. Some Water Authorities found the need to make this alteration without waiting for an 'official' revision and the Scottish Development Department (1979) also sub-divided Class 2, although not Class 1 (see Appendix 3.3.).

When deciding the future standard to be attained by a discharge, the class into which the receiving river has been placed is one of the factors to be considered. It is frequently the case that the pollution in a Class 4 river is the result of the presence of a large proportion of industrial effluents and it is very unlikely that the river can be readily brought to the condition of Class 1. Accordingly the standard of quality sought for such effluents should be sufficient to ensure improvement to Class 2 (or Class 3 in unfavourable circumstances).

3.6. OBJECTIVES AND PRIORITIES

The classifications were developed to assist the Water Authorities in the determination of river quality objectives. The National Water Council classification related the uses of a river water to its chemical quality and took account of the EEC Council Directive (1975) on water suitable for abstraction of drinking water. In this Directive Category A1 waters require simple physical treatment and disinfection; A2 waters require normal chemical and physical treatment and disinfection; and A3 waters require advanced treatment. Before final adoption of the river quality objectives consultations were held with local councils, industry, angling associations and environmental groups.

Maintenance of a high quality is most important in connection with potable water supplies and no deterioration can be permitted especially where existing supplies could be affected. As the volume of an effluent discharge is increased, the standard of quality will need to be more stringent in order that the pollution load on the river system does not increase. Where future supplies must be secured, an improvement may well be required to an existing effluent, either to remove or reduce contaminants or because abstractions will bring about a reduction in the dilution available for the effluent. Other important river quality objectives are the removal of risks to public health and the maintenance and restoration of fisheries. Lower in the order of priority are the maintenance and restoration of amenities and of non-potable water supplies for industry.

The demand for water has gone on increasing and whereas, traditionally, water supply authorities have always tried to find unpolluted waters which require minimum treatment to render them fit for supply purposes, they are finding it necessary in many areas to make use of waters which are to a greater or lesser extent polluted. However, it is intended that any future use of A3 Category waters should be considerably reduced. More emphasis is being placed on the need for conservation of water and water reclamation. While there is available sufficient cheap water of the required quality there may be no inclination on the part of an industrialist to consider re-cycling or sequential use of the water, although economies could be effected and, in many cases, valuable raw materials recovered. Increases in the cost of water may bring a greater incentive to adopt re-cycling or use of a lower grade of water where this can be tolerated.

Because of the possibility of readier prosecution by any person or group, in addition to a Water Authority, for a contravention of discharge Consent conditions the Water Authorities in England and Wales carried out an interim review of the Consent conditions, relating them more realistically to the capabilities of existing treatment plants. The power to prosecute was to be extended by the repeal of Section 11 of the 1961 Act in the provisions of the 1974 Act. The new Act also provided for registers available to the public to be maintained which contain up-to-date information with regard to Consents, discharge conditions, samples of effluent and water and the analysis thereof and any consequent appropriate action by the Water Authority.

Whereas the standard of quality recommended by the Royal Commission came to be regarded as a 'norm' for the great majority of fully-treated effluents from inland sewage disposal works, it was not considered that the same concept should be applied to industrial effluents, for which standards needed more often to be tailored to suit individual circumstances. These circumstances will be brought increasingly into consideration in connection with all effluent discharges in the future.

The condition of a river does not depend solely upon its content of effluents and available dilution, but also on such matters as gradient, depth, rate of flow, presence or absence of weirs and the character of its bed. All of these along with the uses of the river water should be taken into account in deciding the required standard for an effluent. For 30 years nationwide the authorities responsible for the rivers have been able to accumulate information regarding these factors and, with a considerable increase in the continuous monitoring of the quality of river water at key points, will have a much greater knowledge as a background against which to judge the impact of a polluting discharge.

Such a background has not been established in the case of the seas around the coast and tidal waters generally, although there are some notable exceptions with regard to some estuaries such as the Thames, for which there are the extensive records of the London County Council, and some others where intensive surveys have been carried out. In fixing discharge standards the Water Authorities must bear in mind their objectives and priorities as to what has still to be achieved for the sake of the relevant waters and should also give regard to the capability of treatment plant and the burden of the cost thereof.

Many directives are emanating from the European Economic Community as part of the environmental programme embarked upon in 1973. The directives affecting Water Authorities include those dealing with:

  (i) the quality of surface water for abstraction of drinking water,
 (ii) the quality of bathing water,

(iii) pollution caused by certain dangerous substances discharged to the aquatic environment,
(iv) the quality of freshwaters needing protection or improvement in order to support fish life, and
(v) the quality of drinking water.

Other directives approved or drafted concern water quality requirements for shellfish and pollution by titanium dioxide waste and wood-pulp mill discharges. Still more directives are under discussion and individual dangerous substances so far considered include cadmium, mercury and the pesticides, eldrin, dieldrin and aldrin.

Members of the Community have been persuaded away from a sole approach of fixed emission standards in favour of that of environmental quality objectives. Water Authorities are anxious that the limited funds available to them should be used to the best advantage towards the achievement of their own considered objectives rather than full compliance with EEC Directives, which may be of dubious benefit in certain circumstances.

It will be some time before the full effects of the piecemeal implementation of the Control of Pollution Act 1974 are evident and a considerably longer period will elapse before all the many European Directives are formally published and the relevant action taken thereon. Meanwhile the improvement of our rivers will continue in what has been described in the past as 'an exercise in gradualness'.

Despite repeated periods of financial restrictions and economies by public bodies, during which it was always stated that no deterioration should be permitted, the work on the control of pollution of the nation's watercourses has been steadfastly carried out with remarkable benefits in some areas where rivers have been rehabilitated as fisheries and with their recreation and amenity values restored.

The rate at which further improvement can be achieved and the time it will take to realise the longer-term water quality objectives will depend mostly on the availability of capital for investment in the works which are still required.

ACKNOWLEDGEMENT

The author wishes to thank the Severn–Trent Water Authority for permission to make this contribution. However the views expressed are not necessarily those of the Authority.

APPENDIX 3.1. CONDITIONS NORMALLY APPLIED TO EFFLUENTS FOR DISCHARGES TO STREAMS

The following are typical of the conditions normally imposed by a Water Authority in Consents for discharges of sewage or trade effluent. The application of these conditions is subject to variation according to local circumstances and the merits of each particular case and other conditions may be added where appropriate.

Fully Treated Domestic Sewage Effluent

For flows up to that obtained by the application of formula A* the effluent discharged to the stream shall not —

(i) have a BOD (5 days) in excess of 20 mg/litre;

(ii) contain Suspended Solids in excess of 30 mg/litre;

(iii) exceed . . . cubic metres or litres per day under dry-weather flow conditions (the flow normally being the design capacity of the water reclamation works).

At water reclamation works where flows up to that obtained by the application of formula B* are given full treatment the following conditions apply when the flow receiving treatment at the works is in excess of that obtained by the application of formula A.

The effluent discharged to the stream shall not —

(i) have a BOD (5 days) in excess of 30 mg/litre;

(ii) contain Suspended Solids in excess of 40 mg/litre.

In some instances where it is desirable to protect the quality of river water used for potable water supplies or a fishery which contains a large proportion of sewage effluent the following condition may be imposed —

The effluent discharged to the stream shall not contain ammoniacal nitrogen (as N) in excess of 10 mg/litre. (At some sewage works the ammoniacal nitrogen concentration is limited to 5 mg/litre during the months of April to September or May to October inclusive.)

When the sewage contains significant quantities of trade effluent, further conditions may be imposed such as —

The effluent discharges to the stream shall not:

(i) have a permanganate value (4 h) in excess of 20 mg/litre; (this is being replaced by COD value);

*Formulae A and B are given at the end of this appendix.

(ii) contain arsenic, cadmium, chromium, copper, lead and nickel in total in excess of 0.5 mg/litre;
(iii) contain zinc in excess of 0.5 mg/litre;
(iv) contain uncomplexed cyanide (as CN) in excess of 0.1 mg/litre;
 (v) contain monohydric phenols (as C_6H_5OH) in excess of 0.5 mg/litre;
(vi) contain total phenols (as C_6H_5OH) in excess of 2 mg/litre;
(vii) contain sulphides (as H_2S) in excess of 1.0 mg/litre.

When the effluent, after dilution to x times its volume with standard water of hardness 25 (or 250) mg/litre, is tested by the method described in Appendix 2 of the Report of the Committee on Fish Toxicity Tests set up by the Ministry of Housing and Local Government, not more than five fish shall die.

For small domestic sewage treatment plants serving four houses or less or with a capacity of less than 2250 litres/day, the conditions limit the BOD and Suspended Solids to 40 mg/litre and 60 mg/litre respectively.

Trade Effluent

As well as conditions similar to those for a domestic sewage effluent containing significant quantities of trade effluent, other conditions may be imposed such as the following:

The effluent discharged to the stream shall not:

(i) contain non-volatile matter extractable by light petroleum in excess of 5mg/litre;
(ii) have a pH value less than 5 nor greater than 9;
(iii) contain other specified inorganic or organic chemicals in excess of . . . mg/litre;
(iv) have a temperature in excess of 25°C;
(v) have a rate of discharge in excess of . . . litres per second.

When the trade effluent consists solely of cooling water, the conditions limit the permanganate value, the BOD and Suspended Solids to not exceeding 5 mg/litre. If the cooling water is abstracted from a river or canal, the conditions allow an increase of 2, 3 and 5 mg/litre in the permanganate value, BOD and Suspended Solids respectively on the quality of water abstracted. Other quality conditions as necessary will also be imposed on cooling water discharges.

Storm Sewage Tank Effluent

The effluent discharges to the stream shall not contain Suspended Solids in excess of 150 mg/litre; the rate of discharge of effluent to the stream shall be limited to the amount by which the rate of flow at the storm sewage separating weir is at the time of discharge in excess of . . . litres per second (the figure obtained by the application of formula A) and the discharge of effluent shall take place for only so long as an overflow is occurring from the storm sewage tanks.

Storm Sewage Overflows on Foul Sewers

The rate of discharge of the effluent to the stream shall be limited to the amount by which the rate of flow in the outfall sewer at the storm overflow weir is, at the time of discharge, in excess of . . . litres per second (the figure obtained by the application of formula B or the carrying capacity of the sewer if this is greater).

Storm Sewage Overflows at Sewage Pumping Stations

The rate of discharge of the effluent to the stream shall be limited to the amount by which the rate of flow in the sewer(s) draining to the pumping station is at the time of discharge in excess of . . . litres per second (design capacity of the pumping station).

Emergency Overflows from Sewage Pumping Stations

The discharge of the effluent to the stream shall be limited to an overflow from the sump when the pumping station ceases to operate due to circumstances outside the control of the Water Authority (or the . . . District Council) and it is not reasonably practicable to dispose of the sewage otherwise.

Effluent from Surface Water Sewers

The effluent discharged to the stream shall consist only of surface water.

More Stringent Standards

Should the dilution for the effluent available in the stream be small or the use of water from the stream be such that a higher than normal standard of effluent is required, more stringent standards than those indicated above are imposed.

The following statutory statement is incorporated in all Consents—

The terms of this Consent will not, without the consent in writing of the person to whom this Consent is given (or his successor), be altered before the expiration of the period ending with the   day of   19 .

For Discharges to Underground Strata
The following are the standards normally imposed by an Authority in Consents for discharges of sewage effluent from small sewage treatment plants to underground strata when there is considered to be no possibility of danger of pollution of underground water supplies.

(i) The discharge shall consist only of sewage effluent.
(ii) The volume of effluent discharged to underground strata shall not exceed. . . litres per day.
(iii) No part of the sub-surface irrigation system shall be within 10 m of any stream.

In the case of larger volumes of sewage effluent and trade effluent, if it is decided that Consent can be given, more restrictive conditions controlling the quality of the discharge are generally imposed.

*Formulae
The rate of flow for discharges from storm sewage tanks and storm sewage overflows is determined by the formulae recommended in the Final Report of the Technical Committee on Storm Overflows and the Disposal of Storm Sewage. These are as follows—

Storm sewage tank effluent—formula A

$$\frac{3PG + I + 3E}{24 \times 60 \times 60} \text{ litres per second}$$

Storm sewage overflows—formula B

$$\frac{DWF + 1360\,P + 2E}{24 \times 60 \times 60} \text{ litres per second}$$

where DWF = dry-weather flow in litres per day;
P = population;
G = average domestic water consumption in litres per head per day;
I = infiltration water in litres per day;
E = volume of industrial effluent, in litres discharged to the sewer in 24 h.

APPENDIX 3.2. NATIONAL WATER COUNCIL: SUGGESTED CLASSIFICATION OF RIVER QUALITY

River Class	Quality criteria	Remarks	Current potential uses
1A	Class limiting criteria (95 percentile) (i) Dissolved oxygen saturation greater than 80%. (ii) Biochemical oxygen demand not greater than 3 mg/litre. (iii) Ammonia not greater than 0.4 mg/litre. (iv) Where the water is abstracted for drinking water, it complies with requirements for A2^a water. (v) Non-toxic to fish in EIFAC terms (or best estimates if EIFAC figures not available).	(i) Average BOD probably not greater than 1.5 mg/litre. (ii) Visible evidence of pollution should be absent.	(i) Water of high quality suitable for potable supply abstractions and for all other abstractions. (ii) Game or other high class fisheries. (iii) High amenity value.
1B	(i) DO greater than 60% saturation. (ii) BOD not greater than 5 mg/litre. (iii) Ammonia not greater than 0.9 mg/litre. (iv) Where water is abstracted for drinking water, it complies with the requirements for A2^a water.	(i) Average BOD probably not greater than 2 mg/litre. (ii) Average ammonia probably not greater than 0.5 mg/litre. (iii) Visible evidence of pollution should be absent. (iv) Waters of high quality which	Water of less high quality than Class 1A but usable for substantially the same purposes.

APPENDIX 3.2. (contd.)

River Class	Quality criteria	Remarks	Current potential uses
	(v) Non-toxic to fish in EIFAC terms (or best estimates if EIFAC figures not available).	cannot be placed in Class 1A because of high proportion of high quality effluent present or because of the effect of physical factors such as canalisation, low gradient or eutrophication. (v) Class 1A and Class 1B together are essentially the Class 1 of the River Pollution Survey.	
2	(i) DO greater than 40% saturation. (ii) BOD not greater than 9 mg/litre. (iii) Where water is abstracted for drinking water, it complies with the requirements for A3^a water. (iv) Non-toxic to fish in EIFAC terms (or best estimates if EIFAC figures not available).	(i) Average BOD probably not greater than 5 mg/litre. (ii) Similar to Class 2 of RPS. (iii) Water not showing physical signs of pollution other than humic colouration and a little foaming below weirs.	(i) Waters suitable for potable supply after advanced treatment. (ii) Supporting reasonably good coarse fisheries. (iii) Moderate amenity value.
3	(i) DO greater than 10% saturation. (ii) Not likely to be anaerobic. (iii) BOD not greater than 7 mg/litre.^{b}	Similar to Class 3 of RPS.	Waters which are polluted to an extent that fish are absent or only sporadically present. May be used for low grade industrial abstraction purposes. Considerable potential for further use if cleaned up.
4	Waters which are inferior to Class 3 in terms of dissolved oxygen and likely to be anaerobic at times.	Similar to Class 4 of RPS.	Waters which are grossly polluted and are likely to cause nuisance.
X	DO greater than 10% saturation.		Insignificant watercourses and ditches not usable, where objective is simply to prevent nuisance develo...

Note (a) Under extreme weather conditions (e.g. flood, drought, freeze-up), or when dominated by plant growth, or by aquatic plant decay, rivers usually in Classes 1, 2 and 3 may have BODs and dissolved oxygen levels, or ammonia content outside the stated levels for those Classes. When this occurs the cause should be stated along with analytical results.

(b) The BOD determinations refer to 5 day carbonaceous BOD (ATU). Ammonia figures are expressed as NH_4.

(c) In most instances the chemical classification given above will be suitable. However, the basis of the classification is restricted to a finite number of chemical determinants and there may be a few cases where the presence of a chemical substance other than those used in the classification markedly reduces the quality of the water. In such cases, the quality classification of the water should be downgraded on the basis of the biota actually present, and the reasons stated.

(d) EIFAC (European Inland Fisheries Advisory Commission) limits should be expressed as 95% percentile limits.

[a] EEC category A2 and A3 requirements are those specified in the EEC Council Directive of 16 June 1975 concerning the Quality of Surface Water intended for Abstraction of Drinking Water in the Member States.
[b] This may not apply if there is a high degree of re-aeration.

28 January 1977.

APPENDIX 3.3.   SCOTTISH   DEVELOPMENT
DEPARTMENT

	Parameter limits		
Category	*Biochemical oxygen demand mg/litre*	*Dissolved oxygen % saturation*	*Total ammonia as NH_4 mg/litre*
1	5	60	0.9
2	7	50	1.3
3	9	40	—
4	17	10	—
5	> 17	< 10	—

(1) Categories are to be assigned on this basis of the higher numbered (lowest) category given by any of the three parameters.

(2) If there are n samples from a particular site for a sampling period (e.g. 1 year) the category should be determined as follows:

(i) if $n \leq 4$ the category shall be satisfied only if all the samples comply;

(ii) if $4 < n \leq 29$ the category shall be satisfied only if $(n - 1)$ samples comply.

(3) BOD determinations shall be made with ATU where this would have a significant effect on the result. In marginal cases a due allowance may be made when dealing with unsuppressed samples.

4

The Oxygen Balance in Rivers and Pipelines

J.K. WALTERS
Senior Lecturer in Chemical Engineering,
University of Nottingham, UK

Healthy rivers and streams support a wide variety of animal and plant life, all of which require oxygen for respiration. The oxygen present is dissolved in the water and is replenished by reoxygenation from the atmosphere. Pollution in a stream reduces the dissolved oxygen because the polluting materials themselves require oxygen for their own destruction by bacteria. Animals and plants are adversely affected by lower oxygen levels, as we shall see in Chapter 5. The actual level of oxygen in a stream is determined largely by a balance between the oxygen demand of the pollutants and the reoxygenation capacity of the stream. Before we can consider this oxygen balance in detail we must consider the two aspects of it separately. We will begin by considering the oxygen demand of the polluting materials.

4.1. THE BIOCHEMICAL OXYGEN DEMAND (BOD)

The biochemical oxygen demand is a measure of the presence in aqueous solution of organic materials which can support the growth of microbial organisms. It is the most widely known test in the field of water pollution control and measures the quantity of dissolved oxygen consumed in the aerobic microbial oxidation of the water sample within a specified time and at a specified temperature. The conditions specified are normally five days at $20°C$ and the result is knows as the five-day biochemical oxygen demand at $20°C$, commonly abbreviated to BOD_5. Full details of the laboratory procedure can be found in *Standard Methods for the Examination of Water and Waste Water*[15] and will only be given in brief outline here. The sample is diluted with water at $20°C$ and seeded with the appropriate microbial organisms. The diluted sample is divided into two portions, one of which is analysed immediately for dissolved oxygen. The other is placed in a stoppered bottle with no air space and incubated at 20°C in the dark. After five days it is analysed for dissolved oxygen and the BOD_5 of the original sample is calculated from the difference of the two dissolved oxygen analyses and the known dilution.

In the laboratory the measurement of BOD_5 is a static batch process, whereas in a river, stream or pipeline the microbial oxidation occurs within the moving body of water and is a dynamic and continuous process. It is normal to assume that the laboratory test is reasonably representative of the natural processes that occur in a river, although it has been suggested[11] that the rates of oxidation, at least in some rivers,can be much higher than in the laboratory test. The five-day BOD measurements are useful as historical records or as post-mortem examinations after accidental or inadvertent pollutional discharges to a stream, but are no use for direct quality control, because of the length of time of the test. The dissolved oxygen is consumed in reactions which produce new microbial cells from the organic material in the water. With time the older cells die and the organic materials associated with them are themselves consumed in further reactions. This synthesis and lysis of the cells continues until the number of viable cells is greatly reduced and only relatively stable organic materials, rather like humus, remain. The BOD_5 clearly measures only part of this overall process, which is better characterised by the rate constant for the reactions and the overall quantity of oxygen consumed.

4.2. THE STABILISATION OXYGEN DEMAND

The stabilisation oxygen demand is the quantity of dissolved oxygen consumed in the reactions through the point where death of the microbial organisms is essentially complete and only the relatively stable organic materials—the products of reactions and lysed cells—remain. It is essentially a measure of the biologically degradable pollutional load in the water. Instead of using the actual pollutant concentration, the quantity of oxygen required for its oxidation is used, because it is the effect of the pollutant in reducing the oxygen concentration in the water that is important in the context of the environment.

By making biochemical oxygen demand tests for periods of time other than five days or by using respirometric techniques it is possible to build up the oxygen utilisation curve for the waste as a function of time. Three such curves are shown in Fig. 4.1, all of which have the same value for BOD_5.

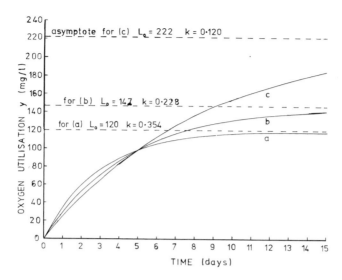

FIG. 4.1. Oxygen utilisation during first-stage BOD. The five-day BOD is 100 mg/litre for all three curves.

The asymptote on the oxygen utilisation axis which each curve approaches at large values of time t is the stabilisation oxygen demand L_0 for that particular waste water and, although the BOD_5 values are the same, the stabilisation oxygen demand values are very different. Waste water (a) is rapidly oxidised, has a larger effect over short time periods and therefore contains material that is rapidly degraded biologically. Waste water (c) on the other hand is only slowly oxidised, has a large effect over long time periods and therefore contains material that is only slowly degraded biologically and which is much more persistent. Waste water (b) is intermediate between (a) and (c).

4.3. THE FIRST-STAGE BOD CURVE

The curves shown in Fig. 4.1 are typical of what is known as the first-stage BOD curve, which is generally modelled as a first-order chemical reaction. The concentration L measured as biochemical oxygen demand of oxidisable material present is the rate-determining factor, provided there is sufficient oxygen present in solution. Sufficient oxygen is generally taken to mean a concentration of at least 20% of saturation. The equation is:

$$\frac{dL}{dt} = -kL \qquad (4.1)$$

or $$L = L_0 e^{-kt} \qquad (4.2)$$

where L = the BOD remaining at time t—the concentration of the
   remaining oxidisable material (mg/litre),
L_0 = the stabilisation oxygen demand (mg/litre),
and k = the rate constant (day^{-1}).

The reactions are quite slow so the time t is measured in days. Neither L
nor L_0 can be measured but the difference between them is the oxygen
utilisation y:

$$y = L_0 - L \qquad (4.3)$$

so that

$$y = L_0(1 - e^{-kt}) \qquad (4.4)$$

which is the equation of the first-stage BOD curve. To evaluate k and L_0 a
curve-fitting procedure must be used, a single measurement of the BOD$_5$
being clearly insufficient. At least two measurements of BOD at different
times are required. Values of k lie in the decade 0.1 to 1.0 day^{-1} at 20°C.
Values of L_0, of course, depend entirely on the quantity of polluting matter
present in the water. Some typical values of both k and L_0 are given in
Table 4.1 from Fair.[5] Values for particular industrial effluents will depend
on the nature of the effluent and analyses should be made to determine k
and L_0. In natural waters a value of k of 0.23 day^{-1} is well established for
large streams flowing with moderate velocity.

Values of the stabilisation oxygen demand of different streams are
additive and may be included in a material balance around the confluence

TABLE 4.1
TYPICAL RATE CONSTANTS AND STABILISATION OXYGEN DEMANDS
20°C*

	$k(day^{-1})$	$L_0(mg/litre)$
Weak waste water	0.35	150
Strong waste water	0.39	250
Primary sewage effluent	0.35	75–150
Secondary sewage effluent	0.12–0.23	15–75
Tap water	<0.12	0–1

*From Fair, Geyer and Okun,[5] with permission.

in the same way as other components. The five-day BOD values on the other hand are *not* additive and are insufficient in themselves to characterise the water. They should only be compared if the rate constants k are the same.

Both k and L_0 depend upon temperature T and in the case of k the van't Hoff Arrhenius equation may be used:

$$\frac{d(\ln k)}{dT} = \frac{E}{RT^2} \tag{4.5}$$

giving

$$k = k_{T_0} \exp\frac{E(T - T_0)}{RTT_0} \simeq k_{T_0} e^{C_k(T - T_0)} \tag{4.6}$$

where E = the energy of activation of the BOD reactions,

T_0 = the reference temperature, usually taken as 293 K,

R = the universal gas constant,

and $C_k = E/RT_0^2$.

We are mostly interested in temperatures near to 293 K so that T in the denominator of the exponential in eqn. (4.6) may be approximated by T_0. E may be taken as 33 kJ/mole and taking T_0 as 293 K (20°C) we find that C_k is 0.046 K^{-1}. At lower temperatures E increases and may be as high as 100 kJ/mole at 273 K (0°C), whereas at temperatures above about 303 K (30°C) E becomes negative and may fall to -24 kJ/mole leading to a decrease in k. However, most streams are close to 20°C so the values given above for E and C_k may be used in the absence of experimental data on the system in question.

The stabilisation oxygen demand was found by Theriault[18] to be linearly dependent on temperature:

$$(L_0)_T = (L_0)_{T_0}[1 + 0.02(T - T_0)] \tag{4.7}$$

The reference temperature T_0 is again usually taken as 293 K (20°C). It is not immediately obvious why L_0 should vary with temperature and indeed Gotaas[8] reported that it did not. Most wastes consist of a mixture of many different organic compounds and L_0 represents the overall effect of all of them. Some may only be degraded if the temperature is high enough and would thus give rise to an apparent increase of L_0 with T.

Example 4.1. At 20°C an effluent has a reaction rate constant of 0.39 day^{-1} and a five-day BOD of 250 mg/litre. The temperature coefficient C_k is 0.046 K^{-1}. Find (*a*) the reaction rate constant at 10°C;

(b) the stabilisation oxygen demand at 20°C and 10°C; and (c) the five-day BOD at 10°C.

Solution

(a) Using eqn. (4.6) $k_{10} = 0.39e^{0.046(10-20)} = 0.246$ day^{-1}.

(b) Using eqn. (4.4) at 20°C: $250 = L_0(1 - e^{-0.39 \times 5})$, hence $L_0 = 291$ mg/litre at 20°C.

Using eqn. (4.7):

$(L_0)_{10} = 291[1 + 0.02(10 - 20)] = 234$ mg/litre.

(c) At 10°C using eqn. (5.4): $y = 234(1 - e^{-0.246 \times 5}) = 166$ mg/litre, i.e. the five-day BOD at 10°C is 166 mg/litre.

The assumption of a first-order reaction for the BOD oxidation is an oversimplification which is adequate for most purposes, but complications can occur for several reasons. Some of these can be incorporated into the first-stage BOD model quite easily:

(i) there may be insufficient microorganisms present to initiate the BOD reactions. A delay or lag then occurs which can be taken into account by replacing t in eqns. (4.2) and (4.4) by $(t - t_0)$, where t_0 is the duration of the lag. The effect is to shift the origin of the curves in Fig. 4.1 along the abscissa to t_0.

(ii) Some waste waters contain chemical reducing agents or may have undergone some anaerobic decomposition. Such waters exert an immediate oxygen demand y_0 and consume a great deal of the dissolved oxygen in a very short time. This may be taken into account by replacing y in eqns. (4.3) and (4.4) by $(y - y_0)$. The effect in this case is to shift the origin of the curves in Fig. 4.1 along the ordinate to y_0.

(iii) The different materials in the waste are oxidized at different rates and the first-order model described so far uses some average value for the rate constant k. This approach is fine for many wastes where the different materials are not too dissimilar. However, if a number of distinct components can be identified and these are found to have widely different rate constants, it is better to apply eqn. (4.1) to each component i in turn. The resulting oxygen utilisation eqn. (4.4) then becomes

$$y = L_0(1 - \Sigma p_i e^{-k_i t}) \qquad (4.8)$$

where L_0 is now the sum of the stabilisation oxygen demands of the individual components and p_i is the fraction of L_0 contributed by component i. It is only worth pursuing this route if the p_i are comparable and the k_i differ by an order of magnitude from each other. An alternative approach is to assume all the components have the same rate constant k but that k decreases with time. In eqn. (4.1) k is then replaced by $k/(1 + at)$ where a is the coefficient of retardation. Integration of this new equation leads to:

$$L = L_0[1 - (1 + at)^{-k/a}] \qquad (4.9)$$

In the limit as $a \to 0$ this equation reduces to the exponential form of eqn. (4.2). Both these approaches were discussed by Gameson and Wheatland[7]. Both give better curve fits than the first-order equation because a greater number of parameters are included. As a consequence more experimental data are required to evaluate the constants. In most cases the simple first-order equation is sufficient.

4.4. THE NITROGENOUS OXYGEN DEMAND

The first-stage BOD curve describes the aerobic bacterial oxidation of carbonaceous compounds. In addition nitrifying bacteria will oxidize ammonia (or ammonium ion) and nitrite to nitrate, *Nitrosomonas* oxidizing the ammonia to nitrite and *Nitrobacter* oxidising the nitrite to nitrate, both bacteria producing bacterial cells with the general formula $C_5H_7NO_2$[12]. The ammonia is first produced by the breakdown of the organic nitrogen materials in the carbonaceous stage so nitrification proceeds slowly at first and then speeds up towards the end of the first stage and slows down again as the ammonia becomes oxidised. An equation describing this nitrogenous oxidation was put forward by Miyake[10]:

$$y_N = \frac{L_N e^{k_N(t - t_1)}}{1 + e^{k_N(t - t_1)}} \qquad (4.10)$$

where y_N is the oxygen consumed in nitrification, L_N is the initial nitrogenous oxygen demand (analogous to the stabilisation oxygen demand L_0 of the first-stage BOD curve) and t_1 is the time at which half the nitrogenous oxidation has been completed. The nitrification rate constant k_N is about five times the first-stage BOD rate constant. Superimposing the oxygen uptake from eqn. (4.10) on the first-stage BOD curve will produce an increase in oxygen utilisation in the region of $t = t_1$. This is clearly shown in Fig. 4.2 where the total oxygen demand $(y + y_N)$ from eqns. (4.4) and (4.10) is plotted for $L_N = 74$ mg/litre, $k_N = 1.2$ day^{-1} and $t_1 = 11$ days. The first-stage curve is curve (b) from Fig. 4.1.

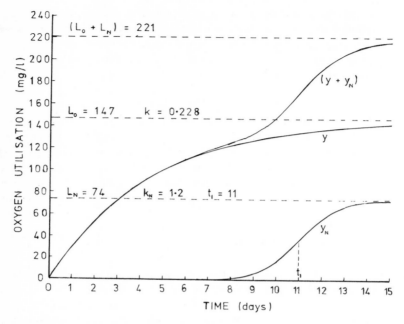

FIG. 4.2. Oxygen utilisation with nitrogenous oxygen demand and first-stage BOD

4.5. THE CHEMICAL OXYGEN DEMAND (COD)

The amount of oxidisable material present in the sample that can be oxidised by a strong chemical oxidant is known as the chemical oxygen demand. The oxidant usually used is a boiling mixture of potassium dichromate and sulphuric acid. The excess dichromate is titrated with ferrous ammonium sulphate and the COD is calculated from the amount of dichromate consumed. For full details of the method the reader should refer to *Standard Methods.*[15] Correlation of COD with BOD is not easy and depends very much on the nature of the organic material in the sample. Some organic compounds are degraded biologically but are not attacked by acid dichromate, for example acetic acid, while the reverse is true for other compounds such as cellulose. The advantage of the COD test is that it is much quicker than the BOD test — a matter of hours rather than days — and it is in common use as a basis for charging by the Water Authorities.

Other oxidising agents can be used, a common one being potassium permanganate when the result is known as the Permanganate Value (PV). It is not such a strong oxidising agent and the COD test with acid dichromate is to be preferred.

4.6. THE ULTIMATE OXYGEN DEMAND (UOD)

The total amount of oxygen required for complete oxidation of the organic material to CO_2, H_2O and NO_3^- is known as the ultimate oxygen demand or UOD. It can be estimated from the stoichiometric coefficients in the reactions:

$$C + O_2 \rightarrow CO_2$$
$$2H_2 + O_2 \rightarrow 2H_2O$$
$$NH_3 + 2O_2 \rightarrow NO_3^- + H^+ + H_2O$$
$$2NO_2^- + O_2 \rightarrow 2NO_3^-$$

so that

$$\text{UOD (mg/litre)} = \frac{32}{12}u + \frac{2 \times 32}{14}v + \frac{32}{2 \times 14}w + \frac{32}{2 \times 2}x - z$$

i.e.
$$\text{UOD} = 2.67u + 4.57v + 1.14w + 8x - z \qquad (4.11)$$

where u = organic carbon (mg/litre as C),

v = organic nitrogen and ammoniacal nitrogen (mg/litre as N)

w = nitrite nitrogen (mg/litre as N),

x = organic hydrogen (mg/litre as H),

and z = organic oxygen (mg/litre as O).

It should be noted that for many degradable organic compounds the number of hydrogen atoms in the compound is twice the number of oxygen atoms and so the last two terms in eqn. (4.11) cancel, i.e. $8x = z$. This is true for carbohydrates such as glucose ($C_6H_{12}O_6$) and for other compounds, e.g., acetic acid (CH_3COOH), glyceraldehyde ($CH_2OH \cdot CHOH \cdot CHO$) and lactic acid ($CH_3 \cdot CHOH \cdot COOH$). However, some compounds have more oxygen so that $8x < z$, e.g., citric acid $C_3H_4OH \cdot (COOH)_3$, while others such as glycerol ($CH_2OH \cdot CHOH \cdot CH_2OH$) have less oxygen so that $8x > z$. Without a detailed knowledge of the constituents of the waste it is usual to assume $8x = z$ and to use only the first three terms in eqn. (4.11) to estimate the ultimate oxygen demand.

4.7. THE BENTHIC OXYGEN DEMAND

The life forms living in the muddy deposits on the bottom of a river are known as the benthos. Purification of the benthic deposits takes place by aerobic oxidation in the surface layers and anaerobic decomposition in the underlying layers. Rate constants for the reactions are one to two orders of magnitude smaller than those for the BOD reactions in the overlying water. The benthic demand remains at a fixed position in the river and therefore affects different waters from moment to moment as the stream flows past. The oxygen demand of the main stream, on the other hand, moves downstream with the river and is subject to a varying benthic demand. The interaction of the two effects on the oxygen consumption of the water is complex, but in many cases the benthic demand is so low and the benthic rate constant so small, that the benthic demand may be ignored in comparison with the mainstream BOD. An exception would be down stream of an outfall with a high Suspended Solids content that settles out to form a high benthic demand.

4.8. DISSOLVED OXYGEN (DO)

The saturation concentration of dissolved oxygen in distilled water at $20°C$ is 9.3 mg/litre. It decreases with an increase of temperature and decreases with an increase of the dissolved solids content. In sea water with about 3.3% wt. dissolved solids the solubility is about 82% that of fresh water. The solubility in domestic waste waters is about 95% that of clean water. The solubility data in Table 4.2 was calculated from the Henry's law constants given in the International Critical Tables.[9] The solubility depends on the partial pressure and since the composition of air may be taken as constant, the solubility may be taken as proportional to the total pressure for variations of atmospheric pressure normally encountered. Thus if atmospheric pressure is 1.0 bar the solubility is about 1.3% less than that given in Table 4.2.

The rate of reaeration of a moving body of water with oxygen from the atmosphere depends on the rate of solution (absorption) through the air/water interface and on the rate of dispersion within the body of water beneath the surface. The driving force for oxygen transfer is the difference between the dissolved oxygen concentration at saturation and the actual concentration present in the water. The simple 'two-film' model serves adequately to describe the transfer of oxygen from the atmosphere to the

TABLE 4.2

SATURATION CONCENTRATIONS OF DISSOLVED OXYGEN IN FRESH
WATER IN EQUILIBRIUM WITH AIR AT 1.013 bar TOTAL PRESSURE

Temp (°C)	DO (mg/litre)	Temp (°C)	DO (mg/litre)	Temp (°C)	DO (mg/litre)
0	14.6				
1	14.2	11	11.1	21	9.14
2	13.9	12	10.9	22	8.98
3	13.5	13	10.7	23	8.83
4	13.2	14	10.4	24	8.68
5	12.8	15	10.2	25	8.54
6	12.5	16	10.0	26	8.40
7	12.2	17	9.84	27	8.26
8	11.9	18	9.65	28	8.13
9	11.7	19	9.48	29	7.99
10	11.4	20	9.31	30	7.86

water. The main resistance to mass transfer is on the liquid side of the
interface so the absorption is liquid film controlled. The gas film resistance
is very small. We may therefore take

$$N = k_L(c_s - c) \tag{4.12}$$

where N = flux of oxygen through the surface $[ML^{-2}T^{-1}]$,
   k_L = mass transfer coefficient $[ML^{-2}T^{-1}\Delta C^{-1}]$ or $[LT^{-1}]$,
   c_s = saturation concentration of oxygen $[ML^{-3}]$,
and c = concentration of oxygen at time t $[ML^{-3}]$.

The rate of dispersion within the underlying water depends on molecular
diffusion in stagnant or slow moving streams and on turbulent eddy
diffusion in fast moving streams. If we assume the water is well mixed, the
rate of change of the oxygen concentration with time dc/dt will be given by
the flux N multiplied by the area of the air/water interface A divided by the
volume of water V beneath that interface. Thus:

$$\frac{NA}{V} = \frac{dc}{dt} = k_L \frac{A}{V}(c_s - c) = r(c_s - c) \tag{4.13}$$

where r is defined as $k_L A/V$ and is known as the reaeration rate constant or
the reoxygenation rate constant. For deep bodies of water with small
surface area such as fjords or lakes in rift valleys, e.g., Loch Ness, V/A is
large and reoxygenation of the deeper layers of water takes place very

slowly. For ordinary rivers V/A is the mean depth H and is of the order of a few metres. Integration of eqn. (4.13) between the limits $(c_0, 0)$ and (c, t) gives:

$$(c_s - c) = (c_s - c_0)e^{-rt} \qquad (4.14)$$

The quantity $(c_s - c)$ is the difference between the saturation concentration of oxygen and the actual concentration and is known as the *dissolved oxygen deficit* and given the symbol D. It is customary to work in terms of D so that eqn. (4.14) may be rewritten as

$$D = D_0 e^{-rt} \qquad (4.15)$$

The dissolved oxygen deficit thus decreases exponentially with time to zero when the water is saturated with oxygen. The rate constant r increases with temperature in accordance with the van't Hoff Arrhenius equation

$$r = r_{T_0} e^{C_r(T - T_0)} \qquad (4.16)$$

where the reference temperature T_0 is usually taken as 293 K (20°C). The temperature characteristic C_r may be taken as 0.024 K^{-1} at the temperatures experienced by most rivers. The value of r depends on the mass transfer coefficient k_L and the mixing characteristics of the water. Owens, Edwards and Gibbs[13] have shown that for British rivers the mass transfer coefficient depends on the river velocity and the mean depth of the river:

$$k_L = 5.33 \, U^{0.67}/H^{0.85} \text{ m day}^{-1} \qquad (4.17)$$

where $U =$ mean velocity of flow (m/s)
$\quad\quad\quad H =$ mean depth (m) (equals V/A)

and hence

$$r = k_L \frac{A}{V} = 5.3 \, U^{0.67}/H^{1.85} \text{ day}^{-1} \qquad (4.18)$$

The mass transfer coefficient is also known as the exchange coefficient. Published values were summarised by Gameson and Truesdale.[6] The range of values encountered are shown in Table 4.3. These values may be used to estimate k_L from a qualitative description of the river if U and H are not known. Churchill, Elmore and Buckingham[3] have related r directly to the stream velocity U and the hydraulic radius R of the river cross-section which is the ratio of the cross-sectional area through which the river flows to the wetted perimeter P—the distance from bank to bank along the bottom of the river:

$$r = 5.2 \, U/R^{5/3} \qquad (4.19)$$

TABLE 4.3
TYPICAL VALUES FOR THE MASS TRANSFER COEFFICIENT
k_L (m/day)*

Types of water	k_L (m/day)
Stagnant water	0.10–0.15
Water flowing at 0.6 m/min	0.25
Sluggish polluted river	0.5
Sluggish clean water about 5 cm deep	1.0
Thames estuary	1.3
Water flowing at 10 m/min	2
The open sea	3
Water flowing at 15 m/min	7
Turbulent lakeland beck	7–50
Water flowing down a 30° slope	20–70

*After Gameson and Truesdale,[6] with permission.

It should be noted that the constants in eqn. (4.17), (4.18) and (4.19) are not dimensionless and SI units should be used with U in metres per second and R and H in metres. It is not wise to claim too great an accuracy for either eqn. (4.18) or eqn. (4.19) so the constants have been rounded off to two-figure accuracy. The ratio R/H of the hydraulic radius to the mean depth is equal to the ratio W/P of the width W to the wetted perimeter. R is therefore always smaller than H. It is considerably smaller for narrow deep streams, but there is very little difference for wide streams. Equations (4.18) and (4.19) do not usually give the same values of r but for streams flowing at 1 m/s with a width to depth ratio of about 7, similar values of r are obtained from the two equations. Open-channel flow equations may be used to estimate the velocity. The simplest is the Chezy–Manning equation:

$$U = R^{2/3} S^{1/2}/n \qquad (4.20)$$

where S = the gradient of the river surface (dimensionless)
and n = the Manning roughness coefficient, selected values of which are given in Table 4.4.

Extended tables can be found in texts on open channel flow such as Chow[2] and Brater and King.[1] In eqn. (4.20) SI units must be used with U in metres per second and R in metres. Usually n is considered to have the same numerical value whatever system of units is chosen and so may be considered to be dimensionless.

TABLE 4.4
MANNING ROUGHNESS COEFFICIENT n

Channel bottom	n
Smooth cement	0.011
Planed timber	0.012
Concrete pipe	0.013
Brick	0.015
Gravel	0.023
Straight canals	0.020
Badly kept canals	0.030
Natural streams	0.030
Natural streams with weeds and stones	0.045
Sluggish weedy streams	0.060
Very weedy streams	0.100

Example 4.2. A river 46 m wide and 2 m deep has a flow of 2.3×10^6 m³ day⁻¹. Estimate the mass transfer coefficient and the rate of reoxygenation.

Solution

River velocity $U = 2.3 \times 10^6 \dfrac{m^3}{day} \times \dfrac{1}{46 \times 2\,m^2} \times \dfrac{day}{24\,h} \times \dfrac{h}{3600\,s}$

$= 0.289\,m/s$

Hydraulic radius $R \simeq \dfrac{46 \times 2}{(46 + 2 + 2)} = 1.84\,m$

Using eqn. (4.17) $k_L = 5.33 \times (0.289)^{0.67}/2^{0.85} = 1.29\,m\,day^{-1}$

Hence, using eqn. (4.18) $r = 1.29/2 = 0.64\,day^{-1}$

Using eqn. (4.19) $r = 5.2 \times 0.289/1.84^{5/3} = 0.54\,day$

4.9. THE DISSOLVED OXYGEN SAG

The concentration of dissolved oxygen in a stream is a balance between processes tending to reoxygenate the stream and those tending to use up the dissolved oxygen. The main balance is between oxygen uptake from the atmosphere and oxygen consumption by the BOD of the stream, but green plant life does have an effect, oxygen being produced by photosynthesis during the day and being reabsorbed at night with the release of carbon dioxide. This action of plants causes a diurnal variation of dissolved oxygen. The amplitude of the variation depends on the number of plants present, the amount of sunlight and the nature of the stream. The amplitude in a clean stream may be as high as $4\,mg/litre$ dissolved oxygen but downstream of an outfall the amplitude is very much less and seldom higher than $1\,mg/litre$. The BOD in the outfall uses the photosynthetic oxygen as it is formed so that the peaks do not build up. It is the downstream region that is of most interest in pollution control and whilst respiration from plants is an important factor in the total oxygen balance, it is not usually included in engineering calculations, because it cannot be relied upon or predicted. Its presence is a bonus and ignoring it will give conservative values for dissolved oxygen. The basic differential equation describing the change of oxygen concentration with time is therefore taken as a combination of eqn. (4.1)—the BOD reaction consuming oxygen—and eqn. (4.13)—the reaeration from the atmosphere. It is usual to work in terms of the dissolved oxygen deficit D ($= c_s - c$) rather than the concentration c, thus:

$$\frac{dD}{dt} = kL - rD \tag{4.21}$$

$$= kL_0 e^{-kt} - rD \tag{4.22}$$

This is the Streeter–Phelps[16] equation. It was first proposed in 1925 and has been widely used ever since. Its main merit is simplicity and, although more complicated expressions have been proposed, it is doubtful whether their use can be justified at the present time in view of the uncertainties over parameters such as k and r already discussed. The Streeter–Phelps equation is a first-order linear differential equation which on integration from $D = D_0$ at $t = 0$ up to (D, t) yields:

$$D = D_0 e^{-rt} + \frac{kL_0}{r - k}(e^{-kt} - e^{-rt}) \tag{4.23}$$

which is the equation of the dissolved oxygen sag curve. The dissolved oxygen deficit increases initially owing to the BOD passing through a maximum and then decreases to zero as reaeration proceeds further downstream. The dissolved oxygen concentration, of course, passes through a minimum and thus gives the name—oxygen sag curve—to the process. The ratio r/k of the reaeration rate constant to the BOD rate constant is known as the self-purification ratio and often given the symbol f. It is an important characteristic of the stream and is subject to less variation than either r or k on their own. Putting $r = kf$ in eqn. (4.23) leads to:

J.K. Walters

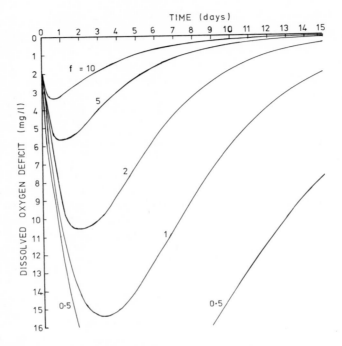

FIG. 4.3. Oxygen sag curves for different values of the self-purification factor f. For all curves $D_0 = 2$ mg/litre, $L_0 = 40$ mg/litre and $k = 0.3$ day^{-1}.

$$D = \frac{L_0}{(f-1)} e^{-kt} \left\{ 1 - \left[1 - (f-1)\frac{D_0}{L_0} \right] e^{-(f-1)kt} \right\} \qquad (4.24)$$

Care must be taken in evaluating this equation (and those that follow) when $f = 1$. In fact it is necessary to put $f = (1 + \varepsilon)$, where ε is small, simplify the equations and then allow ε to tend to zero.

Typical curves are shown in Fig. 4.3 for different values of f. For all curves D_0 is taken as 2 mg/litre, L_0 as 40 mg/litre and k as 0.3 day^{-1}. The curves are characterised by the point of maximum deficit, known as the critical point, and given the general coordinates (D_c, t_c), and the point of inflection (D_i, t_i) where the rate of increase of the dissolved oxygen concentration is a maximum, known as the point of maximum recovery. The critical point is obtained by putting the first derivative dD/dt equal to zero in eqn. (4.22):

$$L_0 e^{-kt_c} = f D_c \qquad (4.25)$$

Also we may put $D = D_c$ and $t = t_c$ in eqn. (4.24) to obtain:

$$D_c = \frac{L_0 e^{-kt_c}}{(f-1)}\left\{1 - \left[1 - (f-1)\frac{D_0}{L_0}\right]e^{-(f-1)kt_c}\right\} \qquad (4.26)$$

We therefore have two equations for the two unknowns kt_c and D_c which can be solved simultaneously to give:

$$kt_c = \frac{1}{(f-1)}\ln\left\{f\left[1 - (f-1)\frac{D_0}{L_0}\right]\right\} \qquad (4.27)$$

$$\text{and } D_c = \frac{L_0 e^{-kt_c}}{f} = \frac{L_0}{f\left\{f\left[1 - (f-1)\frac{D_0}{L_0}\right]\right\}^{\frac{1}{f-1}}} \qquad (4.28)$$

Example 4.3. An effluent with a five-day BOD of 222 mg/litre is discharged at $0.23 \times 10^6 \, \text{m}^3 \, \text{day}^{-1}$ into the river of Example 4.2. The stabilisation oxygen demand of the river upstream of the discharge is 2 mg/litre. The BOD reaction rate constants are 0.23 day^{-1} for the river and 0.39 day^{-1} for the effluent. The temperature is 20°C and all streams are 90% saturated with oxygen at the outfall. Calculate the critical points D_c and t_c downstream.

Solution

For the effluent using eq. (4.4) $222 = L_0(1 - e^{-0.39 \times 5})$ hence $L_0 = 259$ mg/litre. A material balance on the stabilisation oxygen demand at the outfall enables $(L_0)_m$ the value for the mixed flow just downstream to be calculated:

$$(2.3 + 0.23) \times 10^6 (L_0)_m = 0.23 \times 10^6 \times 259 + 2.3 \times 10^6 \times 2$$

hence

$$(L_0)_m = 25.3 \text{ mg/litre}$$

From Table 4.2 the dissolved oxygen saturation concentration at 20°C is 9.31 mg/litre. Hence the dissolved oxygen deficit $D_0 = 9.31(1 - 0.9) = 0.93$ mg/litre. Taking the smaller of the two values of r from Example 4.2, we find that the self-purification factor $f = 0.54/0.23 = 2.35$. So using eqn. (4.28):

$$D_c = \frac{25.3}{2.35\{2.35[1 - 1.35 \times 0.93/25.3]\}^{1/1.35}} = 5.94 \text{ mg/litre}$$

and therefore the dissolved oxygen concentration $= 9.31 - 5.94$ $= 3.37$ mg/litre. From eqn. (4.27):

$$kt_c = (1/1.35)\ln\{2.35[1 - 1.35 \times 0.93/25.3]\} = 0.595$$

and hence $t_c = 0.595/0.23 = 2.59$ days

The point of inflection is obtained by putting the second derivative d^2D/dt^2 equal to zero. Differentiating eqn. (4.24) twice and equating to zero gives, after some algebra:

$$kt_i = \frac{1}{(f - 1)}\ln\left\{f^2\left[1 - (f - 1)\frac{D_0}{L_0}\right]\right\} \tag{4.29}$$

Substituting back into eqn. (4.24) then gives:

$$D_i = \frac{f + 1}{f^2}\cdot L_0 e^{-kt_i} \tag{4.30}$$

The critical point and the point of inflection are related to each other by simpler relationships. From eqns. (4.27) and (4.29):

$$k(t_i - t_c) = \frac{\ln f}{(f - 1)} \tag{4.31}$$

and from eqns. (4.28), (4.30) and (4.31):

$$\frac{D_i}{D_c} = \frac{f + 1}{f^{f/(f - 1)}} \tag{4.32}$$

These are both functions only of f and so in principle f can be determined by measuring the dissolved oxygen content downstream of an outfall, locating D_c and D_i and calculating f from eqn. (4.32) or eqn. (4.31). Unfortunately the right-hand side of eqn. (4.32) is very insensitive to f. It tends to unity as $f \to 0$ and as $f \to \infty$ and is 0.736 (2/e) at $f = 1$. It is symmetrical on a logarithmic scale about $f = 1$. The right-hand side of eqn. (4.31) is a monotonic decreasing function of f. Values of both these

TABLE 4.5
SOME FUNCTIONS OF f

f	0.1	0.2	0.5	1.0	2	5	10
$\dfrac{f+1}{f^{f/(f-1)}}$	0.852	0.802	0.750	0.736	0.750	0.802	0.852
$\dfrac{\ln f}{(f-1)}$	2.56	2.01	1.39	1.0	0.693	0.402	0.256

functions are given in Table 4.5. BOD measurements on samples from the stream may be used to calculate k. The time of flow $t_i - t_c$ between the critical point and the point of inflection may be estimated by dividing the length of reach between D_c and D_i by the stream velocity. Equation (4.31) may then be used to estimate f.

A better method of estimating f is to make joint measurements of the five-day BOD and the dissolved oxygen concentration at points downstream from the outfall. A plot of the dissolved oxygen profile allows the critical point to be determined and a plot of the five-day BOD against distance downstream on log/linear paper allows the BOD rate constant k to be estimated, provided the stream velocity is known. Equation (4.28) may then be used to evaluate f:

$$f = \frac{L_0 e^{-kt_c}}{D_c}$$

$$= \frac{\text{stabilisation oxygen demand at the critical point}}{\text{dissolved oxygen deficit at the critical point}} \quad (4.33)$$

Because both r and k vary exponentially with the absolute temperature T according to the van't Hoff Arrhenius equation, the self-purification factor f, which is the ratio of r to k, will have a similar dependence. Combining eqns. (4.6) and (4.16) we obtain

$$f = f_{T_0} e^{C_f(T - T_0)} \quad (4.34)$$

where
$$C_f = C_r - C_k \quad (4.35)$$

The reference temperature is again usually taken as 293 K (20°C). Using the values of C_r and C_k given before, C_f becomes $-0.022 \, \text{K}^{-1}$ indicating that an increase in temperature reduces f. Values of f are less dependent on temperature than either k or r and generally lie between 1 and 5 at 20°C. Values may be estimated from the nature of the stream using Fig. 4.4.

Example 4.4. The measurements given below were made downstream of an outfall. Calculate the reaction rate constant for the BOD reaction, the stabilisation oxygen demand at the outfall, the river self-purification ratio f and the river reoxygenation rate constant.

Time downstream (days)	0.5	1.0	1.5	2.0	2.5	3.0	3.5
Five-day BOD (mg/litre)	24.8	22.0	19.5	17.3	15.3	13.6	12.1
Dissolved oxygen concentration (mg/litre)	3.72	2.54	1.49	0.91	0.85	1.07	1.48

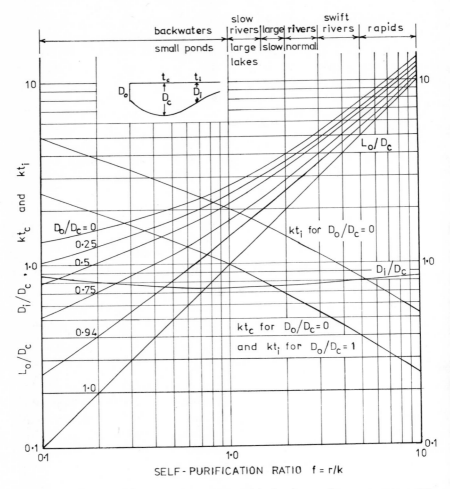

FIG. 4.4. Characteristics of streams at the critical point on the oxygen sag curve. After Fair,[4] with permission.

Solution

Figure 4.5(a) shows a plot of the five-day BOD versus time on log/linear paper. The gradient is -0.24 and the intercept 27.9 mg/litre. Hence k, the BOD reaction rate constant is 0.24 day^{-1} and the five-day BOD at the outfall is 27.9 mg/litre. Using eqn. (4.4) at the outfall gives:

$$27.9 = L_0(1 - e^{-0.24 \times 5})$$

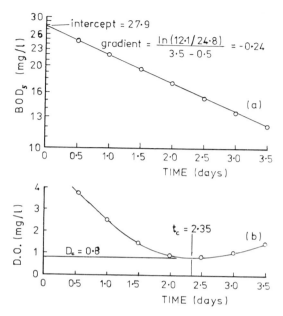

FIG. 4.5. Data from Example 4.4: (a) five-day BOD versus time, (b) dissolved oxygen concentration versus time.

and hence the stabilization oxygen demand at the outfall $L_0 = 39.9$ mg/litre. Fig. 4.5(b) shows the dissolved oxygen concentration versus time, whence $t_c = 2.35$ days and the minimum dissolved oxygen concentration is 0.8 mg/litre. From Table 4.2 the dissolved oxygen saturation concentration is 9.31 mg/litre and hence $D_c = 9.31 - 0.8 = 8.5$ mg/litre. From eqn. (4.2) the stabilisation oxygen demand after 2.35 days can be found as $39.9e^{-0.24 \times 2.35} = 22.7$ mg/litre. Hence from eqn. (4.33) $f = 22.7/8.5 = 2.67$. The reoxygenation rate constant $r = fk = 2.67 \times 0.24 = 0.64$ day^{-1}.

The critical point on the dissolved oxygen sag curve is the most important region of the curve and its coordinates are given by eqns. (4.27) and (4.28) in terms of f and the ratio D_0/L_0. Thus conditions downstream from a given outfall can easily be determined. The converse problem of calculating the outfall conditions when the critical point D_c is specified can be done by trial-and-error solution of eqn. (4.28) for D_0/L_0. However, it is often more convenient to use the graphical method developed by Fair.[4] In principle eqns. (4.27) and (4.28) can be rearranged to give both kt_c and L_0/D_c as functions of f and D_0/D_c. Although analytic expressions cannot be obtained, the results can be depicted graphically as a logarithmic plot of L_0/D_c versus f with D_0/D_c as parameter, as shown in Fig. 4.4 after Fair.[4]

4.10. MAXIMUM ALLOWABLE STREAM LOADING

To avoid complete deoxygenation of a stream the largest dissolved oxygen deficit (D_c) must not exceed the dissolved oxygen saturation value. To support game fish, such as trout and salmon, the dissolved oxygen content must not fall below about 5 mg/litre which corresponds to a deficit of about 4.3 mg/litre at 20°C. From this approach we see that the use to which the stream is to be put determines the maximum dissolved oxygen sag that can be tolerated. From this we can calculate the maximum value of the stabilisation oxygen demand L_0 that we can permit just downstream of an outfall. It is this maximum value of L_0 that is known as the maximum allowable stream loading. The self-purification factor f is determined by the characteristics of the stream, the initial dissolved oxygen deficit D_0 by the conditions prevailing at the outfall and the maximum dissolved oxygen deficit D_c by the use to which the stream is to be put. L_0 can then be found from Fig. 4.4. It should be noted that D_0/D_c always lies between 0 and 1 and that $t_c = 0$ for $D_0 = D_c$, i.e. when the critical point occurs at the outfall. The maximum allowable loading is largest when $D_0 = 0$, when the stream is initially saturated with oxygen, and least when $D_0 = D_c$.

The maximum allowable stream loading $(L_0)_m$ may be related to the stabilisation oxygen demand of the effluent outfall $(L_0)_w$ and the stabilisation oxygen demand of the river $(L_0)_R$ just upstream of the outfall by taking a material balance around the outfall:

$$(L_0)_w W + (L_0)_R R = (L_0)_m (R + W) \tag{4.36}$$

where W = volumetric flow of the effluent outfall,
and R = volumetric flow of the river upstream.

$(L_0)_R$ depends on the previous history of the river upstream and $(L_0)_m$ on the use to which the stream is to be put downstream. The effluent flow W and its oxygen demand $(L_0)_w$ are not independent quantities but must be related by eqn. (4.36). Thus an outfall of known oxygen demand will have an upper bound on the flow rate that can be discharged in order to keep the river oxygen demand within the maximum allowable stream loading. Similarly an outfall of known flow rate will have an upper bound on its oxygen demand for the same reason. This interdependence of $(L_0)_w$ and W is an important point that should be borne in mind when considering an effluent discharge to a river.

4.11. DILUTION REQUIREMENTS

The ratio, R/W, of the river flow to the outfall flow is known as the dilution. From eqn. (4.36) we see that this is related to the maximum allowable stream loading and the stabilisation oxygen demands of the outfall and the river:

$$\frac{R}{W} = \frac{(L_0)_w - (L_0)_m}{(L_0)_m - (L_0)_R} \tag{4.37}$$

The dilution requirement thus depends on the use of the river downstream, the history of the river upstream and the nature of the outfall. It leads naturally to the upper bound on W, the outfall flow rate, discussed before. Similarly for a given dilution, eqn. (4.36) can be rearranged to give the upper bound on the stabilisation oxygen demand of the outfall:

$$(L_0)_w = (L_0)_m \left(1 + \frac{R}{W}\right) - (L_0)_R \cdot \frac{R}{W} \tag{4.38}$$

As an example, let us consider the derivation of the Royal Commission's[14] recommendation of 20 mg/litre BOD for an outfall to a river. The Commission considered that a river containing 2 mg/litre BOD would still retain its self-purification characteristics even when the downstream BOD was doubled to 4 mg/litre. They also considered an eightfold dilution to be attainable in most UK rivers. Inserting these figures: $(L_0)_m = 4$; $(L_0)_R = 2$ and $R/W = 8$ into eqn. (4.38) leads to $(L_0)_w = 20$ mg/litre. Strictly these BOD values should be the stabilisation oxygen demands but it is quite common for five-day BOD values to be used instead. This is satisfactory if the rate constants k are the same (see Section 4.3) as is often so in the case of discharges from sewage works. For a raw sewage which may have an oxygen demand as high as 500 mg/litre the required dilution, from eqn. (4.37), would be $(500 - 4)/(4 - 2)$ which is 248. Such high dilutions are not usually available in UK rivers and hence treatment of the sewage before discharge is necessary. The dilution requirements (R/W) and the maximum allowable stream loading are complementary to each other and are related by eqn. (4.37)

An alternative way of expressing the dilution requirement is in terms of a volumetric river flow per head of population required to avoid odours and nuisances. Clearly such an approach is only applicable to sewage discharges and cannot be used for industrial effluent outfalls. It has been particularly in use in the USA where the river systems are larger and more suitable for the direct discharge of raw sewage. Recommended values of the stream flow Q vary from 6 to 25 m^3/(day)(capita) with a commonly quoted value of 10. The average sewage flow[17] may be taken as 135 litre/(day)(capita) and it contains a BOD loading of about 68 g/(day)(capita), giving a concentration of BOD equal to 68 000/135 or 504 mg/litre which is in agreement with the figure given above. The dilution ratio may be related to Q as $R/W = Q \times 1000/135$ or $R/W = 7.4Q$. Taking Q as 10 then gives $R/W = 74$. This is much smaller than the value of 248 estimated before and implies that this method gives rise to a rather larger BOD in the river downstream of the outfall. We may calculate its value by solving eqn. (4.36) for $(L_0)_m$:

$$(L_0)_m = \frac{(L_0)_w + (L_0)_R \times (R/W)}{1 + (R/W)} \qquad (4.39)$$

and hence in this case $(L_0)_m = (504 + 2 \times 74)/(1 + 74) = 8.7$ mg/litre.

Example 4.5. An effluent outfall with a five-day BOD of 80 mg/litre enters a sluggish stream ($f = 1.2$) which has a stabilisation oxygen demand of 12 mg/litre. Both the effluent and the stream have a dissolved oxygen deficit of 7 mg/litre. If the water downstream of the outfall is not to become anaerobic, calculate the maximum allowable stream loading and the dilution requirement. The BOD reaction rate constant for the effluent is 0.35 day^{-1}. The temperature may be assumed to be 20°C.

Solution
Because the effluent and the stream have the same dissolved oxygen deficit, the dissolved oxygen deficit just downstream D_0 will also be 7 mg/litre. Downstream of the outfall the dissolved oxygen concentration may just fall to zero, so the critical deficit equals the saturation concentration.

$$\therefore \quad D_0/D_c = 7/9.31 = 0.75$$

Also $f = 1.2$, so from Fig. 4.4 $L_0/D_c = 1.98$ mg/litre.

$$\therefore \quad \text{the maximum allowable stream loading } L_0 = 1.98 \times 9.31$$
$$= 18.4 \text{ mg/litre.}$$

For the effluent flow we may use eqn. (4.4) to find the stabilisation oxygen demand:

$$80 = L_0(1 - e^{0.35 \times 5})$$

hence for the effluent $L_0 = 96.8$ mg/litre. Using eqn. (4.37) we find:

$$\text{dilution requirement} \quad \frac{R}{W} = \frac{96.8 - 18.4}{18.4 - 12} = 12.2$$

4.12. PIPELINE FLOW

When an organic material flows through a pipeline there may be sufficient microorganisms present to allow BOD reactions to occur. The rate at which the reactions take place will depend on the number of organisms present but will certainly be significant in a rising main in a sewerage system and may be significant with industrial effluents that have to be pumped some distance. Pipelines are normally operated full of water so there is no possibility of reaeration by oxygen transfer through a free surface. The dissolved oxygen content will therefore decrease as the BOD reactions proceed. The progress of the dissolved oxygen deficit along the pipeline will be given by eqns. (4.21), (4.22) and (4.23) with the reaeration rate constant put equal to zero. Hence,

$$D = D_0 + L_0(1 - e^{-kt}) \tag{4.40}$$

When the dissolved oxygen deficit becomes equal to the saturation concentration c_s at the temperature of the pipeline, the water becomes devoid of oxygen and anaerobic bacteria take over. Putrefaction occurs and may give rise to unpleasant odours. Putting D equal to c_s and rearranging eqn. (4.40) for t gives the time at which anaerobic conditions begin:

$$t = (1/k)\ln[L_0/(L_0 + D_0 - c_s)] \tag{4.41}$$

We may then compare this time with the residence time of the water in the pipeline to determine whether anaerobic conditions will occur or not. If anaerobic conditions are predicted and it is important to avoid them, it will be necessary to provide reoxygenation facilities at intervals along the pipeline.

Example 4.6. The effluent in Example 4.1 is pumped at 10°C at a rate of 50 m³/h through a pipeline 30 cm in diameter to an effluent disposal plant

8 km away. Assuming the effluent is saturated with oxygen initially, how much of the pipeline will be under anaerobic conditions?

Solution

Using eqn. (4.41) the time at which anaerobic conditions begin is given by

$$t = (1/0.246)\ln\left[234/(234 + 0 - 11.4)\right]$$
$$= 0.203 \text{ days or } 4.87 \text{ h}$$

The velocity in the pipe line $= 50\dfrac{m^3}{h} \cdot \dfrac{4}{\pi(0.30)^2 m^2} = 707 \text{ m/h}$

∴ the effluent becomes anaerobic after $707 \text{ m/h} \times 4.87 \text{ h} = 3443 \text{ m}$

∴ length of pipeline under anaerobic conditions
$$= 8000 - 3443 \text{ m} = 4.56 \text{ km}.$$

Example 4.7. To avoid anaerobic conditions in the pipeline in Example 4.6 it is proposed to build reaeration units at appropriate points along the pipeline. Each unit increases the dissolved oxygen to the saturation value. How many units are required?

Solution

From Example 4.6 we must aerate every 3.443 km

∴ we require $8/3.443 = 2.32$ aerations

i.e. after the initial aeration at the start of the pipeline we require two reaeration units along the pipeline. Uniform spacing is recommended giving a spacing of 2.67 km between units.

REFERENCES

1. Brater, E.F. and King, H.W., *Handbook of Hydraulics*, 6th edition. McGraw-Hill, New York, 1976.
2. Chow, V.T., *Open-channel Hydraulics*. McGraw-Hill, New York, 1959.
3. Churchill, M.W., Elmore, H.L. and Buckingham, R.A., The prediction of stream reaeration rates, *Advances in Water Pollution Research*, **1** (1964) 89.
4. Fair, G.M., The dissolved oxygen sag — an analysis *Sewage Works J.*, **11** (1939) 445.
5. Fair, G.M., Geyer, J.C. and Okun, D.A., *Elements of Water Supply and Wastewater Disposal*, 2nd edition. John Wiley and Sons, Inc., New York, 1971.
6. Gameson, A.L.H. and Truesdale, G.A., Some oxygen studies in streams, *J. Inst. Wat. Engrs*, **13** (1959) 175.
7. Gameson, A.L.H. and Wheatland, A.B., The ultimate oxygen demand and course of oxidation of sewage effluents *J. Inst. Sew. Purif.*, Part 2 (1958) 106.

8. Gotaas, H.B., Effect of temperature on biochemical oxidation of sewage, *Sewage Works J.*, **20**, (1948) 441.

9. National Research Council, *International Critical Tables* **3**, 257. McGraw-Hill, New York, 1928.

10. Miyake, K., On the nature of ammonification and nitrification *Soil Sci.*, **2** (1916) 481.

11. *Notes on Water Pollution* No. 10, DSIR, September 1960.

12. *Notes on Water Pollution* No. 52, DSIR March 1971.

13. Owens, M., Edwards, R.W. and Gibbs, J.W., Some reaeration studies in streams *Int. J. Air Wat. Poll.*, **8** (1964) 469.

14. *Royal Commission on Sewage Disposal, 1901–1915, 8th Report*. HMSO, London, 1912.

15. *Standard Methods for the Examination of Water and Wastewater*, 14th Edition. American Public Health Assn. Inc., New York, 1977.

16. Streeter, H.W. and Phelps, E.B., *A Study of the Pollution and Natural Purification of the Ohio River*, Bull. US. Public Health Service, No. 146, 1925.

17. Tebbutt, T.H.Y., *Principles of Water Quality Control*. Pergamon, Oxford, 1971.

18. Theriault, E.J., *The Oxygen Demand of Polluted Waters*, Bull. US. Public Health Service, No. 173, 1927, 141.

5

Biological Effects

D.M. HOLDICH

Lecturer in Zoology, University of Nottingham, UK

5.1. INTRODUCTION

Pollution can be defined simply as an adverse alteration of the environment. As most environments are inhabited by living organisms any adverse alteration to the conditions under which they live may have far reaching effects. Although all organisms pollute their own environment to some extent, such natural pollution is of minor importance when compared with the pollution caused by the activities of man. Due to ever increasing population levels and industrialisation most environments are to some extent unnaturally polluted. The root cause of the problem is man's tendency to dilute and disperse wastes rather than to remove them at source.

Water has always been an obvious diluent for waste from urbanisation, industry and agriculture, but in recent years it has become apparent that even the oceans, although covering some 71% of the earth's surface, have only a limited capacity for receiving pollutants. The limit for most pollutants is a long way off, but the future must be considered as well as the present when planning the disposal of wastes. The need for such planning is perhaps more obvious to the biologist than to the engineer because the former is more aware of the complex interactions between organism and environment, and the effect that any alteration may have. Liaison between different groups of scientists is essential if pollution is not to ruin the environment.

The problem of aquatic pollution is more noticeable in inland and coastal water systems because of the comparatively small amount of diluent present. Although some 3% of the earth's water is fresh, only 0.06% is directly available in the form of lakes and rivers (see Chapter 1), and not all this water is suitable for diluting waste, as it is not in motion. More than half the British coastline is subjected to estuarine and brackish waters and the UK has one of the largest brackish habitat to land ratios in the world.[64] Much of the water draining off the land masses passes through such environments on its way to the oceans. Estuaries have long been the site for industrial development in the UK, e.g., Clyde, Mersey, Severn, Thames, Humber, Tees and Tyne, because of the ready availability of land for building and flowing water for the dilution of wastes. Many bodies of water, as long as they are not too shallow, are, to some extent, self-cleansing. Estuaries, because they are tidal, are usually very efficient in this process. However, because they too have only a limited capacity for receiving man's wastes, some have become virtually dead from the biologist's point of view. The term 'septic tanks of the megalopolis' is an apt picture of certain estuaries.[21]

Many people fail to appreciate the delicate balance of natural ecosystems, and the complexity of the processes which maintain stability. There are probably some 4 000 000 different sorts of extant organism (i.e. species) currently inhabiting the various environments (the conditions in which an organism lives) on earth and yet it is the activities of one of the least numerous of these species which is in danger of upsetting the balance. No species can live in isolation from other members of its community (naturally occurring groups of different species inhabiting a common environment) as it forms part of a dynamic ecosystem (a community and its non-living environment). Within each ecosystem there is an exchange and flow of materials between the component units. If any link in this system becomes unstable, the repercussions may be felt throughout the whole ecosystem and beyond.

This chapter sets out to explain the nature of aquatic ecosystems and the effect that industrial effluents may have on them.

5.2. ECOSYSTEMS

The term ecosystem can be applied to something as large as a desert or as small as the bed of a river. Whatever its size, every ecosystem has in common with others certain components and functional attributes. Ecosystems are not usually discrete entities but are linked with others nearby. All ecosystems are complex interlinking systems which are in ecological equilibrium (i.e. a balance is maintained between total production of living matter and the rate of death and decay over a period of time). However, this equilibrium is delicately balanced and can be upset by environmental

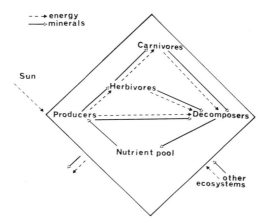

FIG. 5.1.   The basic components of an ecosystem.

changes caused by pollution. Each ecosystem is composed of a number of
basic units between which there is a flow of energy and minerals (Fig. 5.1).
The flow of energy is one way, but that of the minerals is cyclic.

All life depends on energy from the sun and the fact that plants are able to
trap this energy and use it to synthesise organic compounds. Animals
cannot exist without plants and basically 'all flesh is grass'.

The quantity of solar energy entering the earth's atmosphere is approximately $1.4 \times 10^9 \, J \, m^{-2} yr^{-1}$. The amount of radiant energy per unit time
which is actually available varies from one geographic location to another;
in Britain it is approximately $1.0 \times 10^9 \, J \, m^{-2} yr^{-1}$. As much as 99% of this
energy may be lost from plants before it can be utilized, however. The
remainder is used in the process of photosynthesis where it is transformed
into the chemical energy of plant tissue by the reaction:

$$CO_2 + 2H_2O \xrightarrow[\text{green plant}]{\text{light}} (CH_2O) + H_2O + O_2$$

By this process green plants synthesise organic compounds from water
and CO_2 using the energy absorbed from sunlight. Photosynthetic plants
are termed autotrophs and are the primary producers in any ecosystem
(Fig. 5.1). Some man-made ecosystems (e.g., intensive agriculture) have high
productivity levels but natural ecosystems such as estuaries and coral reefs
have even higher levels (Table 5.1).

The total amount of chemical energy stored by green plants per unit area

TABLE 5.1
GROSS PRIMARY PRODUCTIVITY IN THE MAJOR BIOTIC ZONES
(MODIFIED FROM ODUM[47])

Biotic zone	$g/m^2\ day$
Deserts	<0.5
Deep oceans	<1.0
Grasslands, deep lakes, mountain forests some agriculture, shallow seas, continental shelf	$0.5-3.0$
Moist forests, shallow lakes, moist grassland, most agriculture	$3-10$
Some estuaries, coral reefs, alluvial plains, intensive agriculture	$10-25$

per unit time is termed the gross primary productivity. All animals, fungi and most bacteria are heterotrophs, and are either herbivores, carnivores, omnivores, saprophytes or parasites. In other words they need complex organisms as their source of food. However, the gross primary production does not represent the food which is potentially available to the heterotrophs. This is because autotrophs must utilize energy in oxidising organic substances in the process of cellular respiration. Therefore gross primary production minus respiration represents the food energy potentially available to heterotrophs. This is termed 'net primary production' and is normally between 80–90% of gross primary production in natural ecosystems. Heterotrophs do not assimilate all the food they consume and a high percentage of the food of some herbivores may pass out of the body as faeces. Carnivores, however, tend to assimilate a higher percentage of their food. The tissues and the faeces of heterotrophs serve as food for other heterotrophs and decomposers. Ecological systems depend upon the transfer of energy from organism to organism through the various trophic levels of food chains and food webs.

A food chain is a sequence of events in which a plant is eaten by an animal which is in turn eaten by another animal and so on:

$$\text{plant} \rightarrow \text{herbivore} \rightarrow \text{carnivore}_1 \rightarrow \text{carnivore}_2 \rightarrow \text{carnivore}_3.$$

In aquatic systems the bulk of the 'grass' is usually formed by photosynthetic algae such as diatoms and flagellates, generally known as phytoplankton. Feeding on the phytoplankton are herbivorous animals—the zooplanktonts, which in turn are fed upon by carnivorous zooplanktonts, which are then consumed by larger animals such as fish. In nature such food chains rarely occur at such a simple level. In fact the feeding relationships of most higher organisms are extremely complex and the food chain is no longer a linear system but one of interconnecting food chains known as a food web (Fig. 5.2).

In any ecosystem the trophic levels of a food web can be represented as an ecological pyramid or pyramid of numbers (Fig. 5.3). The position occupied by a particular organism is dependent upon its position in a food web. The

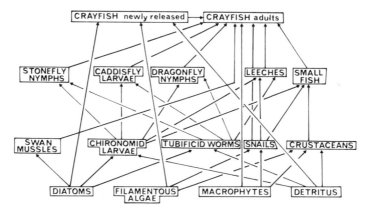

FIG. 5.2. Idealised food web of a freshwater crayfish. (Arrows indicate direction of energy transfer.)

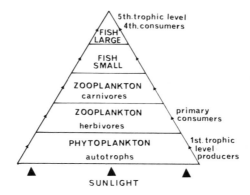

FIG. 5.3 An ecological pyramid. The proportional areas of the sub-divisions approximate, in this example, to the numbers of organisms at each trophic level.

higher the trophic level the lower the number of organisms. The pyramid of numbers treats individuals of all species as equal units, whether they are worms or whales. Two other sorts of pyramid give a different picture of trophic levels. If the total mass of organisms per unit area is considered then a pyramid of biomass can be constructed. However, this implies that organisms yield the same amounts of energy weight for weight. This is not so as many organisms have a large part of their mass composed of non-digestible components such as shell and exoskeletons. Pyramids of biomass do not take into account the production rate (i.e. over a period of time), but are more a measure of the standing crop at any one point in time. Pyramids of productivity, which give a measure of grams of matter produced per square metre per year, give a clearer picture. Pyramids of energy are also used in ecological studies and here each level of the pyramid is represented by the amount of energy utilised by the different feeding types in a given area (e.g. kJ/m^2yr). Whatever the basis of the pyramid, the end result is usually the same, i.e. the pyramid shape. The higher up the pyramid one goes then the fewer the organisms there are, and consequently there is less biomass, less productivity, and usually less energy stored. A top carnivore may assimilate a high proportion of its prey, but it may only conserve some 5% of the energy obtained.

Strangely, the largest living animal, the blue whale, which may reach 30 m in length and weigh 150 tonnes, feeds on very small herbivorous animals, generally called krill. It does so by sieving enormous quantities of this animal from the water using special plates (baleen) inside its mouth. Krill feed directly on phytoplankton and are very numerous in certain parts of the world's oceans. They can yield as much as $100 \ g/m^2$ over large areas of ocean, and compare favourably with cattle production on land. A 90-tonne blue whale may consume some 3 tonnes of krill per day in the summer feeding period. By cutting down on the number of trophic levels involved in its food chain and by having an efficient feeding mechanism the blue whale is able to grow to an enormous size by feeding on an abundant food supply with little expenditure of energy.

The importance of cutting down on the number of trophic levels is due to the fact that the average gross ecological efficiency of many animals is only in the order of 10%, i.e. an animal may only convert this amount of its food intake to growth (Fig. 5.4). This is what is then available as food for other organisms which feed on it. For every 1000 J of plant material consumed by herbivores only 100 J may be passed onto the first-stage carnivore, and only 10 J to a second-stage carnivore. For this reason there have to be many more organisms available as food than there are predators. In nature food chains

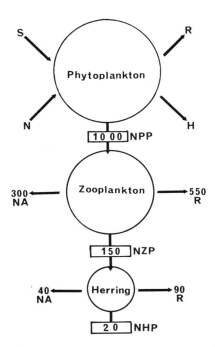

FIG. 5.4. Energy transfer between plant, herbivore and carnivore. The ecological efficiency of the zooplanktonts in this example is 15% and that of the herring 13%. (S, sunlight; N, nutrients; R, respiration; H, heat; NA, non-respired assimilation; NPP, net phytoplankton production; NZP, net zooplankton production; NHP, net herring production.)

with more than five links are rare because of the enormous amount of food needed to support them. Only a small amount of the productivity of one trophic level is then available as food for the next level. The reasons for this low level of energy transfer are shown in Fig. 5.4, which shows what happens to organic matter as it passes through two trophic levels. Of the gross primary production produced by the phytoplankton only 1000 units (i.e. the net primary production) are passed on as food to the zooplankton. Of this 1000 units only 150 are converted to actual flesh which can be eaten by a carnivore such as a herring. Much of the energy obtained by the zooplanktonts from the phytoplanktonts is lost as faeces and is not assimilated; of the amount assimilated a large proportion is used in maintaining the normal bodily functions of the animal and is lost during tissue respiration. The non-respired assimilation remaining is used for growth and reproduction. In some cases this may be what is available to the next trophic level. However, some of the growth may be put into forming non-trophic parts of the body such as a shell and will be of no use to a predator. If the gametes are released from a reproductive individual before it is eaten, then this energy will also be lost to the predator.

From the foregoing account it should be apparent that if any trophic level in an ecosystem is eliminated then this is going to have disastrous effects on higher trophic levels. If one element in a food chain is eliminated a similar effect may occur. However, with a complex food web it is much more difficult to predict the outcome of the removal of one of the components from any one trophic level as many animals are opportunists and may switch their diet. Removal of predators may lead to a population explosion in the trophic level below. Elimination of limpets by oil and detergents on rocky shores often leads to a prolific growth of seaweeds, the growth of which is normally controlled by the herbivorous limpets.[62]

Further information on the complexities of energy transfer and trophic levels can be found in Phillipson[55] and Russell-Hunter.[61]

5.3. LIFE-CYCLES IN THE AQUATIC ENVIRONMENT

One fact which surprises many non-biologists is the enormous diversity of animal life in aquatic ecosystems. Even in the UK virtually every animal group is represented in fresh and/or marine waters. The majority of these animals are invertebrates and perhaps go unnoticed by the non-specialist. Many invertebrates occur in enormous numbers, e.g., over $10\,000/m^2$ for some worms and snails, and therefore play a very important part in aquatic foodwebs and in controlling the levels of important parameters such as oxygen. Natural populations of aquatic larvae of some midges may reduce oxygen levels by 1 mg/litre km in some streams.[19] Such reduction may be important when oxygen levels have already been depleted due to organic pollution.

The complexity of food webs has been mentioned and to this must be added the fact that many organisms have very complex life-cycles. In order to reach adulthood every animal, which is the product of sexual reproduction at least, has to go through a number of growth stages. Some animals resemble their parents at birth but others are markedly different in form, activity and habitat. This may be an advantage as it reduces competition for space and food between young and adults. One advantage of sexual reproduction is that it produces variability. This is important when assessing the effect of pollutants because, if the effect is not too extreme, then there is a good chance that some individuals of a particular species will survive to carry on reproducing. In animals which rely on asexual reproduction, where every individual produced is genetically the same as the parent, there is a much greater chance of elimination if the environment is adversely affected. Many invertebrate animals practise asexual reproduction under favourable conditions so that they can exploit an environment quickly with identical individuals and then, when unfavourable environmental conditions start to set in (e.g. winter), they practise sexual reproduction so that some variability is introduced into the population, thus enhancing survival of the species during this period (e.g., water fleas such as *Daphnia*).

Because of the enormous toll imposed on aquatic organisms by predation and death due to other causes, those low down on the ecological pyramid tend to produce far more young than are actually needed to ensure continuation of the species. Those which do survive to maturity are also often subject to heavy predation. Thorson[65] mentions that a population of foraging oystercatchers (some 30 000 individuals) might consume as many as 642×10^6 cockles over the winter feeding period on some south coast mudflats (this represents a figure of 315 cockles per day per bird in January). Each cockle may produce many millions of larvae and enormous numbers of these are consumed by predators in the plankton at each stage of their development.

Each stage of an animal's development may be subject to different selection pressures and have different susceptibilities to the parameters in its environment. Conner[16] has shown that the larvae of some oysters, shrimps, crabs and lobsters are from 14 to 1000 times (depending on the species) more susceptible to increased levels of copper, mercury and zinc in their environments, than are adults of the same species. The toxicity of industrial wastes is often assessed on adult survival rates and has little meaning where larvae are concerned. Adult American fiddler crabs, for instance, can survive a concentration of 0.18 ppm mercury for at least six weeks, but first-stage larvae die within 48 h.[68] Experiments on the survival of any organism at a particular level of pollutant at a particular time in its life-cycle may yield interesting results, but in order to determine an acceptable level the organism must be able to complete its life-cycle at this level so that the next generation is ensured.

Many animals utilize their larvae to distribute the species in the environment so that new populations may be initiated. Whilst the environment of the adults may be perfectly acceptable to the species, that which the larvae have to pass through may not, so that distribution is restricted to favourable areas only. The common barnacles, which one finds attached to rocks on our coasts, start life as an egg inside the mantle cavity of the parent. Under favourable conditions (e.g., a good food supply) the eggs hatch and are released into the plankton as nauplii larvae. This stage of the life-cycle is used to distribute the barnacles to other localities. During this phase the nauplius sheds its outer skin (exoskeleton) a number of times in order to facilitate growth. Many die during this moulting process because every hair and protuberance is covered by the exoskeleton. After 4–5 such moults the surviving nauplii develop into cyprid larvae, which resemble miniature mussels but with appendages. The function of the cyprid is to find a suitable settling place, usually close to members of its own species, on which it can grow into an adult. The metamorphosis from cyprid to young barnacle is a complex process and is allied to the development of a pupa into an insect. Of 13 000 nauplii successfully hatching only one or two may reach the stage where they are recognisable as barnacles. The life-cycle of the barnacle is summarized in Fig. 5.5.

The larvae produced by many freshwater and marine animals have therefore to be more numerous than the adult stages in order to ensure continuation of the species. The larvae may play an even more important

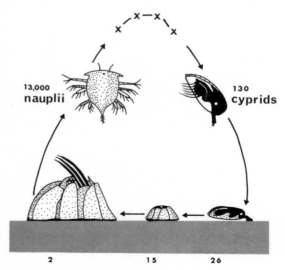

FIG. 5.5.　The life-cycle of an acorn barnacle, showing the numbers surviving to each stage (x indicates a moult). Modified from Thorson.[65]

rôle in some food webs than do the adults. For example, the chironomid midges seen swarming over freshwater habitats in the summer months have aquatic larvae known as blood worms which live in the aquatic sediments. They feed on microscopic plants and detritus and form an important food source for other organisms as they may occur at densities of $10\ 000/m^2$ in some waters. They are fairly resistant to organic pollution, but their removal from the environment by other pollutants would affect a large number of other organisms which utilise them either directly or indirectly as a food source.

From what has been said above it should be clear that all stages in the life-cycle of an organism must be taken into consideration when assessing the possible effect that an effluent may have on the aquatic environment.

5.4. POLLUTANTS IN THE AQUATIC ENVIRONMENT

The list of pollutants discharged in the aquatic environment grows every year, but the main classes which affect organisms are those listed by the Royal Commission on Environmental Pollution.[60] These mainly apply to estuarine and coastal waters, but can also be applied to freshwater in the majority of cases. Those discharged into freshwater are dealt with more fully by the Open University.[49] In brief the main types of pollutants are as follows:

(1) Organic matter—this includes the bulk of sewage, waste from coal mines, saw mills, paper mills, breweries, sugar beet factories and the agricultural industry. The effect of organic pollutants is to decrease the amount of oxygen in the water due to the increased demand for it by decomposing bacteria. Algal blooms may also occur due to enrichment of the water with nitrates and phosphates, the algae may change the levels of O_2 and CO_2 in the water, as well as producing toxins which may be lethal to other organisms.

(2) Poisons—in the form of heavy metals such as mercury, copper, zinc, lead, cadmium, etc., which come from various industrial processes. Biocides of the organochlorine group and PCBs (polychlorinated biphenyls) can also be considered under this heading. Some organisms concentrate such poisons in their tissues and the poison may be further concentrated as it is passed through various trophic levels. In high doses these poisons will have a lethal effect and in sublethal concentrations may well upset the physiological balance of the organism. Compounds of cyanide and sulphide are toxic to aquatic

organisms in low concentrations as they interfere with cell respiration. Free chlorine is used as a biocide in many industrial processes and is toxic in low concentrations.

(3) Oil—this usually reaches the environment by accidental leakage or spillage. However, a certain amount is discharged in the cooling water of oil refineries. In the open sea oil is dispersed fairly rapidly and, although toxic, it does comparatively little harm to aquatic life. In a confined space such as an estuary, however, the effects can be more serious. Besides being toxic oil also has a smothering effect on sessile organisms. (The despersants used to clear oil spills were, in the past, often more toxic than the oil itself to animal life, but that situation has now been rectified.)

(4) Inert suspensions and spoil from mining and drilling at sea—sand, gravel and finely divided matter such as coal washings, china clay waste, pulverised fuel ash, dredged material, sewage sludge. These have the effect of causing turbidity, reducing light penetration and of smothering benthic organisms. Sewage sludge may also contain toxic materials.

(5) Radioactive discharges—mainly from nuclear power stations and fuel processing plants. Radionuclides may have a toxic and possible mutagenic effect.

(6) Cooling water—seawater and freshwater which is used by some factories for cooling plant and which is then returned to the aquatic environment as a thermal effluent sometimes as much as 12°C above ambient water temperature. Increases in temperature cause the oxygen content to decrease and the rate of decomposition of sewage and other organic material to increase. On occasions cooling water may also be used to purge pipes so that the effluent may contain toxic chemicals.

The literature concerning the effect of pollutants on aquatic organisms is enormous and for this reason each of the pollutants mentioned above are discussed further below, although this is by no means a complete coverage. For reviews of this topic see Hynes,[31] George,[23,24] Hood,[29] Lockwood,[34] Vernberg and Vernberg,[66] Vernberg et al.[67]

5.4.1. Organic Pollution (with particular reference to freshwater environments)

Freshwater sometimes contains considerable amounts of organic matter. In rivers this material is often moved into estuarine environments, but in lakes and some reservoirs there is a considerable build up of organic matter. In lakes enrichment from man-made sources can lead to premature ageing.

When discharged into freshwater ecosystems sewage has usually been subjected to primary and secondary treatment so that its oxygen demands are only small. However, the treatments do not remove inorganic salts such as nitrates and phosphates completely (much of the phosphorus coming from detergents in the sewage). Both nitrates and phosphates are essential for plant growth and whilst plants need more of the former there is often 2.5 times as much phosphate as nitrate available in polluted waters. Additional phosphates and nitrates are added to freshwater environments from water draining off agricultural land. If the phosphate content of the water is excessive and the nitrate content low this will encourage the growth of nitrogen fixing plants such as blue-green algae which are of little use as food. Excessive enrichment with plant nutrients will lead to the rapid growth of certain plant species at the expense of others. Those species eliminated by this process of eutrophication are often the ones needed by herbivores for food. The classic case of eutrophication is Lake Erie in North America.[32] Here a very beautiful lake was ruined by increased input of domestic and industrial waste from a rapidly expanding local population. The input of nutrients from sewage led to an increase in the phytoplankton levels from 81/ml in 1929 to 2432/ml in 1962 and to an increase in the bacterium *E. coli* from 175/100 ml in 1913 to 449/100 ml in 1946. The situation became so bad in the 1960s that bathing was prohibited in some areas. Oxygen concentrations in the lake were reduced to such a low level in some parts that only very tolerant animals could survive (e.g., in 1961 84% of the total benthic fauna in the western end were tubificid worms). Commercial fish stocks were severely depleted, especially those of the lake trout. On a smaller scale, increased input of sewage coupled with the increasing use of fertilizers on the surrounding land are leading to eutrophication of Blelham Tarn in the Lake District, although eutrophication is not normally a problem in the UK.[49]

Due to the discharge of effluents containing organic matter many rivers in the UK have high BOD loads; however, this is not all due to domestic sewage, e.g., only 15% of the BOD in the River Tees comes from this source, the rest coming from industry. Treated natural products create high demands for oxygen in rivers, e.g. 7% of the total pollution load in Scotland in terms of BOD comes from distillery wastes discharged into the Moray Firth.[60]

The oxygen demands of decomposers of organic matter may be so great that conditions become anaerobic, then the activity of anaerobic decomposers leads to the production of hydrogen sulphide and methane. Any

D.M. Holdich

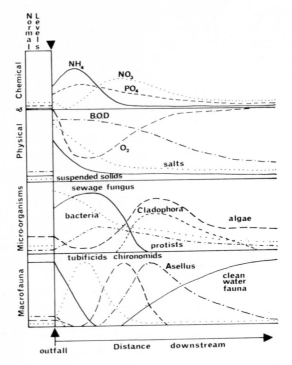

FIG. 5.6.   The effect of an organically based effluent on a river and its communities.
Modified from Hynes.[31]

reduction in the oxygen levels of the aquatic environment will lead to
substantial changes in the fauna and flora. Figure 5.6 shows what can
happen downstream from the entry of an organic effluent. Due to an
increase in BOD levels the oxygen content is reduced and this reduces the
normal clean-water fauna and flora. Plant nutrients are added with the
effluent and this may lead to an increase in certain plants such as
Cladophora. The fauna below the outfall will consist of pollution-tolerant
species which may reach very high numbers, owing to a lack of competition
and predation and an excess of food. Below the outfall there is then a
predictable succession of physical, chemical and biotic components of the
river but it is rarely as clear cut as in Fig. 5.6. In still waters, such as lakes
and reservoirs, the effect can be even more acute because of the slower rate
of oxygen transfer; however, the larger algal populations may compensate
for this to some extent. Deep, still bodies of water are often self-purifying,

but in the summer months heat from the sun causes the formation of a thermocline which separates off a warm upper layer of water from the deeper colder water. Water, and any pollutants it contains, running into such still water will tend to mix with the upper epilimnion first because it will normally have a higher temperature than the colder hypolimnion. If enrichment of the epilimnion occurs then decaying plant material will sink into the hypolimnion where it will be further decomposed. However, because of the thermocline water mixing is reduced and oxygen cannot be transported into the hypolimnion to replace that used by decomposing organisms—therefore anaerobis may result, which will have a profound effect on other organisms in the hypolimnion.

Whilst many areas of high population density are situated on estuaries, the Midlands area of the UK is a long way from the sea and consequently rivers in that area tend to get overburdened with pollutants.[48] The most serious pollutant is sewage and under low summer flow 95% of the discharge of the River Tame is effluent; downstream on the River Trent at Nottingham the level is reduced to 40%. The problem of low oxygen levels in the rivers is alleviated somewhat by aeration due to weirs and the input of cooling water and sewage effluent at a high flow rate; however, as already pointed out, most of the cooling water is somewhat above ambient. The Severn–Trent Water Authority monitors water quality by chemical and biological means, and Woodiwiss[73] has developed a 'biotic index' for assessing water quality in the catchment area. This is relatively simple to use compared with chemical methods and relies on the occurrence, in flowing water, of certain key animals exhibiting varying degrees of pollution tolerance coupled with the actual number of selected animal groups present (Table 5.2). This index, which in essence measures species diversity, works well over the whole year but seasonal differences in the occurrence of certain groups can give conflicting results if observations are only made every few months. The Department of the Environment[18] has also developed a biological classification for more widespread use. When compared with their chemical classification (Table 5.3) there is good agreement for the most and least polluted rivers, but only moderate agreement for the intermediate classes. On a more simple basis the oxygen sag curve as shown in Fig. 5.6 can be used as an indication of the state of a river. Measurements of oxygen levels in the River Thames showed that there was a steady decline from the 1890s to the late 1950s for some 40 km below London Bridge.[9] In the 1950s some stretches of the river were anaerobic. The problem had mainly been caused by organic pollution and toxic outfalls from industry. In addition, pollution took from two days to

TABLE 5.2

THE 'BIOTIC INDEX' AS USED BY THE SEVERN–TRENT WATER AUTHORITY

			Total number of 'groups' present				
			0–1	2–5	6–10	11–15	16+
Clean	Plecoptera nymph present	More than one species	—	7	8	9	10
		One species only	—	6	7	8	9
	Ephemeroptera nymph present (*Baetis rhondani* excluded)	More than one species	—	6	7	8	9
		One species only	—	5	6	7	8
	Trichoptera larvae and/or *B. rhondani* present	More than one species	—	5	6	7	8
		One species only	4	4	5	6	7
	Gammarus present	All above species absent	3	4	5	6	7
	Asellus present	All above species absent	2	3	4	5	6
	Tubificid worms and/or blood worms present	All above species absent	1	2	3	4	—
Polluted	All above types absent	Species not requiring dissolved oxygen may be present, e.g. *Eristalis tenax*.	0	1	2	—	—

The key organisms on the left-hand side are first identified, e.g., *Asellus*. The total number of groups are then calculated and read off along the top line. By following the column down below this to the key organisms line the index can be calculated.

The term 'group' for the purposes of the index means any one of the following: each known species of Hydracarina, Coleoptera adults and larvae, Diptera larvae other than Simulidae, Neuroptera larvae, Plecoptera larvae, Crustacea, Mollusca, Hirudinea, Annelid worms excluding genus *Nais*, Platyhelminthes; each known genus of Ephemeroptera larvae but excluding *Baetis rhodani*; each family of Trichoptera larvae, Chironomidae larvae but excluding *Chironomus thummi*, Simulidae larvae; genus *Nais* (Annelida); *Baetis rhondani* (mayfly) and *Chironomus thummi* (blood worms).

The index works best in running water. Based on Woodiwiss.[73]

TABLE 5.3
COMPARISON OF LENGTHS (IN KILOMETRES) BY BIOLOGICAL AND CHEMICAL
CLASSIFICATION OF NON-TIDAL RIVERS IN ENGLAND AND WALES IN 1973[18] (COURTESY:
HMSO)

Biological class	Chemical class				Total lengths
	Class 1	Class 2	Class 3	Class 4	
Class A	17 657	655	77	0	18 389
Class B	3 418	1 725	130	10	5 283
Class C	386	1 022	666	286	2 360
Class D	88	200	328	774	1 390
Total length	21 549	3 602	1 201	1 070	27 422

Those stretches of rivers unclassified from the biological point of view (i.e. 8 505 km) have not been included in the table.

Chemical class 1 = unpolluted; 2 = doubtful quality; 3 = poor quality; 4 = grossly polluted.

Biological class A = rivers with a widely diverse invertebrate fauna including appreciable proportion of stonefly and mayfly nymphs, caddis fly larvae and freshwater shrimps when ecological conditions are favourable. Good mixed coarse fishing. Salmon, trout and grayling, when purely ecological factors favour these fish.

Biological class B = stonefly and mayfly nymphs may be restricted. Caddis fly larvae and freshwater shrimps usually present in reasonable numbers. Invertebrate population as a whole quite varied.

Biological class C = variety of macroscopic invertebrates restricted, population dominated by the hoglouse, *Asellus aquaticus*. Freshwater shrimps may be present, mayfly nymphs (except *Baetis*) and caddis fly larvae relatively rare. Moderate to poor fisheries. Fish population restricted.

Biological class D = macroscopic invertebrates absent or restricted to pollution tolerant forms such as oligochaete worms and chironomid larvae. Rivers thought to be incapable of supporting fish life.

six weeks to clear the mouth of the Thames depending on the volume of river flow. The ebb and flow of water in any tidal river may move effluents upstream as well as downstream thus adding to the problem of dilution. The reduction in oxygen levels in the River Thames had a catastrophic effect on animal life below London Bridge. However, in recent years, because of the reconstruction and replacement of sewage works, oxygen concentrations are increasing to much higher levels. Coupled with this there has been a remarkable recovery in the fauna (e.g. 91 species of fish in 1976) indicating that many species now find the water suitable for breeding.

5.4.2. Poisons

Three types of poison are particularly important with regard to aquatic life—heavy metals, pesticides and PCBs.

Many heavy metals present in water are essential to organisms in trace amounts; however, large amounts of certain metals are now appearing in areas such as estuaries. Owing to the concentrating effects of food chains (see below) they sometimes reach toxic levels. Mercury and silver are the most toxic, followed by cadmium, zinc, lead, chromium, nickel and cobalt. Mercury is known to have sub-lethal effects in low concentrations. Fiddler crabs, *Uca pugilator*, maintained in 0.18 ppm Hg for six weeks survived but showed extensive damage to the gill tissue, and analysis of these tissues revealed a concentration of 17 ppm Hg.[68]

Once added to the environment, most heavy metals are there for good. Creeks in south Cornwall are heavily polluted with tin and copper from mines and yet support large populations of rag worms at least. These rag worms have become adapted to live at high metal levels but ones from unpolluted areas soon die if placed in the same environment.[12] The real problem of metal toxicity usually comes higher up the food chain and animals which have not had the chance to acquire a tolerance may be exposed to damaging doses of contaminated food.

From the evidence available it appears that marine animals show a marked diversity of tolerances to heavy metals, e.g. some copepods are killed by 3 ppm copper, some barnacles by 10 ppm, but mussels can be bright green with the metal and still survive. Surprisingly mussels with 'green sickness' do not contain high general levels of copper in the blood; it is mainly confined to special cells in the blood. Another sort of cell compartmentalises zinc in the same manner in mussels.

One aspect of heavy metal pollution which is concerning biologists is the effect of mercury on the photosynthesis rate of phytoplanktonts. Uptake of radioactive carbon can be inhibited by 50% at only 1 ppb and yet the water quality standards set up by some countries allow for 5 ppb in drinking water. Organo-mercury fungicides were used in the experiments (*New Scientist*, **3**, 1970, p. 363) and at 50 ppb uptake of carbon was halted. As much of the new oxygen entering the atmosphere comes directly from the activities of phytoplanktonts, there is some cause for concern.

Some animals can concentrate mercury in their tissues whether it is in the environment in high amounts or not. In 1970 it was found that tuna fish contained twice the acceptable level of mercury in some localities and pollution was indicated. However, specimens from museums which had been caught many years previously also contained high amounts. The

TABLE 5.4

METAL LEVELS IN NATURALLY OCCURRING SHORE POPULATIONS ON THE SOUTHERN SIDE OF THE BRISTOL CHANNEL*

Metal	Locality	Plant Fucus	Herbivores Littorina	Patella	Carnivore Nucella	Sea bed sediment	Seawater µg/litre
Zinc (ppm)	Portishead	800	—	580	—	440	52
	Brean	380	340	310	3,100	420	31
	Minehead	240	140	180	550	—	21
	Open Sea	—	—	—	—	—	10
Cadmium (ppm)	Portishead	220	—	550	—	4.2	5.8
	Brean	50	140	200	425	1.6	2.0
	Minehead	20	25	50	270	—	1.0
	Open Sea	—	—	—	—	—	0.1
Lead (ppm)	Portishead	8.5	—	8.5	—	150	2.5
	Brean	0.9	0.6	9.0	27.0	150	1.4
	Minehead	—	0.1	3.0	8.0	—	0.8
	Open Sea	—	—	—	—	—	0.03

*From data in Butterworth et al.[14]

0.5 ppm Hg level acceptable for mercury in American foodstuffs was exceeded a hundredfold in shellfish consumed by the Japanese fishing communities around Minemata. Regular consumption of such high levels resulted in a build up of mercury in their tissues which had very distressing consequences.

The Bristol Channel and Severn Estuary in the UK have recently become the focus of attention by a number of research teams, e.g., Butterworth *et al.*,[14] Nickless *et al.*,[45] Peden *et al.*,[50] and the Institute of Marine Environmental Research at Plymouth is concentrating its efforts into building a mathematical model of this area. Very high levels of cadmium, lead and zinc have been found in shore-dwelling organisms on the north and south sides of the Channel (Table 5.4). The cadmium levels in the seaweeds at Portishead are the highest in the British Isles. The zinc load of dogwhelks reaches 3100 ppm at Portishead. The highest concentrations of heavy metals are near Avonmouth and there is then a regular decrease towards the sea.

It has been estimated that only 25% of the DDT which has been put on the land to date has reached the sea[60] and yet it has a marked effect at quite low concentrations. The solubility of DDT in seawater is 1 ppb; however, it is more soluble in oil and tends to accumulate in the lipid pool of organisms. It tends to become more concentrated as it moves from one trophic level to another due to the process of biological magnification: 0.000 05 ppm in water → 0.04 ppm in plankton → 0.42 ppm in clams → 18.5 ppm in herring gulls are the results of a typical series of measurements.[74] Unless it reaches great concentrations, it is relatively harmless to animals when stored in fat. However, when the fat is mobilised, as it might be under conditions of stress, it is released into the blood where it has a more dramatic effect. Fish and invertebrates are very susceptible to organo-chlorine compounds, which they absorb directly from seawater as well as via food. For example, 5 ppm DDT has been found to result in 100% failure of development in freshwater trout—mortality mainly occurring at the time of yolk sac assimilation; commercial species of crabs and shrimps were killed within 20 days at 0.2 ppb.[22] Some workers have reported that DDT levels may vary in concentration with the time of the year in fish. This can also apply to other accumulated pollutants and reports of build-ups in the environment should be treated with caution unless all-year-round analysis has been carried out—spot checks are misleading.

Another organo-chlorine compound—dieldrin—which is used in sheep dips and as a seed dressing, as well as in some industrial processes is more harmful than DDT and is thought to be partially responsible for the current decline in predatory birds. It tends to accumulate from one trophic level to another and, when it reaches predatory birds, it seems to affect their calcium metabolism and they consequently lay eggs which have abnormally thin shells. This has greatly reduced the number of young being hatched.[59]

PCBs are used in a number of manufacturing processes and reach the environment by way of effluents. As with DDT they are non-biodegradable and persist in the environment for a very long time. PCBs have a sub-lethal effect on many animals low down in food webs by altering their blood chemistry, disturbing their growth and gonad formation, interfering with thermal acclimation mechanisms, and by lowering their resistance to disease. Higher up the food chains, however, when PCBs have been concentrated, by predatory birds for instance, they may affect the production of sex hormones and cause sterility. The kidneys also become enlarged and paralysis may set in. PCBs were found in large doses in many seabirds, especially guillemots, which were washed up in their thousands on the west coast of Britain in 1969.[28] It is not known whether PCBs were the prime cause of death, but it seems highly probable that environmental stress (e.g., shortage of food) and the toxicant together could have been responsible. Addison[1] reviews what is known about the effect of chlorinated hydrocarbons on aquatic organisms.

5.4.3. Oil

Unlike other pollutants crude oil and fractions of oil are virtually insoluble in water and float on its surface. When spilt in large bodies of water the oil tends to be rapidly dispersed and diluted and most of the volatile elements are lost to the atmosphere by evaporation. The volatile components of the oil are most toxic to organisms and consequently the oil decreases in its toxicity with time. The residue which is left is less toxic, but can cause a great deal of damage to diving birds and to sessile organisms on the shore. As many as 500 000 seabirds may be killed by oil per year in the North Sea and North Atlantic. The oil affects their insulation and buoyancy so that they lose body heat rapidly and may have difficulty in floating. If they preen their contaminated plumage then they may ingest the oil and die from its toxic effects. On the shore many organisms which are attached to solid substrata are smothered by the oil. If they can close their shells, as can many molluscs and barnacles, then they may avoid the oil to some extent. Very little is known about the toxicity of the various fractions of oil to aquatic organisms. Corner *et al.*[17] have reviewed what is known about the effect of hydrocarbons on marine zooplankton and fish, and Nelson-Smith[40-42] reviews the biological consequences of oil pollution and the effect which various cleaning operations have. It was, perhaps, the Torrey Canyon disaster of 1967, when over 118 000 tonnes of oil were spilt off the coast of S.W. Britain, which stirred up interest in the effects of oil pollution. The effects of this disaster have been well documented.[15, 62] It would appear that no long-lasting damage has been done to shores in S.W. Britain. The effects of the more recent Amoco Cadiz disaster have been reported by Spooner.[63]

Regular exposure to small quantities can have a more long-lasting effect than a single exposure to a large amount. Discharges from refineries in Southampton Water may contain only 10–20 ppm oil but the flow rate may be 6825 litres/day.[42] As this has been happening since the early 1950s, it has had a marked effect on the local salt-marsh community. Similarly, Milford Haven refineries intermittently discharge small volumes of oily effluent across rocky shores. Over the last 10 years this has killed off many of the herbivores, so that brown algae dominate whereas limpets and barnacles did so before.

When oil is spilt it is very quickly attacked by a variety of micro-organisms which break down the various components. The oil need not cause excessive damage if left alone. However, methods used to remove it are often more damaging than the oil itself. The 12 700 tonnes of detergent used to clear British beaches after the Torrey Canyon spill had a drastic effect on shore life. Smith[62] reported that the detergent BP 1002 (now no longer in use) killed a variety of sub-littoral organisms in low concentrations (e.g., sea anemones 25 ppm; crustaceans 5–25 ppm; bivalve molluscs 0.5–2 ppm; red seaweed 10 ppm). One of the most toxic fractions of crude oil is the low boiling point aromatic hydrocarbons and some of the original oil-dispersing detergents were dissolved in such fractions. Hydrocarbons which are ingested by marine organisms pass through the gut wall and become part of the lipid pool. When they become part of the fatty tissues they are protected from microbial attack and can be transferred from one trophic level to another.

Very little appears to be known about the effect of oil and its various fractions on freshwater organisms. Oil is often spilt from motor vessels or gets into rivers and lakes via drains from the land and some reaches freshwater via cooling water. Organisms which either float near or on the surface, such as plants, and those which come to the surface for air, such as some insects, are most likely to be affected.

5.4.4. Inert suspensions
A variety of solid, but non-toxic, materials are disposed of into the aquatic

environment.[60] Large deposits (some 16×10^6 tonnes) of sewage sludge, pulverised fuel ash, colliery waste and various industrial wastes are tipped either directly into fresh and marine waters or out at sea. They all have the effect of increasing turbidity and consequently reducing light levels and of smothering organisms and their habitats. Perkins[52] and Moore[38] have reviewed the effects of inorganic particulate suspensions on marine life. China clay waste was tipped in large quantities into certain Cornish rivers where it was subsequently carried out into nearby bays. The deposits have led to the elimination of the local fauna.[30] Other clay-based industries (e.g., pottery and brick manufacture) deposit material in rivers where they may have a similar effect. Edwards[20] mentions that in suspension the solids may cause thickening of trout gill lamellae which may lead to eventual asphyxiation of the fish. On the river bed the sediment may interfere with spawning sites and decrease the amount of food available for fish. The River Ebbw in South Wales is fishless for much of its length after the input of effluents from coal washings and steel plants. However, the tributaries support a varied fish population, e.g., eel, roach, stickleback, minnow, bullhead, stone loach and trout.

5.4.5. Radioactive discharges

Little is known about the threshold of radiation damage to aquatic organisms, but in some cases very small amounts have been shown to have a lethal or mutagenic effect.[37] Certain marine organisms tend to concentrate radionuclides and are used by the Authorities to indicate the levels in the environment. Seaweeds may concentrate metal radionuclides by factors in the range of 10^3 to 10^4 and oysters have been found to concentrate zinc-65 by a factor of 10^5.[51,57] The greatest concentration of radionuclides is in the top 5 cm of water and is absorbed either through the body surface or with the food. Algae appear to be fairly resistant; they have a large surface area and when rapidly dividing can concentrate a large amount. Some radionuclides do not become excessively concentrated as they move from one trophic level to another, either in the assimilated form in the tissues or in the unassimilated form in the gut lumen, and in some cases decreases in the amount have been reported.[7] Radionuclides can be concentrated by organisms a long way from their point of origin and oysters gathered some 250 miles from the nuclear source were found to contain 200 000 times more radioactive zinc than the surrounding water. However, not all radioactive material gets so far. Perkins *et al.*[54] reported that ruthenium-106 from the Windscale reactor originally discharged into the Solway Firth and carried out to sea was subsequently carried back into

TABLE 5.5

CONCENTRATION OF STONTIUM-90 IN
CERTAIN ORGANISMS FROM VARIOUS
TROPHIC LEVELS IN PERCH LAKE,
ONTARIO. LAKE WATER ARBITRARILY
DEFINED AS 1*

Lake water	1
Bottom sediment	180
Aquatic plants	280
Minnows	950
Clam tissue	730
Perch flesh	5
Perch bone	3000
Beaver bone	1300
Muskrat bone	3500

*From data in Wilson *et al.*[72]

the estuary and absorbed on particulate material. This eventually became incorporated into salt-marshes or was deposited on rocky shores where it was taken up in the food of some organisms, e.g., mussels, where it was concentrated by a factor of 15.

Radionuclides sometimes get into the environment by accident and become concentrated into organisms at high trophic levels. Strontium-90 leaking from a nuclear reactor near Perch Lake, Ontario, became concentrated from one trophic level to another and was especially pronounced in the bones of certain vertebrates where it replaced calcium during bone formation (Table 5.5).[72]

Multiple factor interaction and physiological stress play an important part in an animal's susceptibility to radiation. In the euryhaline fish *Fundulus* the LD_{50} (dose large enough to kill 50% of the test animals) was markedly affected with sodium-22 efflux in combination with temperature and salinity stress. An increased salinity at temperatures above 20°C increased mortality but in lowered salinity mortality was reduced at temperatures below 20°C. It is possible that the higher temperatures enhance radiation sensitivity by limiting osmo-regulatory capabilities.[69]

5.4.6. Cooling water

As temperature is one of the main limiting factors in biological systems the problem of the disposal of water heated above ambient in the process of cooling equipment or condensing steam can be serious. Small rises in temperature may lead to a general speeding up of biological processes, but rises of 5–10°C have clear biological consequences. Above 40°C most organisms are eliminated in a river, but they may appear again downstream as the temperature falls. Trout may die at temperatures as high as 25°C and their eggs will not hatch at temperatures above 14.5°C. Carp, however, can tolerate 35–38°C. The previous history of an animal will affect its reaction to increased temperature, i.e. those which have been acclimated to higher temperatures will survive better when faced with high temperature than those which have not. Temperature has a direct influence on toxicity—at a given concentration of pollutant a rise of 10°C doubles the effect of the toxicant and halves the survival time. Poisons are therefore more toxic in the summer months. As water levels may also be lower at this time the increase can be even more marked.

Thermal effluents may induce earlier breeding in some species. This usually has no harmful effect as long as sufficient food is available for the young stages. However, if food is seasonal and hatching takes place before the food appears, there will be mass mortality. If, due to increased temperature of its surroundings, a species manages to speed up its breeding cycle, then more generations may be produced per year. This can have serious consequences to man if the species happens to be a pest, e.g., barnacles and mussels as foulers of ships and other man-made structures such as inlet and outlet pipes; gribbles and shipworms as borers of wooden structures. Survival of introduced species (e.g., via the ballast tanks of ships) may occur due to increased temperatures in ports and docks, as has happened in Swansea Docks, where the temperature may be 10°C above ambient.[39] The American hardshelled clam is now breeding so successfully in Southampton Water that it supports a thriving shellfish industry.[3]

One third of Britain's electricity is generated by 18 power stations along the River Trent; the amount of electricity generated has earned the area the name 'Megawatt Valley'. Some $364–455 \times 10^6$ litres of cooling water are evaporated from the cooling towers per day. Large volumes of water are taken from the Trent for cooling purposes. At Ratcliffe-on-Soar 5455×10^6 litres/day are needed for cooling; this circulates around a closed system but the 59×10^6 litres lost per day from the cooling towers has to be replaced by river water. Some 204×10^6 litres/day may be taken in from the river at a maximum and some 145×10^6 litres are returned as heated effluent. The overall effect is to raise the river temperature by some 10°C; however, at the same time large amounts of oxygen are added to the water. The effect on life is minimised in some instances because the warm water lies as a layer on the cooler water below. Warinner and Brehmer[71] have shown that the community composition and abundance of marine benthic organisms at the entrance to York River, Virginia, USA was affected by thermal discharges from a power station over a distance of 300–400 m from the discharge. However, in the River Trent there seems to have been little change which can be attributed to increases in temperature although the life-cycles of some animals have been speeded up.[5]

At Hunterston Nuclear Power Station on the Clyde Estuary large volumes of cooling water are discharged into the sea and this has the effect of raising the temperature 8–10°C above ambient. Chlorine is added to the water at 0.5 ppm to kill off bacteria and prevent settlement of (but not kill) mussels in the pipes. Larvae of planktonic and benthic animals are taken in with the cooling water. The larvae of a bivalve mollusc common in the surrounding sands has a six-hour LD_{50} at 32.75°C and so is unlikely to be affected by the passage through the tubes. The intertidal amphipod *Urothoe* and the gastropod mollusc *Nassarius* start breeding some two months earlier than normal in the sands around the power station.[8]

Massive fish kills are occasionally reported from the aquatic environment and in a few cases this can be attributed to thermal effluents. In Long Island Sound 18 generating stations discharge between 11 and 15×10^9 litres of cooling water per day directly into the Sound or its estuaries. During the summer months the water temperature adjacent to the stations may reach 38°C whereas ambient may be only 23°C. Young and Gibson[75] have reported that masses of migrating menhaden fish were killed on three occasions in 1971 because they swam into the layer of hot effluent water lying on top of the Sound water. This fish had been shown to be killed by thermal shock at a temperatures above 33°C in the laboratory, so it is not surprising that the effect in the field was so dramatic.

As the oxygen content of water decreases with increases in temperature, any problems connected with oxygen depletion will be aggravated by increases in temperature.

5.5. ESTUARIES

Nowhere is the effect of water pollution more noticeable than in an industrialised estuary. Whilst vast regions of the sea are virtually unexploited, coastal and estuarine environments have been so exploited that some are biologically dead. Drainage systems accumulate in estuaries and bring with them wastes produced by man. As stated by Hood,[29] several of the pollutants discharged into the sea have the capacity to make significant change to the ocean environment as a medium for life and ultimately to diminish its usefulness to the rapidly increasing human population. It is in man's own interests to clean up the estuarine environment because, as was shown earlier (Table 5.1), estuaries are amongst the most productive ecosystems of the world. Estuaries have only a certain capacity for receiving and disposing of liquid and particulate effluents without indigenous organisms being harmed. Each estuary differs in its ability to cope with pollutants, although in most the pollution load is decreased greatly by biological breakdown and by the diluting effect of tidal flow.

The third report of the Royal Commission on Environmental Pollution[60] suggested two simple biological criteria for the management of estuarine water, namely that migratory fish be able to pass through at all states of the tide and that the muddy bottom be sufficiently developed to be able to support the fauna essential for sustaining sea fisheries. Many estuaries do not meet these demands. At one time there was a significant shellfish and fishing industry in the Mersey estuary based on mussels, periwinkles, shrimps and a number of fish. Some 227×10^6 litres of sewage are pumped into the Mersey estuary each day virtually untreated and containing high levels of heavy metals and PCBs. This has had a disastrous effect on the organisms, most of which have now been eliminated.

Estuaries can be defined as 'semi-enclosed coastal bodies of water having full connection with the open sea and within which seawater is diluted with water derived from land drainage'.[58] Estuaries may be only transient phenomena in terms of the earth's geological history and the fauna is therefore essentially opportunistic.[8] Although every estuary is unique, they all have one feature in common, i.e. they are subject to tidal fluctuations, and most have some inflow of freshwater which typically overlies the more saline water. Salinity varies considerably over the tidal cycle and between seasons. Inflowing river water tends to be colder than seawater in winter and warmer in summer, so that estuarine temperature fluctuations are larger than those of near-shore water or the open sea.

Estuaries typically contain large amounts of silt and due to this turbidity is high and light penetration poor. The estuarine floor is usually covered with muds which are rich in organic detritus. This detritus largely consists of terrestrial, fluvial and salt marsh vegetation from upper tidal levels. As a consequence of the poor light penetration photosynthesis by the normal type of primary producer—the microalgae—is reduced. Estuaries tend to act as a nutrient trap, but much of this is wasted because the high turbidity levels restrict high phytoplankton production which would normally utilise them.[4] In estuaries, therefore, the primary production mainly comes from the organic components of the detritus, which are converted to secondary

D.M. Holdich

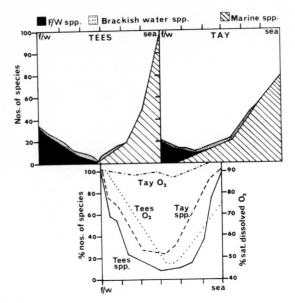

FIG. 5.7. Comparison of the distribution of the fauna and oxygen levels in the polluted Tees Estuary and non-polluted Firth of Tay. Modified from Open University.[49]

production by mud-dwelling primary consumers such as worms and molluscs.

Truly estuarine organisms are few in terms of the number of species present, but many species which live in the neritic environment (the shallow water over the continental shelf) use estuaries as nursery grounds. Towards the middle reaches of an estuary the number of species usually drops markedly (Fig. 5.7). In the River Tees, Alexander et al.[2] found that the decline in the number of species corresponded with a decline in oxygen concentration due to pollution (Fig. 5.7). However, on comparing their results with the Tay estuary, which was unpolluted, they found the same species decline in the middle reaches, but that oxygen levels were high (Fig. 5.7). From this it seems likely that it is the rapid and regular salinity changes in middle reaches of estuaries which might cause this region to be a particularly harsh one for organisms to become adapted to.[35] Barnes[8] has also suggested that the low level of spatial diversity (i.e. mud flats) of the environment may play some part in the reduction in species number, i.e. the number of niches are few and species diversity is not encouraged. However, the abundant food supply in estuaries allows those species which do exist to attain a very high biomass thus making estuaries such productive environments. Superficial examination of an estuary makes it difficult to conceive how it could be very productive. However, upon closer examination of the muddy shores it is usually apparent that, whilst species diversity is low, those species present occur in enormous numbers. McLusky[36] has recorded a figure of $42\,000/m^2$ for the small gastropod snail, *Hydrobia ulvae* in the Clyde estuary. Densities of $7000/m^2$ for the relatively large ragworm, *Nereis diversicolor* have been recorded in the muds of small estuaries on the N. Lincolnshire coast. At low tide this worm occurs at the exclusion of most other macrofaunal sedentary animals and is fed upon by various wading birds. At high tide, however, the area is invaded by flatfish, gobies, eels, crabs and prawns, all of which feed on the worms to some extent.

Gray[26] has shown by contrast that the Tees estuary contains very few macro-invertebrates (i.e. retained by a 0.5-mm sieve) or fish. The River Tees is widely regarded as being grossly polluted.[56] Prior to 1930 the estuary supported a flourishing fishing industry, including salmon. By 1937 salmon had been eliminated and other fish were on the decline. Falling oxygen levels caused by the input of untreated sewage and high amounts of cyanide from iron and steel works are thought to have been the main culprits. Despite its large population Teesside discharges much of its sewage untreated into the Tees. The five-day BOD load increased from $14\,000\,kg/day$ in 1931 to $221\,550\,kg/day$ in 1966[56] as a consequence of population and industrial expansion (which is still increasing as new steel works, oil terminals and power stations are being built). Much of the development has taken place on land reclaimed from intertidal sediments. Despite its apparent sterility Gray has shown that the meiofauna (i.e. that retained by a 0.1-mm sieve) of the muds has a biomass some 50 times greater than the macrofauna, which is unusual for the estuarine environment. The biomass was found by Gray to vary between 44 and $225\,g/m^2$ and was mainly composed of meiofaunal worms at very high densities ($206\,551/m^2$ for oligochaetes and $80\,107/m^2$ for polychaetes). So, although the macrofauna of the Tees appears to have been adversely affected by pollution its meiofaunal element still makes it a very productive estuary.

There are considerable differences in the ability of different species to tolerate any one pollutant and, as mentioned, tolerance levels may also be related to the stage of the life-cycle of the organism concerned. This makes it very difficult to predict how much of a particular pollutant can safely be put into the aquatic environment. The problem is heightened in estuaries because of the very nature of the environment which puts animals under some degree of stress. Some fish migrate through estuaries from rivers to the open sea in order to breed (eels), others such as lampreys and salmon migrate in the opposite direction to breed. As these fish have to adapt to different environmental conditions in the process of the migration they may become particularly susceptible to the effect of pollutants during the transitional stages. Environmental factors can increase the lethal effect of toxicants. Vernberg and Vernberg,[68] for instance, have shown that at a salinity of 30‰ and a temperature of 25°C fiddler crabs could live for very long periods in seawater with 0.18 ppm Hg. They also survived long periods in low salinity seawater with a high temperature (5‰, 35°C), but the addition of sub-lethal concentrations of mercury resulted in an LD_{50} averaging 22 days for male and female crabs.

The problem of synergism is one which is receiving a lot of attention from research workers experimenting on estuarine animals in particular and multiple factor interaction studies are producing very valuable results.[70] The experimental combinations involving the main estuarine parameters coupled with pollutants and the various stages of an organism's life-cycle are extremely numerous and it is unlikely that they will be worked out fully for any organism for some time to come.

5.6. SUB-LETHAL EFFECTS OF POLLUTANTS ON AQUATIC ORGANISMS

Many experiments carried out by scientists on the effect of pollutants on aquatic organisms result in the death of the experimental animals—or at least 50% of them. In such experiments the median lethal response or median tolerance limit (TL_m) is determined to assess the toxicity of the pollutant. This is the experimental condition which kills 50% of the test organisms. In aquatic studies it is usual to discuss toxicity in terms of concentration of the applied factor in the water.[53] It is difficult to estimate how much of an experimental pollutant, for instance, is actually experienced by the test organism because it is contained in the surrounding water. In the UK it is usual to express the concentrations used as the 24-, 48- or 96-h LC_{50}. This is the concentration required (in ppt, ppm or ppb) to kill 50% of the test organisms in a given time. For instance ragworms from Restronguet Creek in Cornwall, where the water is polluted with copper, have a 96-h LC_{50} of 2.3 ppm Cu whereas worms from unpolluted sites have a 96-h LC_{50} of 0.54 ppm Cu.[12] From such experiments little information relevant to sub-lethal effects can be obtained as 50% of the population has been killed (i.e. all biological activity has ceased). Lethal limits should really only be considered as boundaries within which the experiments are carried out — the aim of toxicity studies should be to assess the sub-lethal effects of the factor on the test organism.

The metabolism of an organism is said to govern the efficiency of the ecosystem in the long run. Therefore, if pollution levels which indicate impairment of metabolism could be detected, action could be taken before the effect of the pollutant becomes critical. Beadle[11] has suggested that incipient ill health of an organism might be reflected in abnormalities in ion fluxes before any other symptoms appear. Nimmo et al.[46] have shown that cadmium affects the structure of the exoskeleton, particularly the gills, in a number of marine shrimps. Such changes should be detectable long before the animal dies. However, caution must be exercised in analysing any results involving metabolic and structural changes in an organism, as care must be taken to ensure that they are not due to changes associated with the organism's life-cyle or with its state of inanition. Even the degree to which the organism is parasitised may affect the results. Seasonal sensitivity to pollutants is something else which must be taken into consideration. It has been shown that certain molluscs are far more susceptible to oil dispersants during the months when they are reproducing.[43] Obviously therefore an LC_{50} experiment may give different results at different times of the year and a factor which is lethal in some months may have only sub-lethal effects during others.

Very little work has been done on the long-term effects of pollutants in the aquatic environment. An organism may survive being exposed to a pollutant, but it may be impaired in some way which is not immediately noticeable. George[23] has shown that whilst the polychaete worm, *Cirriformia tentaculata*, normally breeds throughout the year, individuals which had recovered from near lethal doses of two oil dispersants, BP 1002 and Essolvene, never developed gametes. Such a sterilising effect could in the long-term prove lethal to the population, as there would be no recruitment to it to replace individuals once they had died from 'natural' causes.

5.7. BIOLOGICAL MONITORING OF THE AQUATIC ENVIRONMENT

To maintain a relatively healthy aquatic environment in an industrial area it must be continuously kept under surveillance by monitoring.

All biological systems are continuously changing and it is important from the monitoring point of view to distinguish between natural changes and those caused by man. Changes in biological systems can be measured in various ways, e.g., species diversity, time of onset of maturation, reproductive success.[33,44]

Continual monitoring of the aquatic environment is essential if long-term trends are to be noticed. Limited, random surveys are of little use. The various Water Authorities measure many parameters frequently, if not continuously, in some cases, but measurement of certain parameters involves time-consuming chemical methods. In recent years biological indices such as those developed by Woodiwiss[73] and the Department of the Environment[18] have become a popular way of assessing the health of a stretch of running water. Such indices enable one to obtain an on-the-spot check of water quality. They may also indicate intermittent pollution which might not be detectable by one-off chemical checks. Bryce *et al.*[13] have used various indices to compare macro-invertebrate species diversity in the River Lee to some effect. Hellawell[27] has recently reviewed the methods used in the biological surveillance of rivers.

For change to be detected it is essential that base-line studies of the environment are made first to assess the components of the environment under study and any natural changes which might be occurring. Ideally such studies should be made before the event, but this is usually not the case. One important aspect of such studies is to identify 'key' species which control the structure of the community—however, first the community structure itself must be understood.[33] Baker[6] has outlined the problems involved in choosing such key species in the marine environment. Such key species may be used as indicator organisms and Baker lists five groups which may be used for the purpose of monitoring:

(a) bioassay organisms—to be selected and used as laboratory agents to detect the presence and/or concentration of toxic pollutants;
(b) accumulators—organisms which take up and accumulate chemicals in measurable quantities;
(c) exploiters—organisms whose presence indicates the probability of pollution; these may be abundant in polluted areas due to lack of competition from other species;
(d) detectors—these are species which respond to pollutants or environmental change by changing their normal biological pattern;
(e) sentinels—organisms which are sensitive to aquatic pollutants and which are put into the environment as early warning devices, or to measure the effect of pollutants in the natural environment.

Goldberg[25] has suggested that the blue mussel, *Mytilus edulis*, be used as an indicator of marine pollution due to its wide occurrence and the ease with which it can be collected. He envisages workers in a number of countries monitoring the state of health of mussel populations so that they can be used to indicate the build up of pollutants, thus allowing action to be taken if possible before a critical level has been reached. Bayne[10] has commented on such proposals.

Interpretation and understanding of raw data obtained from monitoring programmes requires a multidisciplinary approach. Only by this approach will future changes be predicted and safe levels determined for the input of pollutants via effluents into our ecosystem.

REFERENCES

1. Addison, R.F., Organochlorine compounds in aquatic organisms: their distribution, transport and physiological significance. In *Effect of Pollutants on Aquatic Organisms* (ed. A.P.M. Lockwood) 127–143. Cambridge University Press, London, 1976.
2. Alexander, W.B., Southgate, B.A. and Bassindale, R., *Survey of the River Tees II. The Estuary—Chemical and Biological*. Tech. Pap. Wat. Poll. Res., London, 1935.
3. Ansell, A.D., Lander, K.F., Coughlan, J. and Loosemore, F.A., Studies on the hard-shell clam *Venus mercenaria* in British waters. *J. Appl. Ecol.*, 1 (1970) 63–82.
4. Arthur, D.R., Summarising review. In *The Estuarine Environment* (eds. R.S.K. Barnes and J. Green) 123–133. Applied Science Publishers, London, 1972.
5. Aston, R.J., Field and experimental studies on the effects of a power station effluent on Tubificidae (Oligochaeta, Annelida). *Hydrobiologia*, 42 (2–3), (1973) 225–242.
6. Baker, J.M., Biological monitoring—principles, methods and difficulties. In *Marine Ecology and Oil Pollution* (ed. J.M. Baker) 41–53. Applied Science Publishers, London, 1976.
7. Baptist, J.P. and Lewis, C.W., Transfer of Zn-65 and Cr-51 through an estuarine food chain. In *Symposium on Radioecology* (eds. D.J. Nelson and F.C. Evans) 420–430. USAEC Conf-67053, Oak Ridge, Tenn. USA, 1969.
8. Barnes, R.S.K., *Estuarine Biology*. Edward Arnold, London, 1974.
9. Barrett, M.J., Predicting the effect of pollution in estuaries. *Proc. R. Soc. Lond. B.*, 180 (1972) 511–520.
10. Bayne, B., Watch on mussels. *Mar. Poll. Bull.*, 7 (12) (1976) 217–218.
11. Beadle, L.C., Physiological problems for animal life in estuaries. In *The Estuarine Environment* (eds. R.S.K. Barnes and J. Green) 51–60. Applied Science Publishers, London, 1972.
12. Bryan, G.W., Some aspects of heavy metal tolerance in aquatic organisms. In *Effect of Pollutants on Aquatic Organisms* (ed. A.P.M. Lockwood) 7–34. Cambridge University Press, London, 1976.

13. Bryce, D., Caffoor, I.M., Dale, C.R. and Jarrett, A.F., *Macro-invertebrates and the Bioassay of Water Quality, a Report Based on a Survey of the River Lee.* Nelpress, London, 1978.
14. Butterworth, J., Lester, P. and Nickless, G., Distribution of heavy metals in the Severn Estuary. *Mar. Poll. Bull.,* **3** (5) (1972) 72–74.
15. Cabinet Office, *The Torrey Canyon.* HMSO, London, 1967.
16. Conner, P.M., Acute toxicity of heavy metals to some marine larvae. *Mar. Poll. Bull.,* **3** (12) (1972) 190–192.
17. Corner, E.D.S., Harris, R.P., Whittle, K.J. and Mackie, P.R., Hydrocarbons in marine zoöplankton and fish. In *Effect of Pollutants on Aquatic Organisms* (ed. A.P.M. Lockwood) 72–105. Cambridge University Press, London, 1976.
18. Department of the Environment, *River Pollution Survey of England and Wales— Updated 1973. River Quality and Discharges of Sewage and Industrial Effluents.* HMSO, London, 1975.
19. Edwards, R.W., The effect of larvae of *Chironomus riparius* Meigen on the redox potentials of settled activated sludge. *Ann. Appl. Biol.,* **46** (1958) 457–464.
20. Edwards, R.W., *Pollution.* Oxford University Press, London, 1972.
21. de Falco, P. Jr., The estuary—septic tank of the Megalopolis. In *Estuaries* (ed. G.H. Lauff) 701–703. Am. Ass. Adv. Sci., Publ. No. 83., Washington DC, 1967.
22. Food and Agricultural Organisation, *Pollution: an International Problem for Fisheries.* World Food Problems No. 14. FAO, Rome, 1971.
23. George, J.D., Sub-lethal effects on living organisms. *Mar. Poll. Bull.,* **1** (7) (1970) 107–109.
24. George, J.D., Can the seas survive? Long term effects of pollution on marine life. *Ecologist,* **1** (9) (1971) 4–9.
25. Goldberg, E.D., The mussel watch—a first step in global marine monitoring. *Mar. Poll. Bull.,* **6** (7) (1975) 111.
26. Gray, J.S., The fauna of the polluted River Tees estuary. *Est. Coastal Mar. Sci.,* **4** (1976) 653–676.
27. Hellawell, J.M., *Biological Surveillance of Rivers.* Water Research Centre, Stevenage and Medmenham, 1978.
28. Holdgate, M.W., *The Sea Bird Wreck in the Irish Sea, Autumn 1969.* Natural Environment Research Council Publ. Ser. C. No. 4. 1971.
29. Hood, D.W., *The Impingement of Man on the Oceans.* Wiley-Interscience, New York, 1971.
30. Howell, B.R. and Shelton, R.G.J., The effect of china clay on the bottom fauna of St. Austell and Mevagissey Bays. *J. Mar. Biol. Ass. UK,* **50** (1970) 593–607.
31. Hynes, H.N.B., *The Biology of Polluted Waters.* University Press, Liverpool, 1960.
32. Kormondy, E.J., *Concepts of Ecology.,* 2nd edition Prentice Hall Inc., New Jersey, 1976.
33. Lewis, J.R., Problems and approaches to baseline studies in coastal communities. In *Marine Pollution and Sea Life* (ed. M. Ruivo) 401–404. Fishing News (Books) Ltd., West Byfleet, 1972.
34. Lockwood, A.P.M., *Effect of Pollutants on Aquatic Organisms.* Cambridge University Press, London, 1976.
35. Macan, T.T. and Worthington, E.B., *Life in Lakes and Rivers.* Collins, London, 1972.

36. McLusky, D.S., *Ecology of Estuaries*. Heinemann Educational Books Ltd., London, 1971.
37. Mellanby, K., *The Biology of Pollution*. Edward Arnold, London, 1972.
38. Moore, P.G., Inorganic particulate suspensions in the sea and their effect on marine animals. *Oceanography and Marine Biology Annual Review*, **15** (1977) 225–263.
39. Naylor, E., Effects of heated effluents upon marine and estuarine organisms. *Adv. Mar. Biol.*, **3** (1965) 63–103.
40. Nelson-Smith, A., The effects of oil pollution and emulsifier cleansing on shore life in S.W. Britain. *J. Appl. Ecol.*, **5** (1968) 97–107.
41 Nelson-Smith, A., Biological consequences of oil pollution and shore cleansing. *Field Studies*, **2** (1968) 73–80.
42. Nelson-Smith, A., Effects of the oil industry on shore life in estuaries. *Proc. R. Soc. Lond. B.*, **180** (1972) 487–496.
43. Nelson-Smith, A., Biological consequences of oil spills. In *The Marine Environment* (eds. J. Lenihan and W.W. Fletcher) 46–69. Blackie, Glasgow, 1977.
44. Natural Environment Research Council, *Biological Surveillance*, NERC Publ. B. 18., 1976.
45. Nickless, G., Stenner, R. and Terrille, N., Distribution of cadmium, lead and zinc in the Bristol Channel. *Mar. Poll. Bull.*, **3** (12) (1972) 188–190.
46. Nimmo, D.W.R., Lightner, D.V. and Bahner, L.H., Effects of cadmium on the shrimps *Penaeus duorarum, Palaemonites pugio* and *P. vulgaris*. In *Physiological Response of Marine Biota to Pollutants* (eds. F.J. Vernberg *et al.*) 131–183. Academic Press, New York, 1977.
47. Odum, S., *Fundamentals of Ecology*, 3rd edition. W.B. Saunders and Co., London, 1971.
48. Open University, *Rivers and Lakes*. S2–3 (3) *Environment*. Open University Press, Bletchley, 1972.
49. Open University, *Clean and Dirty Water*. PT272 (5) *Environmental Control and Public Health*. Open University Press, Bletchley, 1975.
50. Peden, J.D., Crothers, J.H., Waterfall, C.E. and Beasley, J., Heavy metals in Somerset marine organisms. *Mar. Poll. Bull.*, **4** (1) (1973) 7–9.
51. Pentreath, R.J., The monitoring of radionuclides. In *Biological Accumulators*, 9–26. FAO, Rome, 1976.
52. Perkins, E.J., *The Biology of Estuaries and Coastal Waters*. Academic Press, London, 1974.
53. Perkins, E.J., Measurements of biological response. In *Marine Pollution* (ed. R. Johnston) 505–585. Academic Press, London, 1976.
54. Perkins, E.J., Williams, B.R.H. and Goodman, J., *The Biology of Solway Firth in Relation to the Movement and Accumulation of Radioactive Materials. V. Radioactivity in Fauna*. United Kingdom Atomic Energy Authority PG Report 752(CC), 1966.
55. Phillipson, J., *Ecological Energetics*. Edward Arnold, London, 1966.
56. Porter, E., *Pollution in Four Industrialised Estuaries*. HMSO, London, 1973.
57. Preston, A., The concentration of Zn-65 in the flesh of oysters related to the discharge of cooling pond effluents from CEGB nuclear power station at Bradwell-on-Sea, Essex. In *Radioecological Concentration Processes* (eds. B.

Aberg and F.P. Hungate) 995–1004. Pergamon Press, Oxford, 1966.

58. Pritchard, D.W., What is an estuary: physical viewpoint. In *Estuaries* (ed. G.H. Lauff) 3–5. Am. Ass. Adv. Sci., Publ. No. 83. Washington, DC, 1967.

59. Ratcliffe, D.A., Changes attributable to pesticides in egg breakage frequency and eggshell thickness in some British birds. *J. Appl. Ecol.*, 7 (1970) 67–115.

60. Royal Commission on Environmental Pollution, *Pollution in Some British Estuaries and Coastal Waters, 3rd report.* HMSO, London, 1972.

61. Russell-Hunter, W.D., *Aquatic Productivity.* Collier Macmillan Ltd., London, 1970.

62. Smith, J.E., '*Torrey Canyon*': *Pollution and Marine Life.* Cambridge University Press, London, 1968.

63. Spooner, M.F., Amoco Cadiz oil spill. *Mar. Poll. Bull.*, 9 (11) (1978) 281–310.

64. Stewart, W.D.P., Estuarine and brackish waters—an introduction. In *The Estuarine Environment* (eds. R.S.K. Barnes and J. Green) 1–9. Applied Science Publishers, London, 1972.

65. Thorson, G., *Life in the Sea.* World University Library, London, 1971.

66. Vernberg, F.J. and Vernberg, W.B., *Pollution and Physiology of Marine Organisms.* Academic Press, New York, 1974.

67. Vernberg, F.J., Calabrese, A., Thurberg, F.P. and Vernberg, W.B., *Physiological Responses of Marine Biota to Pollutants.* Academic Press, New York, 1977.

68. Vernberg, W.B. and Vernberg, F.J., The synergistic effects of temperature, salinity and mercury on survival and metabolism of the adult fiddler crab, *Uca pugilator. Fishery Bulletin*, 70 (2) (1972) 415–420.

69. Vernberg, W.B. and Vernberg, F.J., *Environmental Physiology of Marine Animals.* Springer-Verlag, New York, 1972.

70. Vernberg, W.B., de Coursey, P.J. and O'Hara, J., Multiple environmental factor effects on physiology and behaviour of the fiddler crab, *Uca pugilator.* In *Pollution and Physiology of Marine Organisms* (eds. Vernberg, F.J. and Vernberg, W.B.) 381–425. Academic Press, London, 1974.

71. Warinner, J.E. and Brehmer, M.L., The effects of thermal effluents on marine organisms. *Air and Water Pollution International Journal*, 10 (1966) 277–289.

72. Wilson, E.O., Eisner, T., Briggs, W.R., Dickerson, R.E., Metzenberg, R.L., O'Brien, R.D., Susman, M. and Boggs, W.E., *Life on Earth*, Sinauer Assoc., Inc., Connecticut, USA, 1973.

73. Woodiwiss, F.S., The biological system of stream classification used by the Trent River Board. *Chemistry and Industry*, 11 (1964) 443–447.

74. Woodwell, G.M., Toxic substances and ecological cycles. *Scientific American*, 216 (3) (1967) 24–31.

75. Young, J.S. and Gibson, C.I., Effect of thermal effluent on migrating Menhaden. *Mar. Poll. Bull.*, 4 (6) (1973) 94–95.

6

Physical and Chemical Treatment

J.K. WALTERS

Senior Lecturer in Chemical Engineering, University of Nottingham, UK

6.1. INTRODUCTION

There are a wide variety of processes available for the treatment of waste waters from industrial as well as domestic sources. The exact choice of processes will depend on the nature of the industry, the regulations governing the discharge of effluents and the availability and economics of the water supply. In this chapter we shall consider the physical and chemical processes that are used in the treatment of effluents. Physical processes are used mainly for the removal of suspended solids from water; chemical processes mainly for the removal of dissolved solids. Biological processes are also used extensively, but they will be discussed separately in the next chapter. The removal of solid particles is common to many industries. Particles that settle readily are easily removed by sedimentation or flotation, two processes that are widely used, but smaller particles and colloids must first be coagulated and flocculated before sedimentation. The result is a clear liquid overflow, which is usually sent to the sewer, and a sludge containing a large percentage of solids. Table 6.1 lists several

TABLE 6.1
SEPARATION OF SOLID PARTICLES

Colloidal	Suspended	Sludge	
Coagulation	Sedimentation	Vacuum filtration	
Flocculation	(clarification and	Centrifugation	Incineration
	thickening)	Wet combustion	Tipping
	Flotation	Lagooning	Pyrolysis
	Filtration	Grass plots	

127

TABLE 6.2
REMOVAL OF DISSOLVED SOLIDS

	Inorganic	Organic
Evaporation	Oxidation/reduction	Aerobic oxidation
Ion exchange	Precipitation	Anaerobic digestion
Membrane processes	Neutralisation	Activated sludge
Electrodialysis	Algae harvesting	Trickling filters

NaOH

processes for the disposal of the sludge as well as listing the processes for removing suspended and colloidal materials. The disposal of sludge will be considered in further detail in Chapters 8, 10 and 11 and will not be discussed here.

The removal of dissolved materials from waste water presents different problems to the removal of suspended solids. Inorganic and organic materials generally require different methods of treatment. The methods available are listed in Table 6.2. The removal of organic materials depends largely on biological processes, which are considered in Chapters 7 and 8, and it is processes for the removal of inorganic materials that will be considered later in this chapter.

6.1.1. Volume and strength reduction

In addition to treatment processes as such, there are several methods that may be used by industry to reduce both the strength and volume of the effluent. The process itself could be modified to reduce the amounts of pollutants that enter the effluent streams. The replacement of starch as a sizing agent in the textile industry by cellulose compounds with a much lower BOD may be cited as an example. Equipment could be modified. In the dairy industry the redesign of milk churns, so that they drained faster and more completely, not only reduced the waste milk loading in the effluent stream but also produced a saving in milk.[9] Water could be recycled within the plant itself so that less is required from the supply and less is discharged to the sewers. This is applicable to all industries. In the past water has been considered a cheap and plentiful raw material and little attention has been paid to the water quality and quantity actually *needed by the process*. When examined closely it is often found that less water is required and that a lower quality water is quite adequate. One paper mill observed by Nemerow[9] reduced its water consumption by 50% during a water shortage without drop in production, but unfortunately, despite

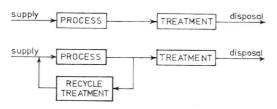

FIG. 6.1. The once-through and recycle systems.

savings to the mill, the water usage returned to its original volume after the shortage was over. This shows all too clearly the low value put on water supplies by industry at that time. Charges for water supply and for discharge to sewers have both increased enormously in recent years and it is in the interest of industry to reduce its usage of water on both counts. Figure 6.1 shows the once-through and recycle systems for water usage. It is quite possible that fewer treatment facilities would be required for a recycle system than for a once-through system and the overall effluent disposal problem would be considerably reduced.

In new plants water usage and effluent disposal should be considered as an integral part of the plant design. In that way considerable economies may be made. To modify an existing plant is more difficult and usually more expensive. Nevertheless reduction in volume of effluent even at the expense of an increase in strength may result in an overall saving as demonstrated in the example given in Chapter 2.

6.1.2. Segregation
Segregation of different effluents from the same works can be advantageous and in some cases essential. It often results in two types of waste; a strong waste of small volume that can be treated by methods specific to the pollutants concerned and a weak waste of large volume that will require less treatment. An example where it is essential to segregate the wastes is in the treatment of effluents from electroplating plants: cyanide wastes must be oxidised in alkaline solution whereas chromate wastes must be reduced in acid solution. The two wastes may then be mixed to neutralise them and the metals precipitated as the hydroxide. A detailed description of the reactions involved will be found in Chapter 8.

6.1.3. Equalisation or balancing
These are alternative names for the process that is essentially the converse of segregation. It is used in industries which have a wide variety of processes

on the same site. The wastes are held in holding tanks with a retention time at least equal to the cycle time of the plant so that fluctuations in strength and flow are smoothed out to give an effluent of uniform consistency. For example, a chemical company may find it advantageous to equalise its acid wastes over a one-day period to even out the alkali requirement for neutralisation. If an alkaline waste from another plant is available, it will be even more advantageous to run this into the equalisation tanks to effect the neutralisation and thus avoid peak concentrations of either acid or alkali.

A coalmining company combined a modification of its process with equalisation of two wastes to remove two pollution problems: the process was modified so that the raw coal was washed with acid mine waste water rather than with water from the public supply. The mine waste water was neutralised at the same time as the coal was washed free of impurities. Typical analyses showed that before the modification the mine water had a pH of 3 and an iron content of 550 ppm, while after the modification the final effluent had a pH close to 7 and an iron content of only 1 ppm, so that the overall problem of effluent disposal was very much diminished.

6.2. SEDIMENTATION

Sedimentation is used to remove suspended solids from waste waters by gravitational settling of the solids through the water. Quiescent conditions are necessary for good separation and these are obtained by allowing the waste water to flow at low velocity through a tank of large cross-sectional area. With proper design the solids settle to form a sludge at the bottom of the tank and clear water is taken from the top of the tank by allowing it to flow over a weir into a collection channel. The sludge is removed either by raking it to a discharge point at the bottom of the tank for withdrawal or by using vacuum suction. In either case the sludge product is known as the 'underflow' and it contains an appreciable quantity of water. The clear liquid product is known as the 'overflow' and should contain no solid material. If the sedimentation tank is poorly designed with insufficient area, it will still function but either the overflow will contain solid particles or the underflow will be more dilute than desired. The main problem in design, therefore, is to determine the cross-sectional area of the sedimentation tank needed to produce the desired concentration of sludge in the underflow. In plan view sedimentation tanks may be either rectangular or circular. The rectangular tanks may be of much larger capacity and are often used as the primary sedimentation tanks at large sewage works. The side-elevation is

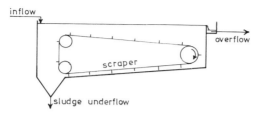

FIG. 6.2. Rectangular sedimentation tank.

FIG. 6.3. Rectangular sedimentation tank (Courtesy of Severn–Trent Water Authority).

shown in Fig. 6.2. The submerged scraper may be operated as shown or from an overhead movable gantry as illustrated in the photograph in Fig. 6.3. The radial flow tank in Fig. 6.4 is generally more common with the rotating rake moving the sludge to the underflow withdrawal point. The photograph in Fig. 6.5 shows a nearly empty tank, the vertical pipes attached to the rakes being for vacuum withdrawal of sludge. The upper regions of a sedimentation tank are in fact clarifying the liquid overflow and the lower regions are thickening the sludge underflow. Sedimentation tanks are therefore also known as clarifiers if the overflow is of more interest and as thickeners if the sludge is important. Below a certain particle size, which

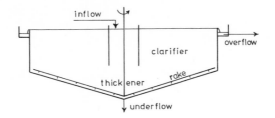

FIG. 6.4. Circular radial flow sedimentation tank.

FIG. 6.5. Interior details of radial flow sedimentation tank (Courtesy of Severn —
Trent Water Authority).

depends on the material concerned, the settling velocity becomes so small
that removal by sedimentation is not possible. Such particles must be first
coagulated before settling can take place and reference should be made to
Section 6.4.

6.2.1. Simple Settling of Discrete Particles

The simplest theory of settling assumes that discrete particles are present
which do not interfere with one another while settling. The particles move
horizontally at the same speed as the water but settle vertically under the

influence of gravity at a steady speed known as the *terminal velocity*. An expression for this may be obtained by equating the weight less the buoyancy of the particle to the frictional drag produced by the relative motion of the particle through the water:

$$(\rho_s - \rho)gV = C_D A \frac{\rho u^2}{2} \tag{6.1}$$

where ρ_s is the density of the particle, ρ the density of the water, V the volume of the particle, A the cross-sectional area of the particle, g the acceleration due to gravity, C_D the drag coefficient and u the terminal velocity of the particle. This may be rearranged to give:

$$u^2 = \frac{2gV(\rho_s - \rho)}{C_D A \rho} = \frac{4gd(\rho_s - \rho)}{3C_D \rho} \tag{6.2}$$

for spheres of diameter d. The drag coefficient C_D is related to the particle Reynolds number Re, which is defined as $\rho u d/\mu$ where μ is the viscosity of the water. Thus C_D is a function of u and eqn. (6.2) would in general have to be solved by trial-and-error. However at low and high values of the Reynolds number, there are simple relationships between C_D and Re:

$$Re < 1 \qquad \text{Stokes's Law} \qquad C_D = 24/Re \tag{6.3}$$
$$Re > 1000 \quad \text{Turbulent} \qquad C_D = 0.44 \tag{6.4}$$

and eqn. (6.2) may be solved explicitly for the terminal velocity u. Unfortunately it is the intermediate region that is of more interest and, although the Schiller and Naumann equation:

$$1 < Re < 1000 \text{ Transition} \qquad C_D = 24(1 + 0.15Re^{0.687})/Re \tag{6.5}$$

applies, it does not enable explicit values of u to be calculated. A better method that avoids trial-and-error is to rearrange eqn. (6.2) to give

$$C_D Re^2 = \frac{4g\rho d^3(\rho_s - \rho)}{3\mu} \tag{6.6}$$

Values of $C_D Re^2$ are available and are tabulated against Re in handbooks such as Perry[12] and presented graphically in texts such as Coulson and Richardson.[3] The procedure is to calculate $C_D Re^2$ from eqn. (6.6) and look up the corresponding value of Re. The terminal velocity u is then found from the definition of Re given above.

It is important to emphasise that this approach applies only to discrete particles settling without mutual interference. With more concentrated

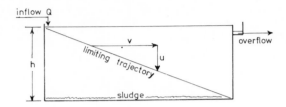

FIG. 6.6. Velocities in a sedimentation tank.

suspensions the settling velocity depends on concentration and the more complicated model to be described in the following sections must be used. In an ideal sedimentation tank, the water is assumed to move at a uniform velocity v horizontally and the particles are assumed to settle at their terminal velocity u. The particles move horizontally with the water so the particle horizontal velocity is also v. Figure 6.6 shows the components of the particle velocity on these assumptions. If t is the retention time of the water in the tank, all particles with terminal velocities greater than h/t will reach the bottom of the tank and be retained. For a tank of cross-sectional plan area A and water volumetric flow Q, the retention time $t = Ah/Q$ and hence h/t is equal to Q/A. Hence all particles with a terminal velocity greater than Q/A will be removed. The quantity Q/A is known as the *surface overflow rate* and is an important parameter in design.

6.2.2. Settling of More Concentrated Suspensions

As the concentration of solids is increased, interparticle forces come increasingly into play and reduce the settling velocity. A number of different types of settling can occur:

(i) *Zone Settling*: above about 500 mg/litre the particles of floc are close enough together for the interparticle forces to hold them in fixed positions relative to one another, so the floc settles *en masse* with a distinct interface between the settling floc and the clear liquid above it. This is probably the most common type of settling to occur in sedimentation tanks.

(ii) *Hindered Settling*: in suspensions with concentrations greater than about 2000 mg/litre there is a significant flow of water upwards past the settling solids owing to the displacement of the water by the solids. The apparent settling velocity is thereby reduced.

(iii) *Compressive Settling*: at the bottom of a sedimentation tank the solids concentration is high, the particles are in contact and the

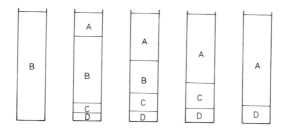

FIG. 6.7. Laboratory batch sedimentation test.

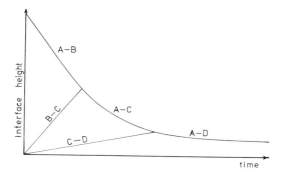

FIG. 6.8. Characteristic settling curve.

weight of the particles is partly supported by the layers of solid below. Consolidation of the sludge takes place slowly.

Zone settling is the most important in the design of sedimentation tanks and may be demonstrated in the laboratory by shaking up a uniform suspension in a large measuring cylinder and allowing it to stand. Figure 6.7 shows what happens as time proceeds. Clear liquid (A) forms at the top and a sharp interface between that and the region of constant composition (B) falls steadily. Sludge (D) builds up at the bottom and is subject to compressive settling on a much longer timescale. An intermediate region of variable composition (C) must occur and contain all compositions between those in regions B and D. A plot of interface position versus time is shown in Fig. 6.8, the position of the clear liquid interface, the curved line, being known as the characteristic settling curve for the material. The slope of the straight lines B–C and C–D is a measure of the velocity with which those

J.K. Walters

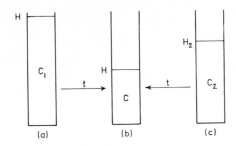

FIG. 6.9. Model for predicting sedimentation rate at concentration c_2 from known settling curve at concentration c_1

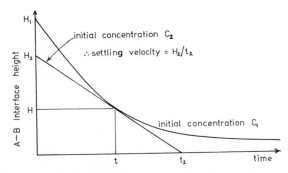

FIG. 6.10. Estimation of sedimentation rate at concentration c_2 from known settling curve at concentration c_1.

interfaces are propagated upwards. The characteristic settling curve must be determined in the laboratory to provide information on which the design of a sedimentation tank may be based. Originally several tests had to be made at different concentrations to provide sufficient information, but using the approach taken by Kynch[6] the sedimentation rate at a particular concentration can be estimated from the characteristic settling curve of a less concentrated suspension. In Fig. 6.9 it is assumed that (b) can be reached in time t either from a uniform concentration c_1 with a clear liquid interface height of H_1 or from a greater concentration c_2 at a height H_2. A material balance then gives

$$H_1 c_1 = H_2 c_2 \tag{6.7}$$

Suppose that the characteristic settling curve for concentration c_1 has been determined and is as shown in Fig. 6.10 and we wish to find the

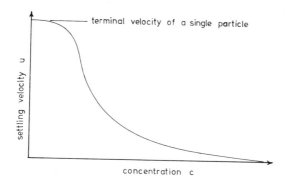

FIG. 6.11. Typical settling velocity versus concentration curve.

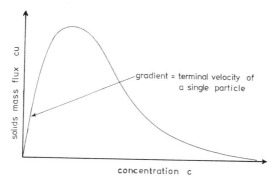

FIG. 6.12. Typical solids mass flux versus concentration curve for batch settling.

sedimentation rate for any selected c_2. The corresponding height H_2 is calculated from eqn. (6.7) and marked on the ordinate. From there a line is drawn tangential to the settling curve for c_1 to cut the abscissa at t_2. The point at which this line touches the curve represents (b) in Fig. 6.9 and the sedimentation rate for concentration c_2 is H_2/t_2. This construction can be repeated for different values of c_2 and a sedimentation rate versus concentration curve built up as in Fig. 6.11. The solids flux (mass per unit area per unit time) is an important parameter given by the product cu. It can be calculated from Fig. 6.11 and is found to pass through a maximum when plotted as a function of c as shown in Fig. 6.12. The flux is zero at two points: at the origin where c is zero and at some other concentration where the particles are so close together that no further movement is possible. So

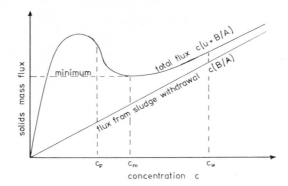

FIG. 6.13. Typical solids mass flux versus concentration curves for continuous underflow withdrawal.

far we have considered batch settling; with a continuous system of underflow withdrawal the sedimentation rate is increased by the downward superficial velocity of the underflow withdrawal (B/A) where B is the underflow volumetric rate and A is the cross-sectional area of the tank. Thus the total solids mass flux becomes $c(u + B/A)$ and we find from Fig. 6.13 that this total flux passes through a minimum. The solid material enters the sedimentation tank at the feed concentration c_F and leaves at the underflow concentration c_u. All concentrations between c_F and c_u must exist somewhere in the tank and therefore the critical region is where c_m occurs and the total solids flux is a minimum. The minimum area A required for the tank is then given by dividing the mass throughput of solids M by the minimum flux, so

$$A \geq \frac{M}{c_m(u_m + B/A)} \tag{6.8}$$

where u_m is the sedimentation rate corresponding to the concentration c_m. For a volumetric feed flow to the tank of F and proper operation so that the overflow is free from solids, the mass throughput of solids is given by:

$$M = Fc_F = Bc_u \tag{6.9}$$

Substituting $B = M/c_u$ from eqn. (6.9) into eqn. (6.8) and solving for the area A leads to

$$A \geq \frac{M}{u_m}\left(\frac{1}{c_m} - \frac{1}{c_u}\right) \tag{6.10}$$

Clearly Fig. 6.13 cannot be plotted until the area A is known and, since the area is the quantity we are trying to calculate, this presents a difficulty. The best way out of this dilemma is to plot $(1/c - 1/c_u)/u$ versus c for values of c between the feed concentration c_F and the underflow concentration c_u. This function is proportional to the right hand side of eqn. (6.10) and it passes through a maximum at $c = c_m$ and $u = u_m$. The required area of the sedimentation tank is then obtained by multiplying this maximum by the solids throughput M.

The above analysis is a combination of theories presented in the literature, a good review of which has recently been given by Pearse.[10]

Example 6.1. Determine the cross-sectional area of a thickener to produce an underflow solids concentration of 0.7 kg suspended solids/litre from a feed slurry of 0.2 kg solids/litre at a total solids mass throughput of 3000 kg/h. The characteristic settling curve, determined in the laboratory, is shown in Fig. 6.14.

Solution
We must first construct the sedimentation rate as a function of concentration: various concentrations are selected between the feed and underflow concentrations and eqn. (6.7) used to calculate the corresponding value of H_2. From each of these points on the ordinate of Fig. 6.14 a tangent is drawn to the curve, the slope of which gives the sedimentation rate for that composition. One such tangent is shown in Fig. 6.14 for a

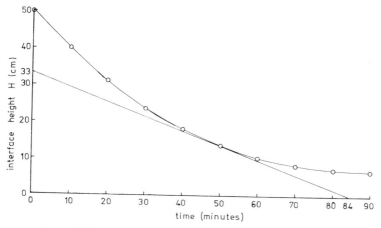

FIG. 6.14. Characteristic settling curve for Example 6.1.

TABLE 6.3
CALCULATIONS FOR SEDIMENTATION TANK DESIGN

c	H_2	u	$\dfrac{1}{c}$	$\left(\dfrac{1}{c}-\dfrac{1}{c_u}\right)$	$\dfrac{100}{u}\left(\dfrac{1}{c}-\dfrac{1}{c_u}\right)$	$\left(u+\dfrac{B}{A}\right)$	$c\left(u+\dfrac{B}{A}\right)$
$\dfrac{kg}{litre}$	cm	$\dfrac{cm}{h}$	$\dfrac{litre}{kg}$	$\dfrac{litre}{kg}$	$\dfrac{h.litre}{metre.kg}$	$\dfrac{cm}{h}$	$\dfrac{kg.cm}{h.litre}$
0.20	50	61	5.00	3.57	5.9	79	15.8
0.24	42	37	4.17	2.74	7.5	55	13.1
0.27	37	29	3.70	2.27	7.9	47	12.6
0.30	33	24	3.33	1.90	8.0	42	12.5
0.32	31	21	3.12	1.69	7.9	39	12.6
0.4	25	15	2.50	1.07	7.0	33	13.2
0.5	20	10	2.00	0.57	5.4	28	14.2
0.6	17	7	1.67	0.24	3.2	25	15.2
0.7	14	5	1.43	0	0	23	16.2

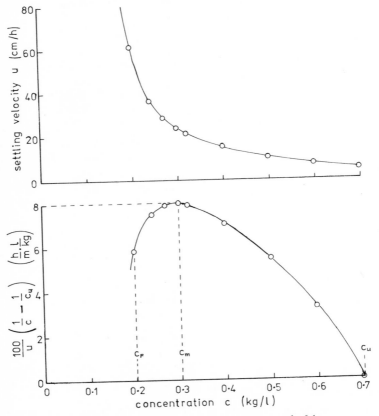

FIG. 6.15. Graphical calculations for Example 6.1.

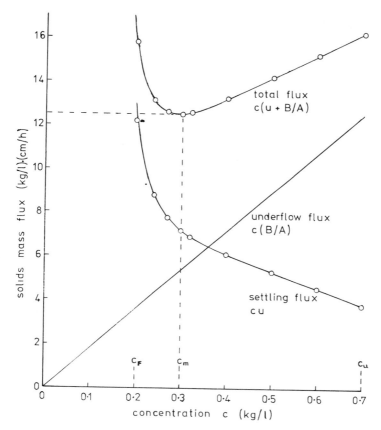

FIG. 6.16. Solids mass flux graphs for Example 6.1.

concentration of 0.3 kg/litre. The subsequent calculations are tabulated in Table 6.3, and plotted graphically in Figs. 6.15 and 6.16. From Fig. 6.15 the maximum value of $(100/u)(1/c - 1/c_u)$ is 8.0 and hence from eqn. (6.10) with $M = 3000$ kg/h we find that

$$A \geq 8.0 \frac{\text{h.litre}}{\text{metre.kg}} \times 3000 \frac{\text{kg}}{\text{h}} \times \frac{1}{1000} \frac{\text{metre}^3}{\text{litre}} = 24\text{m}^2$$

i.e. the required cross-sectional area is at least 24 m².

6.2.3. Sludge Blanket Sedimentation

When very small particles are present, which would not settle in normal sedimentation tanks, but which will flocculate given time, a sludge blanket

J.K. Walters

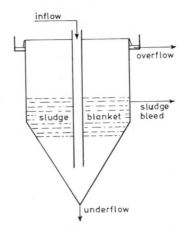

FIG. 6.17. Sludge blanket sedimentation tank.

may be allowed to build up in the tank. This is shown schematically in Fig. 6.17. It is important to control the sludge withdrawal and bleed carefully to avoid losing the blanket, which acts as a filter for the small particles. Such systems take a long time to build up in a clean tank, but are very successful, once the blanket has grown to a sufficient thickness, in producing a clear overflow. They are more appropriately used as clarifiers than thickeners.

6.3. DISSOLVED AIR FLOTATION

Pressure flotation of suspended solids can be achieved by aerating the effluent stream under a pressure of some 3 to 5 atm and then reducing the pressure suddenly. The dissolved air then comes out of solution in the form of very small bubbles, which adhere to the particles of suspended solids causing them to float to the surface where they are skimmed off as a scum. The bubbles are approximately 10 to 100 μm in diameter and rise according to Stokes's Law which is given by a combination of eqns. (6.2) and (6.3). Clarified liquid is removed from the bottom of the tank. In concept flotation is similar to sedimentation except that the solids move upwards instead of downwards. The rise velocity of the solids/air mixture is of the same order as the settling velocities in sedimentation tanks. The two systems in

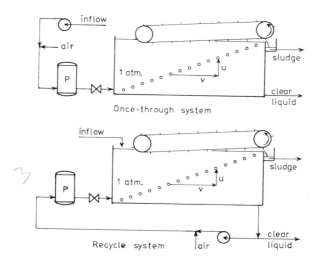

FIG. 6.18. Once-through and recycle dissolved air flotation systems.

common use are shown in Fig. 6.18. In the once-through system the whole of the inflow is pressurised and all the suspended solids pass through the pump. The recycle system has the advantage that the suspended solids do not pass through the pump, and that the rise velocity is increased because of the lowering of the solids concentration. A larger flotation tank is, however, required. The air/solids mass ratio (A/S) is an important factor in the performance of a flotation unit and is usually in the range 0.01 to 0.05. The residence time in the flotation tank is about half an hour and the retention time in the air pressurisation vessel is a few minutes.

6.3.1. Theory of Dissolved Air Flotation

The solubility of air in water follows Henry's Law over a wide range of pressures and the air released when the pressure is reduced from P atmospheres down to 1 atm is given by:

$$a = H(fP - 1) \qquad (6.11)$$

where a is the air released at atmospheric pressure in mg/litre, H is Henry's law constant for air in water in mg/litre per atmosphere, and f is the fraction of saturation attained in the pressurisation vessel. For the once through system with a feed concentration c_F(mg/litre), the air/solids mass ratio is given by:

$$\frac{A}{S} = \frac{H(fP-1)}{c_F} \tag{6.12}$$

and for the recycle system with a ratio R of recycle to feed flow rate:

$$\frac{A}{S} = \frac{RH(fP-1)}{c_F} \tag{6.13}$$

Combining eqns. (6.2) and (6.3) we may obtain an expression for the velocity of rise u of air bubbles of diameter d as:

$$u = \frac{d^2g}{18\mu}(\rho - \rho_a) \tag{6.14}$$

where μ is the viscosity of the water of density ρ and ρ_a is the effective density of the air/solids mix. Usually ρ_a is significantly less than ρ and may be ignored. Inserting the values of μ and ρ for water then gives:

$$u = 545\,000\,d^2 \tag{6.15}$$

for u measured in m/s and d in metres. For the range of bubble size encountered in dissolved air flotation, u lies in the range 3.3 mm/min for $d = 10\,\mu$m up to 330 mm/min for $d = 100\,\mu$m. In Section 6.2.1 it was shown that particles with terminal velocities greater than the surface overflow rate would be separated by sedimentation. The same arguments apply to flotation and bubbles with rise velocities greater than the *surface loading rate*, i.e. the volumetric throughput of the flotation tank per unit area, will have time to reach the top of the tank and be separated. Surface loading rates of about 10 mm/min are usual, corresponding to a bubble size of approximately 17 μm.

Example 6.2. An activated sludge of concentration 3000 mg/litre and volume flow 4 litre/s is to be thickened in a pressurised recycle flotation system. The air/solids mass ratio is to be 0.01 and the recycle pressure is 4 atm. If the pressurising system dissolves air to half its saturation level what recycle rate should be used? If the surface loading rate is to be 10 mm/min what area of flotation cell is required? Take the Henry's law constant for air in water as 24 mg/litre atm.

Solution
Using eqn. (6.13) we have:

$$0.01 = \frac{R \times 24 \times (0.5 \times 4 - 1)}{3000}$$

and hence $R = 1.25$

The recycle rate is therefore $1.25 \times 4 = 5 \, \text{litre/s}$

The flotation tank area $= \dfrac{\text{total volume throughput}}{\text{surface loading rate}}$

$$= \frac{(4 + 5)\,\text{litre/s} \times 10^{-3}\,\text{m}^3/\text{litre}}{10\,\text{mm/min} \times 10^{-3}\,\text{m/mm}} \times \frac{60\text{s}}{\text{min}}$$

$$= 54\,\text{m}^2$$

6.4. COAGULATION AND FLOCCULATION

To remove colloidal particles by sedimentation, they have first to be coagulated so that the particle size is increased to a value suitable for sedimentation. Chemical coagulents are usually added which reduce the electrical field surrounding a colloid particle, thus destabilising the colloid and making it possible for such particles to come together and flocculate during mechanical agitation. High valent metal ions such as Al^{+++} or Fe^{+++} are commonly used for coagulation and in addition polyelectrolytes may be added as aids to flocculation. In some cases polyelectrolytes alone may be sufficient for the coagulation stage too. To be effective the coagulant must be rapidly distributed throughout the body of water. This rapid mixing is done by a high-speed propeller or turbine in a mixing tank with a retention time of only a few minutes. The coagulation and flocculation that follow take a rather longer time of up to an hour and require rather gentler agitation. The inorganic coagulant most often used is aluminium sulphate (alum) $Al_2(SO_4)_3 . 14H_2O$. In aqueous solution below pH 7, the aluminium ion is hydrolysed in stepwise fashion:

$$Al^{+++} + H_2O \rightleftharpoons AlOH^{++} + H^+$$

$$AlOH^{++} + H_2O \rightleftharpoons Al(OH)_2^+ + H^+$$

In addition polymeric cations are formed in mildly acidic solution giving rise to platelike polymers. The general reaction may be written:

$$mAl^{+++} + nH_2O \rightleftharpoons Al_m(OH)_n^{(3m-n)+} + nH^+$$

A thorough study of such hydroxyaluminium complexes has been made by Bersillon et al.[1] who quote equilibrium constants for several of the above

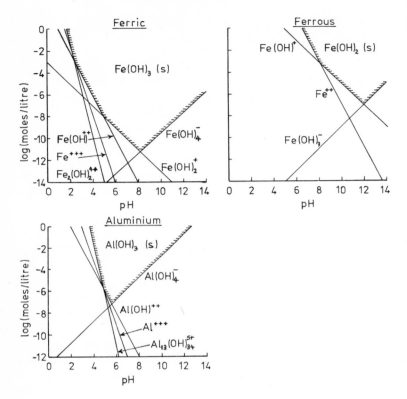

FIG. 6.19. Solution equilibria for some hydroxides.[13]

reactions up to $m = 13$, $n = 34$. They suggest that precipitation of solid species is more likely to occur as the polymeric forms rather than as the simple $Al(OH)_3$. However, a flocculant hydroxide precipitate is formed by hydrolysis and this includes the colloid particles. The solubility of the hydroxide is strongly pH dependent as can be seen from Bertillon's equilibrium data or from Weber's[13] graphs as shown in Fig. 6.19. The best results are obtained between a pH of 5 and 7. Outside this range alum is not used as a coagulant.

Ferric salts such as the sulphate or the chloride may be used between a pH of 5 and 11 and again several forms of the hydroxide exist as shown in Fig. 6.19. At higher pH ferrous salts such as the sulphate (copperas) $FeSO_4 \cdot 7H_2O$ are suitable. The useful range of pH for these ferrous salts is from 10 to 14.

Ferric and ferrous salts are both cheaper than alum, but the hydroxide precipitates are brown in colour and can lead to residual rust staining in the water, which may be unacceptable in some industries. Aluminium hydroxide is white and does not lead to such problems.

The range of pH and metal ion concentration required for satisfactory precipitation of the metal hydroxide can be estimated from Fig. 6.19. Dosages of aluminium ferric or ferrous salts required to destabilize the colloids are always larger than those required to precipitate the hydroxide, because the destabilisation is brought about by the polymeric complexes that exist in solution and which would be absorbed on to the colloidal particles. The correct dosage of coagulant depends on the colloid concentration and the pH of the water and must be determined by appropriate laboratory tests. Excess coagulant has been shown to restabilise the colloid, so as little coagulant as possible should be used.

6.4.1. Polyelectrolyte Flocculation

Polyelectrolytes are water-soluble polymers with many adsorption sites which are available for adsorption on to the colloid particles. One polymer molecule can therefore become adsorbed on to several colloid particles thus forming a bridge between particles and producing a stable floc. Such polymers may be anionic (negatively charged) or cationic (positively charged) or even nonionic. Many proprietory brands are available and the manufacturers should be consulted for details. Some examples of the types of molecules that are suitable are:

Nonionic: polyethylene oxide

$$[-CH_2-CH_2-O-]_n$$

polyacrylamide (PAM)

$$\left[-CH_2-CH- \atop \quad \overset{|}{CO} \atop \quad \overset{|}{NH_2} \right]_n$$

Anionic: polystyrene sulphonate (PSS)

$$\left[-CH_2-CH- \atop \quad \overset{|}{C} \atop HC \nearrow \searrow CH \atop HC \searrow \nearrow CH \atop \quad \overset{|}{C} \atop \quad SO_3^- \right]_n^{n-}$$

polyacrylic acid (PAA)

$$\left[-CH_2-CH- \atop \quad \overset{|}{CO} \atop \quad \overset{|}{O^-} \right]_n^{n-}$$

Cationic: quaternary polyamide   polydiallyldimethylammonium
                                               (PDADMA)

$$\left[-CH_2-\overset{\displaystyle CH_3}{\underset{\displaystyle CH_3}{\overset{|}{\underset{|}{N^+}}}}-CH_2- \right]_n^{n^+} \left[\begin{array}{c} CH_2 \\ / \quad \backslash \\ -CH \quad CH-CH_2- \\ | \qquad | \\ CH_2 \quad CH_2 \\ \backslash \quad / \\ N^+ \\ / \quad \backslash \\ CH_3 \quad CH_3 \end{array} \right]_n^{n} $$

There is a minimum size of anionic or nonionic polymer, with a molecular weight of the order of a million, for satisfactory bridging between negative colloid particles. Cationic polymers, however, can function as destabilising agents by bridge formation or charge neutralisation or both and may be effective at much lower molecular weights. Restabilisation due to overdosing can occur and there is a direct relationship between the optimum polymer dosage and the colloid concentration. The polymer dosage can be quite critical and the location of the destabilisation region may be markedly affected by pH. Laboratory tests over a wide range of polymer dosage are advisable. A series of samples are set up on a multiple stirrer rig and different amounts of coagulant added to each. After vigorous stirring with a glass rod to disperse the coagulant the samples are flocculated by gentle stirring for about half an hour and then allowed to stand for an hour. The clear liquid layer is then checked for colour and turbidity and the lowest dosage of coagulant that gives satisfactory results noted. A second set of samples is then prepared with a different pH in each. The coagulant dose previously determined is then added and stirring, flocculation and settling carried out as before. The optimum pH and coagulant dosage are thus both determined.

6.4.2. Power Requirements in Flocculation

Flocculation is achieved by fairly gentle agitation of the coagulating water. Too little movement will lead to inadequate flocculation and too much movement to break-up of the floc. Agitation is usually achieved mechanically by paddles but may also be achieved hydraulically by flow through tanks with baffles in them. The power input per unit volume, P is given by the product of the shear stress and the velocity gradient G. By definition the shear stress is the product of the liquid viscosity μ, and the velocity gradient and hence

$$P = \mu G^2 \tag{6.16}$$

Mechanical stirring is usually achieved by a number of rectangular paddles rotated about an axis in the centre of the tank. With the paddles moving with a relative velocity v with respect to the liquid and with a tank volume V, the power input per unit volume is:

$$P = NFv/V \tag{6.17}$$

where F is the drag force exerted by the liquid on each paddle and N is the number of paddles. For a paddle of area A, the drag force is given by

$$F = C_D A \rho v^2 / 2 \tag{6.18}$$

where C_D is the drag coefficient for a flat plate moving through a liquid of density ρ and hence

$$P = N C_D A \rho v^3 / 2V \tag{6.19}$$

or

$$G = (N C_D A \rho v^3 / 2\mu V)^{1/2} \tag{6.20}$$

The relative velocity v is usually taken as about 3/4 of the velocity of the paddle tip and is therefore related to the rotational speed of the paddles by the paddle geometry. For good flocculation G is usually in the range 10 to 100 Hz. With an appropriate design value of G, the tank volume and paddle geometry can be chosen to conform with eqn. (6.20) and from eqn. (6.16) the power input per unit volume P is found to lie in the range 0.1 to 10 W/m^3.

For hydraulic turbulence in a baffled tank, the power input is equal to the product of the pressure loss ρgh and the liquid flow rate Q where h is the head loss from inlet to outlet. Hence

$$P = \rho g h Q / V \tag{6.21}$$

or

$$G = (\rho g h Q / V\mu)^{1/2} \tag{6.22}$$

With such a system the flocculation and sedimentation must be carried out in different tanks, but with the mechanical flocculation it is often possible to perform the flocculation and sedimentation in different parts of the same tank and combine them with sludge blanket sedimentation as shown in Fig. 6.20.

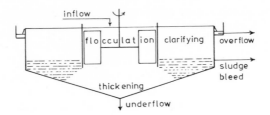

FIG. 6.20. Combined flocculation and sedimentation.

Example 6.3. The flocculation section of a combined flocculation and sedimentation tank is 10 m in diameter and 5 m deep. The tank is fitted with a stirrer consisting of four paddles each 4 m high by 2 m wide, the centre line of the paddles being 3 m from the axis of rotation. The design value of the velocity gradient is 40 Hz and the drag coefficient for the paddles is 1.8. What is the required speed of rotation of the stirrer and the power consumption?

Solution

From eqn. (6.16), $P = 10^{-3} \times 40^2 = 1.6$ W/m^3

Hence the total power consumption $= 1.6 \times (\pi/4) \times 10^2 \times 5 = 630$ W

From eqn. (6.19), $630 = 4 \times 1.8 \times (4 \times 2) \times 10^3 v^3/2$

hence $v = 0.28$ m/s

The velocity of the paddle tip is therefore $(4/3) \times 0.28 = 0.37$ m/s. The paddle tip is 4 m from the axis of rotation and so the angular speed is $0.37 \times 60/(2\pi \times 4) = 0.88$ rpm.

6.5. SAND FILTRATION

For the removal of the final traces of suspended solids sand filtration may be used. Two types of filter are in common use. In both the liquid is passed downwards under gravity through a packed bed of sand particles. The interstices between the particles are completely filled with liquid and a head of liquid above the top surface of the sand provides the pressure needed to drive the liquid through the filter. In a slow sand filter fine sand is used and a low liquid velocity of about 2 m/day is used. The suspended solids get trapped in the interstices of the sand particles near the top of the bed and cleaning is done by the physical removal of the clogged sand at the top. Such filters have been in use for many years for polishing water supplies and can be very large in area. The rapid sand filter with a liquid velocity of about

5 m/h requires a smaller area. Cleaning is done by backwashing with filtrate to fluidise the sand and allow the suspended solids to be flushed out. The washings are returned to the sedimentation tank upstream of the filter. Backwashing is carried out at much higher velocities than the filtration and causes considerable expansion of the bed which must be taken into account when designing the filtration tank.

As the interstices of the sand become filled with suspended solids, the pressure drop across the bed increases as a linear function of time. In practice it is usual to clean the bed either when the pressure drop becomes too large or when an unacceptable amount of material breaks through into the outflow. The rapid filter may require daily washing, the slow filter considerably less frequently.

6.6. AERATION

Aeration of water is an important aspect of the treatment of waste effluents as well as in the reaeration of natural bodies of water such as rivers discussed in Chapter 4. It is used mainly for the treatment of organic effluents where chemical and biological oxidation takes place. Aeration not only introduces oxygen into the water, but also provides sufficient agitation to keep the remaining solids present in suspension. Oxidation of dissolved and suspended materials can then take place. In addition other dissolved gases, such as CO_2 and H_2S, may be expelled from solution along with other odour-producing substances. There are two basic aeration systems available: diffused air in which air is pumped to distributors at the bottom of the tank, where bubbles are formed which rise up through the water, and surface turbines which rotate in the surface and throw droplets of water into the air, so aeration takes place from the atmosphere to the droplets. Submerged turbines can be used with either system to improve agitation and generally to reduce the residence time required for oxidation, but additional power is required.

6.6.1. Diffused Air Aeration

The oxygen transfer rate equation was given in Chapter 4 as:

$$\frac{dc}{dt} = k_L \frac{A}{V}(c_s - c) = r(c_s - c) \qquad (4.13)$$

with the variables defined in Section 4.8. The rate constant r is temperature dependent with a coefficient defined by eqn. (4.16) of $0.024 \, K^{-1}$. Values of

k_L generally range from 10 to 20 m/day which corresponds to a turbulent stream. The surface area A of the bubbles depends on their size which in turn depends on the gas flow rate and the type of air diffuser used. For a sparger system with a number of individual holes the diameter d of the bubbles may be estimated from:

$$d = 1.3G^{0.4}/g^{0.2} \qquad (6.23)$$

where G is the volumetric gas flow per hole. This is satisfactory up to a value of G of about 20 cm^3/s but above that flow the large bubbles formed immediately break up into a collection of smaller bubbles with diameters of about 0.5 cm which is the steady state size for bubbles in a turbulent liquid. A porous plate distributor will produce smaller bubbles but have a larger pressure drop and be more susceptible to plugging with solid particles. Smaller bubbles are an advantage because they provide a larger interfacial area for oxygen mass transfer.

Diffused air aeration is quiet with easy adjustment of the air rate for different conditions. The disadvantages are the crucial positioning of the diffusers to obtain good suspension of the solid particles and the relatively high power consumption. The power requirement depends on the air rate, the depth of water and the pressure drop through the diffusers, and is generally in the range of 2 to 3 kWh/kg O_2 transferred.

6.6.2. Surface Turbines

Surface turbines, rotating in the surface, produce droplets of water which move through the air, become reaerated, and then fall back to the body of the water. In addition they have to create a circulation in the water to distribute the reaerated material throughout the main body of the water. In deep tanks draught tubes may be used to enhance circulation. Power requirements are about 0.5 kWh/kg O_2 transferred, but the overall power needed is generally greater than for diffused air systems, because of the additional power required to give adequate circulation of the liquid and keep the solids in suspension. More oxygen is therefore transferred than in the diffused air system. The surface turbine is highly efficient and gives the best oxygen transfer. Its main disadvantage is that only relatively shallow tanks may be used.

6.6.3. Submerged Turbines

On its own, a submerged turbine requires a separate air supply near the eye of the turbine. The turbine itself breaks up the large bubbles formed to give the characteristic size of bubbles in turbulent water of about 0.5 cm diameter. Power requirements are from 1 to 2 kWh/kg O_2 transferred, but, like the surface turbine, additional power must be supplied to give adequate suspension of the solids present. The net result is a system that is intermediate in oxygen transfer between the diffused air and surface turbine systems. It can be combined with the surface turbine to enable deep tanks to be used but the power requirement is high.

6.6.4. Recent Innovations

A recent innovation is the ICI deep-shaft aeration process.[5] Two shafts (adjacent or concentric) are used and the effluent is circulated rapidly down one and up the other by injection of air to give an air-lift effect. Power requirements of 0.2 kWh/kg O_2 transferred or less are claimed. Advantages of the system are greater contact times between the effluent and the air and greater solubility of oxygen in the effluent at the bottom of the shaft because of the greater pressure. For a shaft depth of 100 m the pressure at the bottom is about 9 atm and the solubility is increased accordingly. This and other recent systems are discussed further in Chapter 7, Section 7.7.5.

A recent paper by Motarjemi and Jameson[8] shows that oxygen transfer efficiencies from very small bubbles are much greater than from bubbles of 0.5 cm in diameter encountered in turbine and most diffused air systems. They suggest that bubbles smaller than 1 mm are desirable for good mass transfer efficiencies. The production of such small bubbles would require additional power, but that aspect was not studied.

6.7. EVAPORATION

Evaporation of pure water from the effluent is clearly only applicable for non-volatile wastes. The heat load is large because of the high latent heat of vaporisation of water and so the process is used mainly by industries which can recycle the concentrated material that remains after the water has been evaporated. The waste must be initially fairly strong with at least 1% total dissolved solids, but the main factor is an economic one: the value of the recycled concentrate must be greater than the cost of the energy required to evaporate the water. Paper mills are one of the main users of evaporation for concentrating the sulphate cooking liquors for reuse. It is also possible to combine evaporative recovery with ion exchange systems in electroplating works to recover metals from plating wastes. Another example is in the handling of radioactive solutions where all the radioactive material must be recovered. Evaporation produces a clean water free of radioactivity and can allow the radioactive material to be recovered in solid form.

6.8. ION EXCHANGE

Ion exchange resins are solid materials with active sites at which ions held on the resin may be exchanged with ions in the water flowing over the resin. An equilibrium exists between the different ions on the resin and in the water. Undesirable ions in the waste water may therefore be removed and held on the resin and replaced by less undesirable ions. Subsequently the resin is regenerated by reversing the reaction by passing a concentrated regenerant solution through the resin. Cation exchange resins have negative active sites and exchange cations. They can therefore be used for removing metal ions such as zinc or copper and replacing them in the waste by H^+ or Na^+ ions. On regeneration a concentrated solution of the metal that has been removed is produced and it is usually possible to recycle this for re-use. Anion exchange resins have positive active sites and exchange anions. Cation resins may be natural zeolites or synthetic polymers containing active groups such as $-SO_3H^-$ while anion resins are synthetic polymeric amines. Many proprietory types are available. The resins are used in the form of a packed bed of particles through which the effluent is passed. Selective exchange of the appropriate ions occurs and a build-up of concentration of the ion that is removed from the water takes place in the resin. This 'front' moves gradually through the packed bed until the resin can remove no more material at which time a 'breakthrough' of the effluent solution occurs. This is undesirable and the effluent should be directed to another fresh bed of resin just before 'breakthrough' occurs. The first bed is then regenerated. Countercurrent moving bed systems are also in use. Ion exchange was originally developed for softening hard water, but it has been successfully developed for recovering valuable materials from a variety of wastes. Notable applications have been found in the treatment of metal plating wastes, the recovery of ammonium nitrate from fertiliser wastes[4] and recently in the recovery of protein from food processing wastes with cellulosic resins. For a resin R, a cation M^+ and an anion A^- the reactions in the resin may be simply represented as:

$$R.H + M^+ \rightleftharpoons R.M + H^+$$
$$R.OH + A^- \rightleftharpoons R.OH + OH^-$$

The forward reactions take place during the passage of the waste water through the resin and the reverse reactions during regeneration. The regenerant for the cation resin is an acid such as sulphuric acid and for the anion resin an alkali such as sodium hydroxide. The regenerant strength is about 10% wt. During operation the resin bed is usually backwashed after the treatment part of the cycle to remove any build up of dirt or solid materials. After regeneration the bed is again rinsed to remove any residual traces of regenerant. During backwashing the resin bed expands and due allowance must be made for this in design of the containing vessel. The capacity of the resin depends on the number of ionic sites present and this is usually expressed as the number of gram-moles of electrons transferred per litre of bed volume.

Example 6.4. A car accessory firm produces 200 m^3/day of plating waste, the main metal component of which is chromate ion at a concentration of 140 mg $CrO_4^=$/litre. The chromate is to be recovered by ion exchange with a five-day interval between regenerations. The waste is passed through a hydroxide anion exchange column with a capacity of 1.2 g moles of electrons/litre of resin. The resin is also rinsed with water, the initial rinsings, with a volume equal to the volume of the bed, being added to the sodium chromate solution. Calculate the diameter of the ion exchange column if the height/diameter ratio is to be 4 and the concentration of the sodium chromate solution. Allow for 50% expansion of the bed during rinsing.
Atomic weights: Na = 23, O = 16, H = 1, Cr = 52.

Solution
$CrO_4^=$ retained on the resin in five days

$$= 140 \frac{mg}{litre} \times 200 \frac{m^3}{day} \times 5\,days \times \frac{1000\,litre}{m^3} \times 10^{-6} \frac{kg}{mg}$$
$$= 140\,kg$$

Because $CrO_4^=$ is a divalent ion, the resin capacity is 0.6 gram-ions of $CrO_4^=$/litre, i.e. $0.6 \times (52 + 4 \times 16) = 70\,g\,CrO_4^=$/litre.

So volume of resin required $= 140\,kg \times 1000 \frac{g}{kg} \times \frac{1}{70g}$

$$= 2000\,litre = 2\,m^3$$

With a 50% expansion of the bed, the column diameter is given by:

$$\frac{\pi d^2}{4} \times 4d = 2 \times 1.5,\ \text{i.e.}\ d = 0.98$$

so a 1-m diameter column should be used. Because NaOH is univalent, the bed capacity during regeneration is 1.2 g-moles NaOH/litre of bed, or $1.2 \times (23 + 16 + 1) = 48$ g NaOH/litre of bed.

So the weight of NaOH required for regeneration

$$= 2000\,\text{litre} \times \frac{48\text{g}}{\text{litre}} \times \frac{\text{kg}}{1000\text{g}} = 96\,\text{kg}$$

at 10% (wt) concentration, weight of water
$$= 864\,\text{kg}$$
i.e. volume of water $\qquad = 864\,\text{litre}$

∴ Concentration of $CrO_4^=$ in Na_2CrO_4 solution is

$$\frac{140\,\text{kg}}{(2000 + 864)\text{l}} \times \frac{1000\text{kg}}{\text{kg}} = 49\,\text{g/litre}$$

6.9. MEMBRANE SEPARATION PROCESSES

Membrane separation processes are governed by the rates of transport of different species through the membrane. Three different processes can be identified and in all three the phenomenon of *osmosis* is important to a greater or lesser extent. Osmosis is the name given to the natural process in which water flows through a semi-permeable membrane from a dilute solution to a stronger solution. Flow ceases when the difference in pressure between the two solutions reaches the so-called osmotic pressure, the value of which depends on the nature of the solute and its concentrations in the two solutions. As an example seawater which contains about 3.3% (wt) dissolved solids has an osmotic pressure of about 25 atm with respect to pure water. Waste water solutions will normally have far fewer dissolved solids and have a correspondingly lower osmotic pressure. If a pressure greater than 25 atm is applied to the sea water side of the membrane, pure water is transported through the membrane and a separation is achieved. This is known as *reverse osmosis* and comparatively high pressure differences are required. It is, of course, necessary that the membrane be impermeable to the solutes and permeable only to water if a pure water product is to be obtained.

The two other membrane processes are *ultrafiltration* in which relatively large molecules, such as polymers or proteins or even colloidal suspensions, are concentrated by removing some solvent and *dialysis* in which low-molecular-weight solutes pass preferentially through the membrane leaving the higher molecular weight molecules behind. Dialysis relies on the greater diffusion rates of low-molecular-weight species in the membrane. Transport of solvent can be prevented, if desired, by maintaining an isotonic (equal osmotic pressure) solution on the other side of the membrane, although in waste treatment processes passage of water through the membrane is usually an advantage. The molarity of high molecular weight materials is quite low even for quite large mass concentrations, so their osmotic pressures are quite low also. The pressure differences required in both ultrafiltration and dialysis are therefore relatively low and may only be from 2 to 7 atm. In addition the membranes used have a more open mesh and a larger porosity.

6.9.1. Reverse Osmosis

In principle, reverse osmosis can be used for the separation and concentration of inorganic or organic substances in aqueous or non-aqueous solutions, provided a suitable membrane can be found. Two properties of the membrane are very important: the chemical nature of the film surface in contact with the solution—it must be inert—and the existence of appropriately sized pores in the surface of the film so that solvent may pass through but not solute. Typical materials are cellulose acetate and polymeric materials such as aromatic polyamides. Many proprietary membranes are available commercially. The material is dissolved in a suitable solvent and a water-soluble filler added. The solution is then cast on to a sheet of glass which has a rim about 0.25 to 0.5 mm high. The solvent is evaporated for a few minutes and then the film is gelled for 1 to 2 h in ice-cold water. The filler is then leached out with warm water to leave a film about 75 to 150 μm thick with a pore size of about 0.01 μm. The film is not of uniform structure throughout its thickness. Under the electron microscope the membrane is seen to be asymmetric, consisting of a dense surface layer

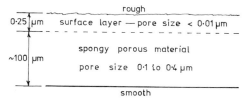

FIG. 6.21. Section through a reverse osmosis membrane.

about 0.25 μm thick on a spongy porous mass underneath as shown in Fig. 6.21. For reverse osmosis applications the concentrated solution should be on the surface layer (rough) side of the membrane and the pure water product on the spongy (smooth) side. If the membrane is used the other way round the water flux will knock off the surface layer and no separation will be achieved. Membranes must be stored in water. In air the membrane dries out and the porous structure is irreversibly changed. Water fluxes are generally between 5 and 15×10^{-4} g/s cm^2.

A number of theories have been put forward to explain the mechanism of reverse osmosis, but most can be approximated by the mass transfer equations:

$$\text{water flux } N_w = A(\Delta P - \Delta \Pi)$$
$$\text{solute flux } N_s = S(c_c - c_d)$$

where ΔP is the applied pressure difference, $\Delta \Pi$ is the difference in osmotic pressure across the membrane, c_c and c_d are the solute concentrations in the concentrated and dilute solutions and A and S are effectively mass transfer coefficients. A is known as the *pure water permeability constant* and is a measure of the ease with which water will pass through the membrane. S is the *solute transport parameter*. For good separation a large value of A and a small value of S are required. For sodium chloride solutions Matsuura *et al.*[7] report values of pure water permeability constant A between 10 and 25×10^{-6} g/s cm^2 atm and values of solute transport parameter S from 0.5 to 25×10^{-5} cm/s in polyamide membranes. Matsuura's paper presents a method of predicting the solute transport parameter for other alkali metal halides and for several organic solutes such as alcohols, aldehydes, ketones and ethers from data on sodium chloride using thermodynamic arguments and should find extensive use.

Reverse osmosis has been largely used for the production of drinking water from brackish waters or sea water and it is now cheaper than distillation. It may also be used for the separation of water from solutions of organic materials and for separating organic azeotropes and isomeric mixtures. In industrial effluent treatment it may be used for producing water of recyclable quality and a waste of increased strength. Commercial plants are in operation for the removal of water from cheese whey and Pepper[11] gives costs of from 31 to 45 p/m^3 of water removal for a 200 m^3/day plant. He also gives costs for a plant processing a molasses fraction by reverse osmosis.

Water fluxes are quite small and consequently a large surface area of membrane is necessary to obtain a significant flow of water. The problem is to provide a large surface area within a small volume. Four main types of membrane units are available:

(a) flat plate units stacked together in a similar manner to a plate-and-frame filter press;

(b) tubular, with porous metal or plastic tubes a few centimetres in diameter to support the membranes;

(c) spiral wound — essentially the flat plate system rolled up into a spiral;

(d) hollow fibre units with hollow fibres about $25-250\,\mu m$ outside diameter with a diameter-to-wall-thickness ratio of from 3 to 5. These are arranged in bundles like a miniature heat exchanger with many millions of fibres in each unit. The water flux is much lower than for the other three types of unit — around $0.1 - 1.0 \times 10^{-4}\,g/s\,cm^2$ but a very large surface area can be arranged in a small space so that the overall throughput is quite substantial, and comparable with that from other types of unit. The flow is from the outside of the fibre inwards because the fibres withstand pressure better in compression than in tension and because it is a fail-safe method since weak fibres will be self-sealing upon collapse rather than be ruptured.

6.9.2. Membrane Fouling

The membranes contain very fine pores and these are easily blocked by a number of different mechanisms. Pretreatment by filtration is necessary to remove suspended solids and in addition solution pH must be controlled on the acid side of neutrality at pH 5 to 6 to prevent both hydrolysis of the membrane and precipitation of calcium carbonate scale. Hydroxides of heavy metals, notably iron and manganese, can be precipitated in the membrane if care is not taken either to precipitate them deliberately in advance by aeration before filtration or to keep them in solution by removing the dissolved oxygen with catalysed sodium sulphite. Other difficulties may be encountered with biological growths and open storage tanks are to be avoided. Flushing the membrane periodically with clean water and occasional chemical cleaning will usually maintain the membrane in good condition. It is also important to maintain a sufficient velocity past the membrane on the high pressure side to prevent excessive polarisation — build-up of solute concentration adjacent to the membrane — which would reduce the water flux.

6.9.3. Electrodialysis

Dialysis of charged ions through a membrane can be achieved by applying an electrical potential across electrodes immersed on either side of the membrane. This is known as electrodialysis in contrast to simple dialysis where pressure is the driving force. In electrodialysis two types of membrane are used: one type permeable to cations and the other type permeable to anions. They are similar to ion exchange resins but made in the form of sheets. Several such cation- and anion-permeable membranes are stacked together alternately between electrodes. In operation the waste solution is fed to one end of all the compartments. The ions move under the influence of the electric field and pass through one membrane so that alternate compartments become depleted of ions and the other compartments have an increased concentration. Weak and strong products are taken from the other end of the unit. Membrane fouling can occur for the reasons discussed in the previous section and similar pre-treatment may be required. The economics of reclaiming nickel sulphate from nickel-plating wastes were discussed by Birkett,[2] who estimated a cost of $6.9 per thousand gallons, which is about 80p/m^3.

6.10. OXIDATION/REDUCTION AND PRECIPITATION

These are straight chemical treatment processes in which chemicals are added to produce an insoluble material by reaction with the dissolved ions in the waste water. The resulting precipitate can then be removed by one of the several methods for removal of suspended solids that were discussed earlier in this chapter. Segregation of wastes that require oxidation from those that require reduction is essential. A good example comes from the electroplating industry where chromate wastes must be reduced in acid solution and cyanide wastes oxidised in alkaline solution. The chemical reactions involved are discussed in detail in Chapter 8, Section 8.4.6. Precipitation of metals is commonly as their hydroxides and is very dependent on pH. Optimal values for several metals are given in Section 8.4.2.

6.11. NEUTRALISATION

Before disposal of strongly alkaline or strongly acid waste waters, the waste has to be neutralised. This can be done by chemical dosing in holding tanks in conjunction with equalisation procedures discussed earlier. If the resulting salts are innocuous direct discharge to the sewers or rivers may be permitted. In other cases further treatment for salt removal may be necessary either to comply with Consent regulations or to recover valuable material in the waste water.

6.12. ALGAE HARVESTING

Algae require nine minor essential elements (Fe, Mn, Si, Zn, Cu, Co, Mo, B and Va) and seven major essential elements (C, N, P, S, K, Mg and Ca) for optimum growth. The use of algae for removing minerals from waste water is still experimental and was discovered by the chance observation that the phosphate content of water leaving sewage works stabilisation ponds was much less than the concentration entering. Other minerals were not investigated but phosphates are probably of most interest because algae appear to be able to assimilate and store considerably more phosphorus than they actually require for growth. It is important to harvest the algae before the water is discharged and before the algae die, because upon death the algae become a nutrient BOD load on the water and the phosphates and other materials are released back to the water. Collection, dewatering and drying are the three stages of harvesting the algae, which can be sold as animal feed supplements. The growth of algae depends on the waste water supplying the inorganic nutrients in a form that can be utilised by the algae. Soluble materials are most readily assimilated and the presence of hardness in the water is an advantage. The processes taking place are the same as those that occur in eutrophication processes in lakes and waterways. In oxidation ponds, however, the process is speeded up so that this method of phosphorus removal becomes a practicable proposition.

6.13. PROCESSES USED FOR WASTE WATER TREATMENT

A variety of industries are listed in Table 6.4[14] together with a tabulation of twelve major types of effluent treatment process that are in use. Each of the twelve is subdivided into different operations labelled a, b, c, etc., so that the operations that have been successfully used in each industry can be seen. Table 6.5[14] indicates clearly that it is the natural products industries listed in the first column that produce wastes that can be treated biologically. The metal, mineral and general manufacturing industries produce wastes that require chemical treatment and appear in the third column. The other industries produce several types of waste which may require biological or chemical treatment.

TABLE 6.4
PROCESSES EMPLOYED FOR THE TREATMENT OF DIFFERENT TYPES OF WASTE WATER

Source of waste water	Processes used											
	1	2	3	4	5	6	7	8	9	10	11	12
Abattoir	ab	abc	bde	bd	b	ab				g	ab	cdf
Adhesives manufacture	bc	b	b	f		a				g	b	b
Anodising	a	b				bdg				a	ab	b
Antibiotics production	abc	b	bed					b	ac	a	abc	
Beet sugar	ab	ab	bc	e		h				h	b	a
Brewing	b	b	be								a	
Canning		ab	eb								ab	
Cattle sheds		ab	be				e			g	g	f
Cider making	bc	b	b	b							b	
Instant coffee	a	b			a						b	g
Coke ovens		bc		f		h	f				ab	f
Dairying	b	ab	bde	b–f	b	a	gb	ab	a	g	abg	dg
Distillery	ab	g	bce			g		ab			a–g	d
Dyeing	bc	b	a	abf		abg	a				ab	a
Egg processing	b	b	b							g	g	
Electroplating	abc					b–eg	ab	a		a	ab	ab
Engineering	a	bcd				bdf					a	c
Fellmongering	a	ab	b			gc					ab	e
Felt manufacture		ab				a				g	a	
Fish meal production								a			c	d
Gas washing (blast-furnace)		b		f		bcg	e				b	a
Glass grinding		b				b					a	
Grain washing	bc	a	b	d						g	ab	
Malting	bc	a	b	d						g	ab	

Meat processing	ab	abc	bde	bd	b	ab		ab		g	ab		cdf
Milk processing	b	ab	bde	b–f	d	a	gb			g	abg	b	dg
Mining		b				a					bc		
Oil refining	a	bc		ef		af	be	ac	a		ab		ae
Pulp and paper	ab	abc	bd	aef		ag					b		
Petrochemicals	ab	c		f		h					b		
Pharmaceuticals	ac	b		f		ga	c	c			a		
Phosphatising		b				gb					a		
Photogravure		b				gd					a		
Pickling of metals		b				gb	ih	a			ah		b
Piggeries		b		d		gf	a			ghd	ag		f
Plastics emulsion	a	b									a		
Phenolic plastics		bc		f		h	c	bc			a		fd
Poultry batteries											g		
Poultry processing		ab	b	bcd		a					ab		a
Quarrying		b				a		a			b		a
Retting flax		b	b	g		ha					bg		
Rubber latex production	ac	ab		f		ga					b	b	
Synthetic fibres	ab	ba	b	f		acg					ab		
Tanning	a	ab	b	b		ga	ab			g	ab		
Textiles		ab	b	bdf		ha					ab		a
Vegetable processing		ab	eb	bf		a				ad	ab		
Wool scouring		abdg	b	a						c	a		c

Note: The above entries are not necessarily complete, not all the processes would necessarily be used at a particular factory and the above listing does not indicate order of use.

TABLE 6.4—*contd*

Key to processes listed in Table 6.4

1. *Preliminary treatment*
   a Segregation of waste streams
   b Balancing of flow
   c Balancing of composition

2. *Solids/liquid separation*
   a Screening
   b Settlement
   c Flotation
   d Centrifugation
   e Hydrocyclone
   f Sand filtration
   g Micro-straining
   h Grass plots
   i Filtration

3. *Biological filtration*
   a Conventional
   b Single filtration with re-
     circulation
   c Double filtration
   d Alternating double filtration
   e High-rate filtration on
     plastics medium

4. *Activated sludge*
   a Conventional
   b Extended aeration
   c Contact stabilisation
   d Oxidation ditch
   e Aerated lagoon
   f Complete mixing
   g Aeration during processing

5. *Anaerobic digestion*
   a Mesophilic digestion of
     sludge
   b Anaerobic activated-sludge
     process
   c Anaerobic filter

6. *Chemical treatment*
   a Coagulation
   b Precipitation
   c Oxidation
   d Reduction
   e Cementation
   f Emulsion breaking
   g pH adjustment
   h Nutrient addition

7. *Physical treatment*
   a Adsorption
   b Reverse osmosis
   c Solvent extraction
   d Air stripping
   e Recirculation
   f Distillation
   g Membrane filtration
   h Crystallisation
   i Electrolysis

8. *Thermal processes*
   a Evaporation
   b Drying
   c Incineration

9. *Sludge conditioning*
   a Inorganic chemicals
   b Polyelectrolytes
   c Heat treatment
   d Freeze thaw

10. *Sludge dewatering*
    a Filter presses
    b Belt presses
    c Rotary vacuum filters
    d Centrifuges
    e Electro-flotation
    f Dissolved air flotation
    g Drying beds
    h Lagoons

11. *Final disposal*
    a To sewer
    b To river
    c To sea
    d To deep wells
    f To soakaways
    g Spreading on land
    h Re-use

12. *Recovery of products*
    a Water for re-use
    b Metals
    c Grease or oil
    d Protein, etc. for animal
      feed
    e Fibres
    f Fertiliser or soil
      conditioner
    g Other products

TABLE 6.5

GROUPING OF PROCESSES ACCORDING TO METHODS OF TREATMENT EMPLOYED
FOR WASTE WATERS

Processes giving waste waters which are easily treated by aerobic biological processes	*Processes giving waste waters containing potentially toxic organic matter but which can be treated biologically under favourable conditions*	*Processes giving rise to waste waters which require chemical rather than biochemical treatment*
Beet-sugar production	Adhesives manufacture	Anodising
Brewing	Carbonisation	Electro-plating
Canning	Dyeing	Engineering
Dairying	Fellmongering	Engraving
Farming[a]	Gas washing	Iron and steel
Fermentation	Pharmaceutical production	Mineral processing
Fish meal production	Plastics manufacture	Mining
Grain washing	Synthetic fibres	Metal finishing
Malting	Tanning	Paint manufacture
Meat processing	Textile processing	Vulcanised fibre production
Milk processing		Wire drawing
Poultry processing		
Starch production		
Vegetable processing		

[a]Contains a proportion of organic matter resistant to degradation.

REFERENCES

1. Bersillon, J.L., Brown, D.W., Fiessinger, F. and Hem, J.D., Studies of hydroxyaluminum complexes in aqueous solution, *J. Research U.S. Geol.Survey*, **6** (3) (1978), 325.
2. Birkett, J.D., Electrodialysis: an overview, *Ind. Wat. Eng*, Sept. (1977), 6.
3. Coulson, J.M. and Richardson, J.F., *Chemical Engineering*, Vol. 2, 3rd Edition. Pergamon, Oxford, 1978.
4. Higgins, I.R., Chopra, R.C. and Roland, L.D., Continuous ion exchange achieves unique solutions in pollution control, *I. Chem. E. Symp. Series*, No. 54 (1978), 105.
5. Hines, D.A., Bailey, M., Ousby, J.C. and Roesler, R.C., The ICI deep shaft aeration process for effluent treatment, *I. Chem. E. Symp. Series*, No. 41 (1975), I:D.

6. Kynch, G.J., A Theory of sedimentation. *Trans. Faraday Soc.*, **48** (1952), 166.
7. Matsuura, T., Blais, P., Pageau, L. and Sourirajan, S., Parameters for prediction of reverse osmosis performance of aromatic polyamide — hydrazide (1:1) copolymer membranes, *Ind. Eng. Chem., Process Des. Dev.*, **16** (4) (1977), 510.
8. Motarjemi, M. and Jameson, G.J., Mass transfer from very small bubbles — the optimum bubble size for aeration. *Chem. Eng. Sci.*, **33** (1978), 1415.
9. Nemerow, N.L., *Liquid Waste of Industry*. Addison–Wesley, 1971.
10. Pearse, M.J., Gravity thickening theories: a review. *Warren Spring Laboratory Report*, 1977.
11. Pepper, D., Reverse osmosis for preconcentration, *The Chemical Engineer*, No. 339, Dec. (1978), 916; Reverse osmosis and ultrafiltration, *I. Chem. E. Symp. Series*, No. 54 (1978), 247.
12. Perry, J.H. and Chilton, C.H. (Eds.), *Chemical Engineer's Handbook*, 5th edition McGraw-Hill, 1973.
13. Weber, W.J. (Jnr.) *Physicochemical Processes for Water Quality Control*. Wiley-Interscience, 1972.
14. Wheatland, A.B., *Notes for Course 'Pollution Abatement and Effluent Control'*, Department of Chemical Engineering, University of Nottingham, 1973.

7

Biological Treatment of Sewage

J.H. HILLS
Lecturer in Chemical Engineering, University of Nottingham, UK
AND
J.C. MECKLENBURGH
*Senior Lecturer in Chemical Engineering,
University of Nottingham, UK*

7.1. NOMENCLATURE

7.1.1. Roman Letters

A	area of clarifier (m^2)
a	g O_2 per g BOD
a'	g O_2 per g live cells
B	live cells/dead cells
b	g live cells per g BOD
b'	g dead cells per g live cells
C	live cells
D	diffusion coefficient (m^2/s)
D	dead cells
E_T	total enzyme concentration
H	depth of clarifier (m)
h	distance from top of filter bed (m)
K	Monod equation constant (g/m^3)
k	constant in eqn. (7.80)
k_1, k_2	constants in eqn. (7.10)
k_e	endogenous rate constant (h^{-1})
k_L	mass transfer coefficient per unit area (m/s)
$k_L a$	mass transfer coefficient per unit volume (s^{-1})
L	length of clarifier (m)
l	distance along clarifier (m)
m	g CH_4 per g BOD

167

m'	g CH_4 per g live cells
P, P'	products
p, q	constants in eqn. (7.80)
Q	liquid flow rate (m^3/h)
Q_h	hydraulic loading of filter m^3/m^3 day
R_A	rate of consumption of substrate per unit area of a film (g/m^2s)
r_m	rate of methane generation (g/m^3h)
r_{ox}	rate of oxygen consumption (g/m^3h)
$\bar{r}_{ox}$	average rate of oxygen consumption (g/m^3h)
r_s	rate of substrate reaction (g/m^3h)
r_x	rate of cell growth (g/m^3h)
r_y	rate of cell death (g/m^3h)
S	substrate
s	substrate concentration (g/m^3)
s^*	substrate concentration at film surface (g/m^3)
T	temperature (°C)
t	time (h)
V	reactor volume (m^3)
v_s	sludge settling velocity (m/h)
W	width of clarifier (m)
w	wetted perimeter (m)
x	live cell concentration (g/m^3)
x^*	live cell concentration within film or floc (g/m^3)
$\bar{x}$	average live cell concentration in reactor (g/m^3)
Y	overall yield of solids
y	dead cell concentration (g/m^3)
z	total solids concentration (g/m^3)

7.1.2. Subscripts

e	in clarifier effluent
in	in reactor inlet
o	in fresh feed
out	in reactor effluent
u	in thickened sludge from clarifier
m	maximum

7.1.3. Greek Letters

α	purge fraction
β	reaction rate constant per unit area of film (m/s)
ε	recycle fraction

Θ	constant in eqn. (7.80)
θ_h	hydraulic residence time (h)
θ_c	cell residence time (h)
θ_{min}	value of θ at washout
λ	distance from surface of slab
μ	maximum specific growth rate (h^{-1})
σ	specific surface of packing (m^2/m^3)
ψ, ψ'	stoichiometric coefficients
$\omega, \omega', \omega''$	stoichiometric coefficients

7.2. INTRODUCTION

Public sewers carry a mixture of industrial and domestic wastes which require treatment before discharge. Figure 7.1 shows the flow diagram and an aerial photograph of a typical sewage treatment works. *Primary treatment*, by screening and settling, removes gross solids and gives an effluent with a BOD of 150–500 mg/litre in dry weather. *Secondary treatment*, usually biological, must reduce this figure to not more than 20 mg/litre BOD with not more than 30 mg/litre dissolved solids (so-called 20:30 effluent). Higher effluent standards or limits on specific ions (nitrate, phosphate) may require *tertiary treatment* of some kind, but this is not common at present. Such treatment includes lagooning, sand filtration, anaerobic denitrification, etc.

This chapter describes the biological methods of secondary treatment, with particular reference to public sewage works, but indicating possible variants when designing for specialised industrial effluents of very high BOD, low nitrogen and phosphorus, etc. Treatment is by means of *aerobic* microbes either suspended in the water (*activated sludge process* and its variants) or attached to an inert support (*trickling filter* and *rotating biological contactor*). The commonest treatments are by activated sludge in large plants and trickling filters in small ones.

Figure 7.2 is a flow diagram of the activated sludge process. Primary effluent and recycled sludge are fed to the aeration tank, where the dissolution of oxygen is promoted by surface aerators (Fig. 7.3) or submerged gas diffusers. The suspension passes to the secondary clarifier, where thickened sludge is withdrawn from the base, while clear effluent passes over a weir to discharge (Fig. 7.4). The sludge, which consists of a mixed population of microbes agglomerated into flocs by a polysaccharide

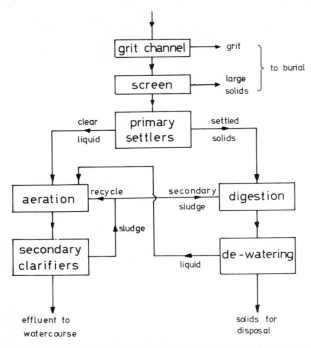

FIG. 7.1(a) (above) Flow diagram of a sewage treatment works and; (b) (below) aerial photograph of Stoke Bardolph sewage treatment works (Courtesy Severn–Trent Water Authority).

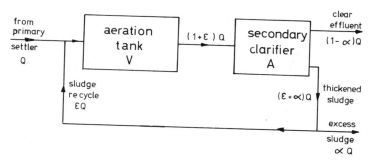

FIG. 7.2 The activated sludge process.

FIG. 7.3 Surface aerators (Courtesy of Severn–Trent Water Authority).

gel, grows in volume in the aerator and a purge stream must be removed before recycle.

This purge, together with solids from the primary settlers, is treated, often by *anaerobic digestion*, to render it inoffensive and easy to dispose of. Part of the solids is converted into CO_2 and methane by anaerobic microbes; the methane serves as fuel to operate the whole works which can be almost self-sufficient in energy. Certain very concentrated industrial wastes may be treated directly by anaerobic digestion, but dilute wastes need too much energy to warm them to the required 35°C.

J.H. Hills and J.C. Mecklenburgh

FIG. 7.4 Secondary clarifier (Courtesy of Severn–Trent Water Authority).

FIG. 7.5 Trickling filter (Courtesy of Severn–Trent Water Authority).

In the *trickling filter* a packed bed of some inert material is coated with microbial slime and waste water sprayed over the top of the bed (Fig. 7.5). Effluent from the foot of the bed, after settling, can be discharged to the watercourse.

7.3. BIOLOGICAL REACTIONS

The *metabolism* of living cells consists of a complex chain of reactions catalysed by highly specific catalysts called *enzymes*. Some of these reactions involve the breakdown of complex molecules into simpler ones with the release of energy (*respiration*); others use some of the breakdown products and the energy to synthesise fresh cellular material, including replacement of the enzymes destroyed by deactivation. Because enzymes are highly specific in their action, any change in the environment upsets the steady-state reaction chain and growth slows down until a fresh set of enzymes has been synthesised to cope with the new situation. Sewage is inherently a variable feedstock and the slow response of the biological system to change leads to severe control problems. The process of adjustment to environmental change is called *acclimatisation* and is an essential preliminary to experimental study.

The overall reaction for cell growth may be written:

$$\text{Reactants} \xrightarrow{\text{cells}} \text{new cells} + \text{products} \tag{7.1}$$

In addition some cellular material is itself oxidised to provide energy to maintain cellular functions. This *endogenous metabolism* leads ultimately to cell death:

$$\text{Live cells} \rightarrow \text{dead cells} + \text{products} \tag{7.2}$$

Dead cells consist mainly of cell walls, which are complex polysaccharides difficult to degrade biologically. The cellular contents, or *cytoplasm*, are released into the medium by *lysis* or cell rupture and serve as substrate for other cells to use.

Energy is obtained by oxidation of part of the nutrient in the medium. In the presence of oxygen *aerobic* microbes decompose organics to carbon dioxide and water. These reactions are highly exothermic and comparatively rapid at ambient temperatures; the major problem for the design engineer is to maintain an adequate supply of oxygen.

Anaerobic microbes break down complex substances into simpler ones in the absence of air or oxygen. Sulphate often serves as ultimate electron acceptor and hydrogen sulphide, responsible for much of the foul smell of sewage, is a common end product. Reactions are much slower than the corresponding aerobic ones and need higher temperatures to achieve acceptable rates: 35°C is a typical value for the mesophilic organisms used in sewage sludge digestion. Heats of reaction are very small and a major engineering problem is the maintenance of above-ambient temperatures in an economical way.

7.4. STOICHIOMETRY

7.4.1. Aerobic Reactions

Sewage being a complex mixture of compounds, the concentration of nutrients is usually expressed in terms of BOD, COD or some similar overall measure based on the weight of oxygen required to oxidise unit weight of nutrient under specified conditions.

Equations (7.1) and (7.2) can be written for aerobic reactions:

$$S + aO_2 \overset{c}{\rightarrow} bC + \psi P \tag{7.3}$$

$$C + a'O_2 \rightarrow b'D + \psi'P' \tag{7.4}$$

where S represents substrate, C live cells, D dead cells and P and P' are other products, mainly water and CO_2.

Typical values for the stoichiometric coefficients in sewage treatment are:

$$a = 0.38 \, \text{g} \, O_2/\text{g} \, BOD_L$$
$$b = 0.58 \, \text{g live cells/g} \, BOD_L$$
$$a' = 1.06 \, \text{g} \, O_2/\text{g live cells}$$
$$b' = 0.25 \, \text{g dead cells/g live cells}$$

BOD_L is the oxygen required for total oxidation of all substrate and of all live cells to dead cells. It is called 'stabilisation oxygen demand' by Walters in this Volume, and 'Ultimate BOD' by some other authors. From the definition, we have, eliminating C between eqns. (7.3) and (7.4).

$$a + a'b = 1 \tag{7.5}$$

The coefficients mentioned, extracted from a range of published data, have been adjusted to obey eqn. (7.5). Exact values for a particular substrate, especially one very different from domestic sewage, should be determined experimentally, by the methods described in Section 7.6.

In aerobic sewage treatment eqn. (7.3) should go to completion to give a low BOD effluent, while eqn. (7.4) should be incomplete if the system is to function, so that there is a net production of live cells and the oxygen requirement is less than the BOD_L. Coefficients b and b' are often called *yields* of their respective reactions.

7.4.2. Growth Limiting Factors

Raw materials for cell growth, which must be provided by the substrate, include nitrogen, phosphorus and other elements in addition to the carbon, hydrogen and oxygen always present. Table 7.1 gives the composition of a

TABLE 7.1
COMPOSITION OF A TYPICAL CELL

Element	% dry weight
C	50
O	20
H	8
N	14
P	3
S	1
Others	4

typical resting cell—an actively growing cell is relatively poorer in N and P and richer in carbohydrate. Using these data and the stoichiometric coefficients above, we can estimate the minimum requirements of these other nutrients for complete removal of BOD as follows:

N $0.08 \, g/g \, BOD_L$
P $0.02 \, g/g \, BOD_L$
S $0.06 \, g/g \, BOD_L$

These are conservative estimates because of the lower N and P requirements of growing cells and practical experience suggests minimum values of 0.04 for N and 0.006 for P.[7]

Domestic sewage contains a large excess of N and P, but some industrial effluents may be deficient, and the removal of BOD, or the settling properties of the sludge will suffer. To treat such effluents they may be mixed with domestic sewage, or calculated amounts of the necessary elements may be added before treatment.

7.4.3. Nitrification

Nitrogen in domestic sewage is mainly present as urea, $CO(NH_2)_2$, and its hydrolysis product ammonia. Nitrifying bacteria can use NH_3 as an energy source and CO_2 as a source of carbon, with an overall reaction—

$$NH_3 + CO_2 + O_2 \xrightarrow{cells} cells + NO_3^- \qquad (7.6)$$

This reaction has a very high oxygen requirement of $4.5\,g\,O_2/g\,N$ as NH_3 and any unreacted ammonia, as well as being toxic to fish, causes a high residual BOD in the effluent. It also has a very low cell yield ($0.07\,g$ cells/gN) which implies low concentrations of nitrifying bacteria in sewage sludge and hence slow reaction. Cell residence times of up to 10 days are needed for complete nitrification.

The final product is nitrate ion NO_3^- and, while there is at present no limit on the concentration of nitrate in effluent, there is some evidence that it is harmful and the inclusion of limits of nitrate in effluent standards in the future seems possible. It can be removed by anaerobic bacteria in a tertiary denitrification stage in which an oxidisable substrate (often methanol) must be added to provide energy and carbon:

$$NO_3^- + \text{substrate} \rightarrow N_2 + CO_2 + H_2O + \text{cells}$$

7.4.4. Anaerobic Reactions

For sludge digestion eqns. (7.1) and (7.2) may be written:

$$S + \omega H_2O \overset{C}{\leftrightarrow} bC + mCH_4 + \psi CO_2 \tag{7.7}$$

$$C + \omega' H_2O \overset{C}{\leftrightarrow} b'D + m'CH_4 + \psi' CO_2 \tag{7.8}$$

Energy yields are low, depending on the substrate, and this leads to low cell yields. Typical values of the stoichiometric coefficients are:

$$b = 0.07\,g \text{ cells/g } BOD_L$$
$$m = 0.21\,g\,CH_4/g\,BOD_L$$
$$b' = 0.25\,g \text{ dead cells/g live cells}$$
$$m' = 0.20\,g\,CH_4/g \text{ live cells}$$

If digestion goes to completion, we can eliminate C from eqns. (7.7) and (7.8):

$$S + \omega'' H_2O = (m + bm')CH_4 + (\psi + b\psi')CO_2 + bb'D \tag{7.9}$$

Neglecting the small quantity of dead cells, the oxygen required to oxidise the $(m + bm')$ methane is equal to that required to oxidise the substrate S, which is the BOD. Since the oxidation of 1 g methane requires $4\,g\,O_2$, we have:

$$m + bm' \leq 0.25$$

7.5. KINETICS

7.5.1. Overall Reaction in a Single Cell

Cellular metabolism consists of a chain of reactions, each catalysed by a different enzyme. Any one of these reactions should obey Michaelis-Menten kinetics:

$$\text{Rate} = \frac{k_1[s][E_T]}{k_2 + [s]} \tag{7.10}$$

where $[E_T]$ is the total concentration of the enzyme in question, $[s]$ is the concentration of substrate and k_1 and k_2 are constants.

For a given cell there will be a whole chain of such reactions and it is reasonable to assume that the overall rate is governed by the slowest step in the chain and that the form of the overall rate equation is similar to eqn. (7.10). Experience bears this out in many cases and the rate of cell growth is given empirically by the Monod equation:

$$r_x = -br_s = \frac{\mu.s.x}{K + s} \tag{7.11}$$

where

r_x = the cell growth rate g/m^3 h
$-r_s$ = the substrate utilisation rate·g/m^3 h
x = cell concentration g/m^3
s = substrate concentration g/m^3 (or BOD)
b = cell yield g cell per g substrate (or BOD)
μ = maximum specific growth rate h^{-1}
K = a constant with units g/m^3

K is the value of s for which the rate is half its maximum value. For high substrate concentrations, $s \gg K$, and eqn. (7.11) becomes zero order in s:

$$\frac{1}{x}r_x = \text{maximum specific growth rate} = \mu \tag{7.12}$$

while for low concentrations, $s \ll K$, it becomes first order:

$$\frac{1}{x}r_x = (\mu/K).s \tag{7.13}$$

Garnett and Sawyer[8] proposed replacing the non-linear eqn. (7.11) over its entire range by eqn. (7.12) for $s > K$ and eqn. (7.13) for $s < K$; this suggestion, known unhelpfully as the 'two-phase theory', leads to mathematical simplifications and is commonly adopted, at least in limiting cases of low or high substrate concentrations.

Equation (7.11) applies to a single, pure substrate. Values of K are typically 1 g/m^3 or less, making zero-order reactions very common. For a mixed substrate, such as sewage, parallel reactions occur, with the more readily metabolisable substances being removed more rapidly. Overall, the rate decreases with time, which means an effective overall order greater than zero. In many cases, this can be accommodated in the form of eqn. (7.11) by increasing the apparent value of K, and values of 40 g/m^3 or more are frequently quoted in sewage treatment.

7.5.2. Mass Transfer Limitations

The flocs of activated sludge and the slime film of trickling filters consist of microbes embedded in a polysaccharide gel. To reach the microbes and react, substrate must diffuse through this gel and such diffusion could become rate limiting. An estimate of the effect can be made with the simplified model sketched in Fig. 7.6. The gel is regarded as a semi-infinite slab with cells distributed uniformly within it at a concentration of x^*. Substrate diffuses into the slab from the surface where $\lambda = 0$ and its concentration is s^*, with a constant diffusion coefficient D. A mass balance at depth λ then yields:

$$\text{Rate per unit volume} = D\frac{d^2 s}{d\lambda^2} = -r_s \tag{7.14}$$

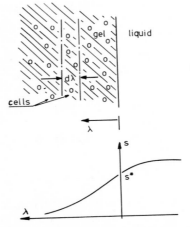

FIG. 7.6 Substrate concentration in a bacterial film.

Boundary conditions on eqn. (7.14) are:

$$\text{at } \lambda = 0 \qquad s = s^* \tag{7.15}$$

$$\text{and } \frac{ds}{d\lambda} \to 0 \quad \text{where } s \to 0 \tag{7.16}$$

An analytical solution for s as a function of λ is not possible if eqn. (7.11) is used as the rate equation, but assuming constant oxygen concentration the limiting forms (7.12) and (7.13) yield:

$$\text{zero order (eqn. 7.12)} \quad s = s^* \left(1 - \lambda \sqrt{\frac{\mu x^*}{2Dbs^*}} \right)^2 \tag{7.17}$$

$$\text{first order (eqn. 7.13)} \quad s = s^* \exp\left(- \sqrt{\frac{\mu x^*}{KDb}} \cdot \lambda \right) \tag{7.18}$$

Equations (7.17) and (7.18) provide an indication of possible diffusional limitation, since s falls effectively to zero above a certain value of λ, and if the radius of the floc, or thickness of the slime film, is greater than this value, no substrate can penetrate to the deepest region to react with the cells. Table 7.2 lists typical values of the parameters in sewage treatment which, when substituted into eqns. (7.17) and (7.18) give limiting film thicknesses ($s < 1\%$ of s_0) of 25 and 65 μm respectively. This agrees with the experimental finding of Kornegay and Andrews[9] that the rate of reaction ceases to increase with film thickness above about 70 μm. Typical activated sludge flocs have diameters from 100 to 1000 μm, so some effect of mass transfer is to be expected, and there are advantages in keeping the floc size small by vigorous stirring.

The actual rate of consumption of substrate per unit area of microbial floc or film can be calculated for the semi-infinite film from:

$$R_a = - D \frac{ds}{d\lambda} \bigg|_{\lambda = 0} \tag{7.19}$$

TABLE 7.2
TYPICAL KINETIC PARAMETERS

D	$5 \times 10^{-6} \, cm^2/s$
K	$20 \, g/m^3$
s^*	$30 \, g/m^3$
μ	$2 \times 10^{-4}/s$
b	0.4
x^*	$10^5 \, g/m^3$

Substituting for s from eqns. (7.17) and (7.18) we obtain

$$\text{zero order } R_A = \sqrt{\frac{2\mu . x^* D}{b}}\ s^{*\,1/2} \tag{7.20}$$

$$\text{first order } R_A = \sqrt{\frac{\mu . x^* . D}{K.b}}\ s^* \tag{7.21}$$

Thus the apparent order on s^* is between $1/2$ and 1 and the overall rate can be represented by eqn. (7.11) with values of μ and K adjusted to allow for diffusion.

Since measurement of the parameters in eqns. (7.20) and (7.21) for a given sludge is almost impossible, it is normal to assume eqn. (7.11) and measure apparent values of μ and K in a fully acclimatised sludge. Such values will then include any diffusional effect. A full treatment of diffusion effects is given by Atkinson.[4]

Oxygen will diffuse more readily than the larger substrate molecules. Its concentration in air-saturated water is given in Chapter 4 (Table 4.2) and is about $8-10\,\text{g/m}^3$. The rate of the activated sludge reaction has been shown to be zero order on oxygen down to concentrations of $0.5\ \text{g/m}^3$. However, to avoid any possibility of anaerobic conditions, dissolved oxygen levels of at least $2\ \text{g/m}^3$ are usually maintained.

7.5.3. Endogenous Metabolism

Oxidation of part of the cytoplasm to provide maintenance energy (endogenous respiration) leads to a decrease in the mass of the individual cell. The reaction is assumed to be first order on cell mass, so that eqn. (7.11) may be modified to give:

$$r_s = -\frac{\mu . s . x}{b(K + s)} \tag{7.22}$$

$$r_x = \frac{\mu . s . x}{K + s} - k_e x \tag{7.23}$$

where k_e is the endogenous rate constant. In addition cells die, as a result of endogenous respiration or otherwise, and dead cells are produced:

$$r_y = b' k_e x \tag{7.24}$$

where y is the concentration of dead cells and b' their yield per unit mass of live cells. Equation (7.24) assumes that all endogenous respiration leads to death, which is not strictly true, and more complex models are available which avoid this assumption.[10]

In practice, live and dead cells cannot be distinguished in sewage sludge. All that is normally measured is the mixed-liquor suspended solids (MLSS) or the mixed-liquor volatile suspended solids (MLVSS)—the latter determined as the loss of weight on heating to $600°C$; the difference is mainly occluded grit. If we assume that the polysaccharide gel is 'dead cells', we can represent the total solids by:

$$z = x + y \tag{7.25}$$

7.5.4. Oxygen Consumption

From eqns. (7.3) and (7.4) the rate of oxygen consumption, r_{ox}, is:

$$r_{ox} = -ar_s + a'r_y/b' \tag{7.26}$$

$$= \left(\frac{a\mu s}{b(K+s)} + a'k_e \right)x$$

Similarly, the rate of methane generation in anaerobic reactions, r_m, from eqns. (7.7) and (7.8) is:

$$r_m = -mr_s + m'r_y/b' \tag{7.27}$$

7.6. DETERMINATION OF PARAMETERS

The kinetic and stoichiometric parameters vary with substrate and with the shape, size and microbial composition of the sludge, so an empirical determination is needed in a laboratory scale or pilot plant reactor. The simplest such determination experimentally is the *batch reactor*, filled with effluent solution and seeded with acclimatised sludge. Aeration and stirring are started and samples taken at predetermined times and analysed for BOD, MLSS and oxygen uptake rate. Details of the procedure can be found in Eckenfelder.[3]

Such a system does not give complete information, but the data give a preliminary indication of the feasibility of the proposed treatment. For more complete data, the Continuous Flow Stirred Tank Reactor (CSTR) must be used in which effluent solution is fed and treated effluent and solids withdrawn continuously. As this system has simpler mathematics, we shall treat it first.

7.6.1. CSTR Reactor

The simple CSTR reactor is known to biologists as a 'chemostat'. With good stirring all concentrations within the reactor are constant and equal to their value in the outlet stream.

Consider a reactor of volume V with a volumetric feed and overflow rate Q. Mass balances on substrate, live cells and dead cells give:

$$Q(s_{in} - s_{out}) = V\frac{\mu s_{out} x_{out}}{b(K + s_{out})} \tag{7.28}$$

$$Q(x_{out} - x_{in}) = V\left(\frac{\mu s_{out} x_{out}}{K + s_{out}} - k_e x_{out}\right) \tag{7.29}$$

$$Q(y_{out} - y_{in}) = V b' k_e x_{out} \tag{7.30}$$

If the feed is filtered, it will contain no solids, so $x_{in} = y_{in} = 0$. Q and V may be combined to give the hydraulic mean residence time $\theta_h = V/Q$. This is the inverse of the dilution rate, which is often preferred by microbiologists. We can then rearrange eqn. (7.30) to give:

$$y_{out} = \theta_h b' k_e x_{out}$$

whence

$$z_{out} = x_{out} + y_{out} = x_{out}(1 + \theta_h b' k_e) \tag{7.31}$$

Similarly eqn. (7.29) gives:

$$1/\theta_h + k_e = \frac{\mu . s_{out}}{K + s_{out}} \tag{7.32}$$

whence,

$$s_{out} = \frac{K(1 + k_e\theta_h)}{\mu\theta_h - (1 + k_e\theta_h)} \tag{7.33}$$

It follows from eqn. (7.33) that s_{out} is independent of s_{in}. As θ_h decreases, s_{out} increases until it reaches s_{in}, at which point no reaction occurs, and all cells are swept out of the system. This condition, known as 'washout', occurs when

$$\theta_h = \theta_{min} = \frac{1 + K/s_{in}}{\mu - k_e(1 + K/s_{in})} \tag{7.34}$$

Figure 7.7 shows the general behaviour of the system as washout is approached. Operation close to washout is unstable and should be avoided. Substituting eqn. (7.32) into eqn. (7.28) gives

$$s_{in} - s_{out} = \frac{\mu . s_{out} x_{out} \theta_h}{b(K + s_{out})} = \frac{(1 + k_e\theta_h)x_{out}}{b}$$

or, substituting for x_{out} from eqn. (7.31)

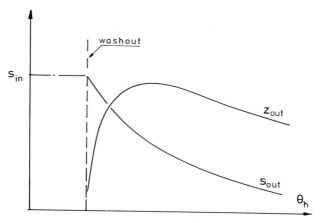

FIG. 7.7 Behaviour of a CSTR reactor. Substrate concentration s and MLSS z versus mean residence time θ_h.

$$z_{out} = \frac{b(1 + b'k_e\theta_h)}{1 + k_e\theta_h}(s_{in} - s_{out}) \tag{7.35}$$

which may be rearranged to give the apparent yield of solids:

$$Y = \frac{z_{out}}{s_{in} - s_{out}} = b \cdot \frac{(1 + b'k_e\theta_h)}{(1 + k_e\theta_h)} \tag{7.36}$$

Since $b' < 1$, Y decreases with increasing θ_h.

From eqns. (7.26), (7.28) and (7.31) the rate of oxygen consumption is:

$$r_{ox} = a(s_{in} - s_{out})/\theta_h + \frac{a'k_e z_{out}}{1 + b'k_e\theta_h} \tag{7.37}$$

Equations (7.32), (7.36) and (7.37) may be used to determine the various kinetic and stoichiometric parameters from data on the variation of s_{out}, z_{out} and r_{ox} with θ_h, as shown below.

Example 7.1. The following data are for the growth of sewage sludge on a glucose medium at $25°C$[11] with additional hypothetical values for

θ_h h	1.54	1.75	2.00	2.50	3.33	5.00	10.53	14.9	45.5
z_{out} mg/litre	70	418	528	556	535	537	490	471	266
$s_{out}(COD_{out})$ mg/litre	847	191	33.9	23.5	26.1	30.7	35.2	23.4	39.2
$r_{ox}(O_2$ rate) mg/litre h	34.3	129	134	110	84	58	30.3	23.2	10.0

oxygen uptake rate. The inlet COD, s_{in}, was constant at $1050\,\text{g/m}^3$. Estimate the various biological parameters:

Solution
From eqn. (7.36) as $\theta_h \to 0 \quad Y \to b$
and as $\theta_h \to \infty \quad$ or $\quad 1/\theta_h \to 0 \quad Y \to bb'$

Thus graphs of Y against θ_h and $1/\theta_h$ should yield values of b and b' by extrapolation to zero. Figure 7.8 shows the appropriate graphs. We conclude that $b = 0.54$ and $bb' \simeq 0.1$ so that $b' \simeq 0.2$. The latter value is very uncertain and could be as low as zero. The low values of Y at low θ_h are discussed below.

Having determined b and b' eqn. (7.36) may be rearranged to give:

$$\frac{b(1-b')}{b-Y} = 1 + \frac{1}{k_e} \cdot \frac{1}{\theta_h}$$

This functional relationship may be plotted to give a straight line of gradient $1/k_e$. Figure 7.9 shows the result; scatter at low values of θ_h (high values of $1/\theta_h$) is very great, but the longer residence time would be

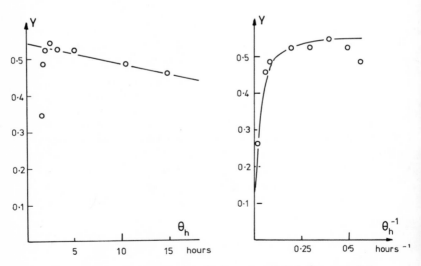

FIG. 7.8 Determination of coefficients b and b' in Example 7.1.

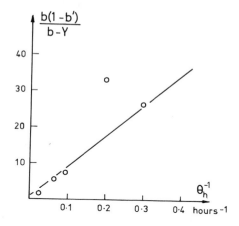

FIG. 7.9 Determination of k_e in Example 7.1.

expected to give the more accurate endogenous parameter estimation. From Fig. 7.9 we obtain $k_e = 0.012\,\mathrm{h}^{-1}$.

Having determined k_e, we can rearrange eqn. (7.32) to give

$$\frac{\theta_h}{1 + k_e\theta_h} = \frac{K}{\mu}\cdot\frac{1}{s_{out}} + \frac{1}{\mu}$$

This may be plotted to give a straight line of gradient $\dfrac{K}{\mu}$ and intercept $\dfrac{1}{\mu}$.

It is evident from inspection of the data that s_{out} does not fall to zero as it should; after $\theta_h \simeq 2.5\,\mathrm{h}$, values fluctuate randomly around $30\,\mathrm{mg/litre}$. Chiu *et al.* discuss this point in their original paper[11] and suggest reasons for it, connected with the non-biodegradable nature of the residual COD. Taking the first four points only, the graph of Fig. 7.10 gives:

$$1/\mu = 1.55\,\mathrm{h} \qquad K/\mu = 19\;(\mathrm{mg/litre})\,\mathrm{h}$$

whence

$$\mu = 0.65\,\mathrm{h}^{-1} \qquad K = 12.3\,\mathrm{mg/litre}$$

Because of the uncertain gradient, the value of K is not very accurate.

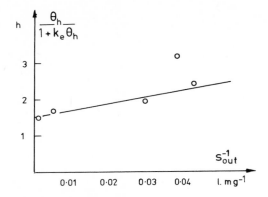

FIG. 7.10 Determination of μ and K in Example 7.1.

From eqn. (7.34) we may calculate θ_{min} at washout

$$\theta_{min} = \frac{1 + \dfrac{12.3}{1050}}{0.65 - 0.012\left(1 + \dfrac{12.3}{1050}\right)} = 1.59 \text{ h}$$

The smallest residence time is, in fact, less than this value, and Y values at both $\theta_h = 1.54$ and $1.75\,$h are well below the smooth curve in Fig. 7.8a. The reason is that sewage is not a pure culture; K, μ, etc, are average values, and near to washout the slower growing organisms tend to be washed out first, changing the average values of the parameters.

Equation (7.37) may be written

$$\frac{r_{ox}\theta_h}{s_{in} - s_{out}} = a + \frac{a'k_e\theta_h}{1 + b'k_e\theta_h} \cdot Y = a + a'b\frac{k_e\theta_h}{1 + k_e\theta_h}$$

which may be plotted to give a straight line of gradient $a'b$ and intercept a. Figure 7.11 shows the result to be

$$a = 0.25 \quad a'b = 0.568 \quad \text{or} \quad a' = 1.05$$

Since this graph is based on simulated data the goodness of fit is better than in the previous figures. The value of a is lower than the typical values in eqn. (7.3) because of the use of COD rather than BOD_L as the substrate concentration. As may be appreciated from the graph, the gradient, and

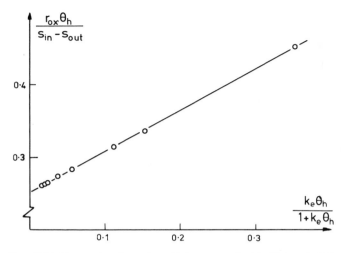

FIG. 7.11 Determination of coefficients a and a' in Example 7.1.

hence a', is likely to be much less accurate than the intercept when real data are used.

7.6.2. Batch Reactors

Equations (7.22) to (7.24) apply with the rate terms represented by time derivatives, thus

$$r_s = \frac{ds}{dt}, \quad r_x = \frac{dx}{dt} \quad \text{and} \quad r_y = \frac{dy}{dt}$$

To obtain s and z as functions of t these equations must be integrated, which is not possible analytically in the general case. However, as the cell concentration is normally large in sewage reactors, $x \gg s$ and to a first approximation we may replace the variable x by its mean value $\bar{x}$ and treat this as constant.

Thus eqn. (7.22) becomes

$$\frac{ds}{dt} = -\frac{\mu.s\bar{x}}{b(K+s)}$$

which on integration gives:

$$K \ln\left(\frac{s_{in}}{s_{out}}\right) + (s_{in} - s_{out}) = \frac{\mu.\bar{x}}{b}t \qquad (7.38)$$

Adding b times eqn. (7.22) to eqns. (7.23) and (7.24) gives

$$br_s + r_x + r_y = b\frac{ds}{dt} + \frac{dx}{dt} + \frac{dy}{dt}$$

$$= b\frac{ds}{dt} + \frac{dz}{dt}$$

$$= -(1 - b')k_e\bar{x}$$

Integrating we find:

$$z_{out} - z_{in} = b(s_{in} - s_{out}) - k_e\bar{x}(1 - b')t$$

or

$$Y = \frac{z_{out} - z_{in}}{s_{in} - s_{out}} = b - k_e\bar{x}(1 - b')\frac{t}{s_{in} - s_{out}} \qquad (7.39)$$

Thus a linear plot of Y against $t/(s_{in} - s_{out})$ should have an intercept b and gradient $k_e\bar{x}(1 - b')$.

Similarly, rearranging eqn. (7.38) we get

$$\frac{\ln s_{in}/s_{out}}{s_{in} - s_{out}} = \frac{\mu\bar{x}}{Kb} \cdot \frac{t}{s_{in} - s_{out}} - \frac{1}{K} \qquad (7.40)$$

and a linear plot of $(\ln s_{in}/s_{out})/(s_{in} - s_{out})$ against $t/(s_{in} - s_{out})$ should have a gradient $\mu\bar{x}/Kb$ and intercept $-1/K$.

Equation (7.26) gives oxygen rate $= -a\,ds/dt + a'k_e\bar{x}$.

Hence oxygen used $= a(s_{in} - s_{out}) + a'k_e\bar{x}t$

or

$$\frac{\text{oxygen used}}{s_{in} - s_{out}} = a + a'k_e\bar{x}\frac{t}{s_{in} - s_{out}} \qquad (7.41)$$

A linear plot of oxygen uptake/$(s_{in} - s_{out})$ against $t/(s_{in} - s_{out})$ should have a gradient $a'k_e\bar{x}$ and intercept a.

From eqns. (7.31), (7.40) and (7.41) we can calculate $K, a, b, \mu\bar{x}, k_e\bar{x}(1 - b')$ and $a'k_e\bar{x}$. Since $\bar{x}$ cannot be found, there is no way that μ and k_e can be obtained from this data. However, if the batch reactor is seeded with sludge of an age similar to that intended for the full-scale plant, $\bar{x}$ will be a constant fraction of $\bar{z}$ the mean MLSS, and design can be made on this basis.

Example 7.2. Estimate the design parameters from the following hypothetical data for the batch growth of sludge on filtered sewage.

t(h)	0	0.5	1.0	1.5	2.0	2.5	3.0	3.5
s(BOD) mg/litre	320	268	217	168	121	77	39	13
z(MLSS) mg/litre	2100	2110	2125	2135	2140	2150	2150	2145
O_2 used mg/litre	0	43	85	126	167	206	243	275

Solution

Plot the data according to eqns. (7.39) (7.40) and (7.41):

$t/\Delta s \times 10^3$	9.62	9.71	9.87	10.05	10.29	10.68	11.40
$(\ln s_{in}/s_{out})$ /$\Delta s \times 10^3$	3.41	3.77	4.24	4.89	5.86	7.49	10.43
$Y \times 10^3$	192	243	230	201	206	178	147
$O_2/\Delta s \times 10^3$	827	825	829	839	848	865	896

The three equations are plotted in Fig. 7.12 and 7.13 and we deduce

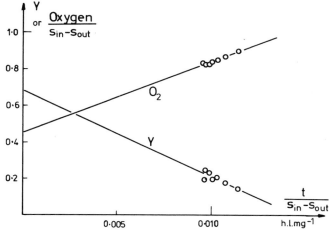

FIG. 7.12 Simulated batch data: yield and oxygen usage in Example 7.2.

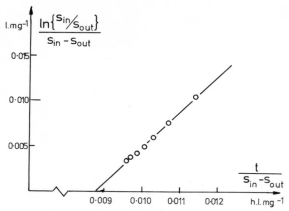

FIG. 7.13 Determination of kinetic parameters from batch data in Example 7.2.

$$b = 0.68 \qquad k_e\bar{x}(1 - b') = 47 \, \text{mg/litre h}$$

$$1/K = 0.0347 \qquad \frac{\mu\bar{x}}{Kb} = 3.96$$

whence $K = 28.8 \, \text{mg/litre} \quad \mu\bar{x} = 77.6 \, \text{mg/litre h}$

$$a = 0.45 \quad a'k_e\bar{x} = 39 \, \text{mg/litre h}$$

It is clear from Fig. 7.12 that the value of b is highly uncertain, because we are using a small difference in the necessarily large MLSS to calculate it. Since s is measured in BOD, we could use eqn. (7.5) to calculate a':

$$a' = (1 - a)/b = 0.81$$

whence $k_e\bar{x} = 48.1$ and $b' \simeq 0.03$

However, a value of b' nearer 0.25 is usual for sewage sludge. The possible errors of each stage are compounded, and the value of b' is very unreliable.

7.7. REACTOR DESIGN

In this section we shall first discuss the activated-sludge system, followed by the trickle filter and other forms of reactor.

7.7.1. Clarifier

The aerator and clarifier of an activated-sludge plant must be designed together, as each affects the design of the other. Clarifier design is quite complex and is dealt with elsewhere in this volume, but the following simple model will serve to illustrate the interactions.

Figure 7.14 shows a horizontal-flow rectangular clarifier of depth H, width W and length L. Effluent from the aerator flowing at $Q(1 + \varepsilon)$ where ε is the recycle fraction, enters at $l = 0$ with a solids concentration z_{out}. We assume that the sludge/clear liquid interface settles at a velocity v_s independent of sludge concentration, until the sludge concentration reaches a maximum value z_m when all settling stops.

Until that moment we have

$$\text{sludge height} = H - v_s t$$

where t is the time taken to flow a distance l along the tank and is given by:

$$t = \frac{HWl}{Q(1 + \varepsilon)} \tag{7.42}$$

Since the aim of the clarifier is also to thicken the sludge as much as possible, the length L should evidently be enough to allow the sludge blanket to reach its maximum concentration z_m. Lengths greater than this achieve no more separation, although they do provide a safety factor (see later). A minimum design is to have the sludge just reach z_m at $l = L$. Since the 'clear' effluent will always contain some solids (e.g., very fine sludge particles which settle slower than v_s) we can perform a mass balance and obtain:

$$z_{out}H = z_u(H - v_s t) + z_e v_s t$$

where z_u and z_e are the solids concentrations in the thickened sludge and 'clear' effluent respectively.

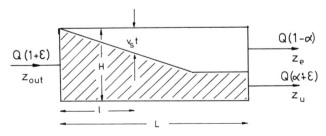

FIG. 7.14 Sketch of a secondary clarifier.

Substituting for t from eqn. (7.42) with $Wl = WL = A$ (the clarifier area)

$$z_{out} = z_u\left(1 - \frac{Av_s}{Q(1 + \varepsilon)}\right) + z_e\frac{Av_s}{Q(1 + \varepsilon)} \qquad (7.43)$$

If the sludge purge rate is αQ, the total underflow is $Q(\alpha + \varepsilon)$ and the total effluent flow is $Q(1 - \alpha)$. A solids balance on the complete clarifier then gives:

$$Q(1 + \varepsilon)z_{out} = Q(\alpha + \varepsilon)z_u + Q(1 - \alpha)z_e$$

or

$$z_{out} = \frac{\alpha + \varepsilon}{1 + \varepsilon}z_u + \frac{1 - \alpha}{1 + \varepsilon}z_e \qquad (7.44)$$

Eliminating z_{out} between eqns. (7.43) and (7.44) gives:

$$z_e\left(\frac{Av_s}{Q(1 + \varepsilon)} - \frac{1 - \alpha}{1 + \varepsilon}\right) = z_u\left(\frac{\alpha + \varepsilon}{1 + \varepsilon} - 1 + \frac{Av_s}{Q(1 + \varepsilon)}\right)$$

$$= z_u\left(\frac{Av_s}{Q(1 + \varepsilon)} - \frac{1 - \alpha}{1 + \varepsilon}\right)$$

Since $z_e \neq z_u$ we must have

$$\frac{Av_s}{Q(1 + \varepsilon)} - \frac{1 - \alpha}{1 + \varepsilon} = 0$$

or

$$A = \frac{Q}{v_s}(1 - \alpha) \qquad (7.45)$$

As just pointed out, this gives a *minimum* value of A. To allow for overloads without washout, the clarifier should be overdesigned.

7.7.2. CSTR Aerator

Referring to Fig. 7.2, we may carry out mass balances over the whole plant (aerator and clarifier):

substrate:

$$Qs_o - (\alpha Q + (1 - \alpha)Q)s_{out} = -Vr_s = V\frac{\mu s_{out}x_{out}}{b(K + s_{out})} \qquad (7.46)$$

live cells:

$$\alpha Qx_u + (1 - \alpha)Qx_e = Vr_x = V\left(\frac{\mu s_{out}x_{out}}{K + s_{out}} - k_ex_{out}\right) \qquad (7.47)$$

dead cells:

$$\alpha Qy_u + (1 - \alpha)Qy_e = Vr_y = Vb'k_ex_{out} \qquad (7.48)$$

Defining the mean cell residence time, θ_c, as the ratio of the mass of cells in the tank to the net rate of removal of cells, we have:

$$\theta_c = \frac{V x_{out}}{\alpha Q x_u + (1-\alpha) Q x_e} \tag{7.49}$$

Similar equations also apply for y and z as it is assumed that no reaction occurs in the clarifier.

Substituting eqn. (7.49) into eqn. (7.47) gives:

$$\frac{V x_{out}}{\theta_c} = V \left(\frac{\mu s_{out} x_{out}}{K + s_{out}} - k_e x_{out} \right)$$

or

$$\frac{1}{\theta_c} + k_e = \frac{\mu s_{out}}{K + s_{out}} \tag{7.50}$$

whence

$$s_{out} = \frac{K(1 + k_e \theta_c)}{\mu \theta_c - (1 + k_e \theta_c)} \tag{7.51}$$

Equations (7.50) and (7.51) have the same form as eqns. (7.32) and (7.33) for the CSTR without recycle, except that θ_c replaces θ_h.

Writing eqn. (7.49) for y and substituting into eqn. (7.48) we have:

$$\frac{V y_{out}}{\theta_c} = V b' k_e x_{out}$$

or

$$y_{out} = b' k_e \theta_c x_{out}$$

Thus

$$z_{out} = x_{out} + y_{out} = x_{out}(1 + b' k_e \theta_c) \tag{7.52}$$

Substituting eqns. (7.50) and (7.52) into eqn. (7.46) we have:

$$Q(s_o - s_{out}) = \frac{V}{b} \frac{1/\theta_c + k_e}{1 + b' k_e \theta_c} \cdot z_{out}$$

whence, substituting $\theta_h = V/Q$,

$$z_{out} = \frac{1 + b' k_e \theta_c}{1 + k_e \theta_c} \frac{b \theta_c}{\theta_h} (s_o - s_{out}) \tag{7.53}$$

Writing eqn. (7.49) for z and substituting $\theta_h = V/Q$

$$\theta_h z_{out} = \theta_c(\alpha z_u + (1-\alpha) z_e) \tag{7.54}$$

Rearranging gives:

$$\alpha = \left(\frac{\theta_h}{\theta_c} z_{out} - z_e \right) \Big/ (z_u - z_e)$$

$$= \left[b\frac{1 + b'k_e\theta_c}{1 + k_e\theta_c}\cdot(s_o - s_{out}) - z_e \right] \Big/ (z_u - z_e) \qquad (7.55)$$

Substituting for z_{out} from eqn. (7.44) into eqn. (7.54) we obtain:

$$\theta_h = \frac{V}{Q} = \frac{\theta_c[\alpha(z_u - z_e) + z_e](1 + \varepsilon)}{\alpha(z_u - z_e) + z_e + \varepsilon z_u} \qquad (7.56)$$

To design a system for given s_o, s_{out} and Q, with sludge properties fixing z_e and $z_u = z_{max}$, we may obtain θ_c from eqn. (7.50). Equation (7.55) may then be solved for α, and substitution of α into eqn. (7.45) gives A, the minimum clarifier area. Equation (7.56) then relates V, the aerator volume to ε the fractional recycle. Since α and z_e are normally small, we have, approximately,

$$V \simeq \theta_c Q \left[\alpha + \frac{z_e}{z_u} \right] \frac{1 + \varepsilon}{\varepsilon} \qquad (7.57)$$

Thus V increases with decreasing ε, and the design involves an economic balance between large capital costs for a large aerator and large pumping costs for a large recycle. Normally the optimum lies in the range $\varepsilon \simeq 0.2 - 0.3$, with $\theta_h \simeq 6$ h.

Aeration requirements can also put a lower limit on V as explained below, while good sludge settling tends to need θ_c values of at least 3 days, even if a smaller value is obtained from eqn. (7.50), so the design involves a large number of interacting constraints.

7.7.3. Aeration

Oxygen use, from eqn. (7.26), becomes:

$$r_{ox} = -ar_s + a'r_y/b' = a(s_o - s_{out})/\theta_h + a'k_e x_{out}$$

Substituting for x_{out} from eqns. (7.52) and (7.53) we find:

$$x_{out} = z_{out}/(1 + b'k_e\theta_c) = b\theta_c(s_o - s_{out})/[\theta_h(1 + k_e\theta_c)]$$

and so
$$r_{ox} = \left[a + \frac{a'bk_e\theta_c}{(1 + k_e\theta_c)} \right] \frac{s_o - s_{out}}{\theta_h} \qquad (7.58)$$

To provide this oxygen air is either bubbled through the liquid, or, more usually, a type of turbine in the liquid surface entrains air and mixes the liquid. Design of such surface aerators is difficult as geometrical considerations affect the performance. Manufacturers usually quote performance in terms of kg O_2 dissolved per kWh of power required, with values typically around 2 kg/kWh. Such measurements are usually made in catalysed Na_2SO_3 solution, ensuring a zero dissolved oxygen concentration whereas healthy activated sludge needs 2 mg/litre of dissolved oxygen (DO) (i.e. about 20% of air saturation), so 30–50% overdesign should be allowed for.

There is also a limit to the oxygen transfer capacity per unit volume of the aerators, as they cannot be placed too close together. Values of mass transfer coefficient $k_L a$ much above 10/h are probably unrealistic, which with an oxygen saturation of 10 mg/litre and a minimum DO of 2 mg/litre gives a maximum oxygen transfer rate of 80 mg/litre h or 2 kg/m³ day. If the calculated oxygen requirement exceeds this value, the sludge will go anaerobic with all the attendant problems of poor settling and the design must be modified to reduce r_{ox} by increasing θ_h — see eqn. (7.58) — and hence increasing V.

Example 7.3. Design a CSTR activated sludge plant and clarifier for the following duty:
$Q = 1000$ m³/h. Inlet BOD 250 mg/litre. Exit BOD 25 mg/litre with 10 mg/litre MLSS. Sludge settles at 0.9 m/h to the maximum concentration of 8000 mg/litre. Recycle 30%. Aerator delivery 2 kg O_2/kWh. Biological data: $a = 0.38$, $a' = 1.06$, $b = 0.58$, $b' = 0.25$, $K = 40$ mg/litre, $\mu = 0.1$/h, $k_e = 0.012$/h.

Solution
Equation (7.50) gives

$$\frac{1}{\theta_c} = \frac{0.1 \times 25}{40 + 25} - 0.012 = 0.02646$$

$$\therefore \; \theta_c = 37.8 \, \text{h} = 1.57 \, \text{days}$$

This is less than the recommended minimum of 3 days, so the higher value will be chosen: $\theta_c = 3$ days $= 72$ h. This leads to an effluent BOD better than required, given by eqn. (7.51):

$$S_{out} = \frac{40(1 + 0.012 \times 72)}{0.1 \times 72 - (1 + 0.012 \times 72)} = 13.97 \, \text{mg/litre}$$

Equation (7.55) gives

$$\alpha = \frac{0.58 \dfrac{1 + 0.25 \times 0.012 \times 72}{1 + 0.012 \times 72}(250 - 13.97) - 10}{(8000 - 10)}$$

$$= 0.00993$$

Equation (7.56) gives

$$\theta_h = \frac{72(0.00993(8000 - 10) + 10)(1 + 0.3)}{0.00993(8000 - 10) + 10 + (0.3 \times 8000)}$$

$$= 3.36\,h$$

Equation (7.58) gives

$$r_{ox} = \left(0.38 + \frac{1.06 \times 0.58 \times 0.012 \times 72}{1 + 0.012 \times 72}\right)\frac{250 - 13.97}{3.36}$$

$$= 46.7\,mg/litre\,h$$

This is below the maximum rate, so the aerators can cope. From eqn. (7.45)

$$A = \frac{1000}{0.9}(1 - 0.00993) = 1100\,m^2$$

Because of the sensitivity of the clarifier to overload (see Example 7.4 below) the actual design should include a safety factor to cope with expected peak loads.

Aerator volume, $V = Q\theta_h = 1000 \times 3.36 = 3360\,m^3$
Oxygen usage $= 3360 \times 46.7 \times 10^{-3} = 156.9\,kg/h$
Aerator power needed $= \frac{1}{2} \times 156.9 = 78.5\,kW$
Purge flow of thickened sludge $= 1000 \times 0.00993 = 9.93\,m^3/h$
Solids purged $= 9.93 \times 8000 \times 10^{-3} = 79.4\,kg/h$

Example 7.4. Investigate the behaviour of the plant designed above to hydraulic overload (increased Q, constant s_o)

(a) assuming that the clarifier is sufficiently overdesigned, and,
(b) assuming the clarifier is at the limit of its operation.

Solution

The above equations are all in terms of cell mean residence time θ_c, so this should be taken as the independent variable. As the system overloads, θ_c falls and s_{out} rises until washout occurs when $s_{out} = s_{in}$. However, throughput Q determines θ_h directly, rather than θ_c and the relationship between θ_h and θ_c is very different in the two cases.

(a) Clarifier overdesigned. Here z_u remains at 8000 and z_e at 10, with slight adjustments of α to allow for removal of all the solids formed. z_{out} remains almost constant, from eqn. (7.44), so that to a first approximation θ_h is proportional to θ_c—eqn. (7.53).

TABLE 7.3
HYDRAULIC OVERLOAD WITH OVERDESIGNED CLARIFIER

θ_c (h)	72	37.8	20	15	14
s_{out} (mg/litre)	13.97	25.0	65.26	147.5	201.4
α	0.0099	0.0113	0.0102	0.0053	0.0019
θ_h (h)	3.36	1.96	0.96	0.42	0.19
Q (m³/h)	1000	1710	3500	8000	17700

TABLE 7.4
HYDRAULIC OVERLOAD WITH CLARIFIER AT LIMIT

θ_c (h)	72	30	20	15
s_{out} (mg/litre)	13.97	33.17	65.26	147.5
α	0.0099	0.0251	0.0385	0.0488
θ_h (h)	3.36	3.31	3.26	3.23
Q (m³/h)	1000	1015	1031	1040

To solve, we obtain s_{out} from eqn. (7.51), $z_{out}\dfrac{\theta_h}{\theta_c}$ from eqn. (7.53), then α from eqn. (7.55), and θ_h from eqn. (7.56). Table 7.3 shows the sort of behaviour found. The effluent is seen to be acceptable at a flowrate 70% above the design value, showing the insensitivity of the system to flow rate changes.

(b) Clarifier at limit. Here, α is related directly to Q (or θ_h) by eqn. (7.45)

$$\frac{Av_s}{Q} = \frac{Av_s}{V} \cdot \theta_h = 1 - \alpha$$

As Q increases, α also increases and z_u falls. Equations (7.44), (7.45), (7.54) and (7.55) contain the four unknowns z_{out}, z_u, α and θ_h (z_e being taken as 10 mg/litre) and any three may be eliminated, leaving a quadratic in the fourth. The results are set out in Table 7.4.

Thus, even a 4% increase in Q leads to a totally unacceptable effluent of 147.5 mg/litre BOD. This result demonstrates the point made above, that the clarifier should be overdesigned to allow for expected peak loads.

7.7.4. Plug Flow Aerator

The design method is essentially similar to that for the batch reactor, with t replaced by the mean fluid residence time per pass.

$$t = \frac{V}{Q(1 + \varepsilon)} = \frac{\theta_h}{1 + \varepsilon} \tag{7.59}$$

If the mean live cell concentration is $\bar{x}$, we may define the mean cell residence time (assuming as before no reaction in the clarifier):

$$\theta_c = \frac{\text{mass of live cells in reactor}}{\text{net removal rate of live cells}} = \frac{V\bar{x}}{Q(\alpha x_u + (1 - \alpha)x_e)} \tag{7.60}$$

In the steady state, the net rate of removal equals the net rate of production, so for live cells:

$$Q(\alpha x_u + (1 - \alpha)x_e) = Q(s_o - s_{out})b - Vk_e\bar{x} \tag{7.61}$$

or from eqn. (7.60):

$$\frac{V\bar{x}}{\theta_c} = Q(s_o - s_{out})b - V\bar{x}k_e$$

whence

$$\theta_h\bar{x} = \frac{\theta_c}{1 + k_e\theta_c} b(s_o - s_{out}) \tag{7.62}$$

Substituting t from eqn. (7.59) into the batch eqn. (7.38) gives:

$$K \ln \left(\frac{s_{in}}{s_{out}} \right) + (s_{in} - s_{out}) = \frac{\mu \bar{x}}{b} \frac{\theta_h}{1 + \varepsilon} \tag{7.63}$$

A substrate mass balance at the reactor inlet gives:

$$Q(1 + \varepsilon)s_{in} = \varepsilon Q s_{out} + Q s_o \tag{7.64}$$

Substituting for $\bar{x}$ from eqn. (7.62) and s_{in} from eqn. (7.64) into eqn. (7.63) we obtain:

$$K \ln \left(\frac{s_o/s_{out} + \varepsilon}{1 + \varepsilon} \right) + \frac{s_o - s_{out}}{1 + \varepsilon} = \frac{\mu \theta_c}{1 + k_e\theta_c} \cdot \frac{s_o - s_{out}}{1 + \varepsilon}$$

or

$$\frac{K(1 + \varepsilon)}{s_o - s_{out}} \ln \left(\frac{s_o/s_{out} + \varepsilon}{1 + \varepsilon} \right) = \frac{\mu \theta_c}{1 + k_e\theta_c} - 1 \tag{7.65}$$

Equation (7.65) is the analogue of the CSTR eqn. (7.50) and differs from it in several ways, notably the dependence of s_{out} on s_o and ε as well as θ_c. A plot

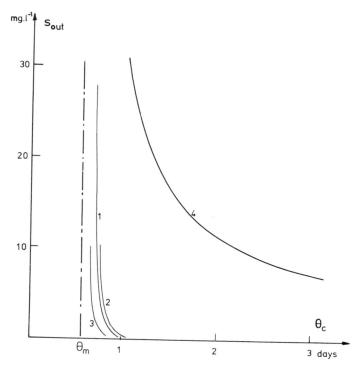

FIG. 7.15 Comparison of the performance of plug flow and CSTR aerators.
$\mu = 0.083/h$, $k_e = 0.003/h$, $K = 28$ mg/litre.
Curve 1: Plug flow $\varepsilon = 0.3$ $s_o = 300$ mg/litre;
Curve 2: Plug flow $\varepsilon = 0.5$ $s_o = 300$ mg/litre;
Curve 3: Plug flow $\varepsilon = 0.3$ $s_o = 500$ mg/litre;
Curve 4: CSTR

of s_{out} against θ_c shows, as expected, that the plug flow reactor achieves a lower effluent concentration for a given value of θ_c (Fig. 7.15). This apparent advantage may not lead to design economy however, since θ_c is determined in many cases by sludge properties, which demand that $\theta_c \geq 3$ days.

Both plug flow and CSTR aerator systems have the same value of θ_c at washout ($s_{out} = s_o$) namely,

$$\theta_{min} = \frac{1 + K/s_o}{\mu - k_e(1 + K/s_o)} \tag{7.66}$$

No reaction is assumed to occur in the clarifier, so the relative proportions of live and dead cells are the same:

$$\frac{y_u}{x_u} = \frac{y_e}{x_e} = \frac{y_{out}}{x_{out}} = B, \text{ where } B \text{ is a constant} \tag{7.67}$$

Since for dead cells, the rate of removal from the system is equal to the rate of production in the aerator:

$$Q(\alpha y_u + (1 - \alpha)y_e) = V\bar{x}b'k_e$$

Substituting from eqn. (7.67) gives:

$$B(\alpha x_u + (1 - \alpha)x_e) = \theta_h\bar{x}b'k_e$$

and hence from eqn. (7.60):

$$B\frac{\theta_h}{\theta_c}\bar{x} = \theta_h k_e\bar{x}b' \quad \text{or} \quad B = b'k_e\theta_c$$

Thus

$$z_j = x_j + y_j = x_j(1 + b'k_e\theta_c) \tag{7.68}$$

where subscript $_j$ can be $_u$, $_e$ or $_{out}$.

From eqn. (7.60) again, $\alpha = \left(\dfrac{\theta_h\bar{x}}{\theta_c} - x_e\right)\bigg/(x_u - x_e)$

and substituting for $\theta_h\bar{x}$ from eqn. (7.62) and x_j from eqn. (7.68) gives:

$$\alpha = \left[\frac{1 + b'k_e\theta_c}{1 + k_e\theta_c}b(s_o - s_{out}) - z_e\right]\bigg/(z_u - z_e) \tag{7.69}$$

A comparison of eqns. (7.69) and (7.55) shows that the design value of α is identical in the two cases. To obtain θ_h we must relate $\bar{x}$ to measurable variables, since only the product $\bar{x}\theta_h$ occurs in the previous equations.

Since we have assumed $\bar{x}$ to be constant in the integration leading to eqn. (7.63), we may make the approximation:

$$\bar{x} \simeq \tfrac{1}{2}(x_{in} + x_{out}) \tag{7.70}$$

Mass balances of live cells at reactor inlet and over the clarifier yield:

$$Q(1 + \varepsilon)x_{in} = \varepsilon Q x_u \tag{7.71}$$

$$Q(1 + \varepsilon)x_{out} = (\alpha + \varepsilon)Q x_u + (1 - \alpha)Q x_e \tag{7.72}$$

Substituting for $\bar{x}$ from eqn. (7.60) x_{in} from eqn. (7.71) and x_{out} from eqn. (7.72) into eqn. (7.70) gives:

$$\frac{\theta_c}{\theta_h}(\alpha x_u + (1-\alpha)x_e) = \frac{\varepsilon x_u}{1+\varepsilon} + \frac{(\alpha x_u + (1-\alpha)x_e)}{2(1+\varepsilon)}$$

Replacing x_j by z_j using eqn. (7.68) and rearranging leads to:

$$\theta_h = 2(1+\varepsilon)\theta_c \frac{\alpha(z_u - z_e) + z_e}{\alpha(z_u - z_e) + z_e + 2\varepsilon z_u} \tag{7.73}$$

If $z_u \gg z_e$ and $\varepsilon \gg \alpha$, this reduces to the same simple eqn. (7.57) as the corresponding CSTR equation, and similar remarks apply.

Aeration requirements are obtained from eqn. (7.26):

$$r_{ox} = -ar_s + a'r_y/b'$$

The overall consumption is given by:

$$\bar{r}_{ox} = a(s_o - s_{out})/\theta_h + a'k_e\bar{x}$$

which with eqn. (7.62) becomes:

$$\bar{r}_{ox} = \frac{s_o - s_{out}}{\theta_h}\left(a + \frac{a'bk_e\theta_c}{1 + k_e\theta_c}\right) \tag{7.74}$$

which is identical to the CSTR eqn. (7.58). However, for the plug flow reactor, oxygen uptake differs along the reactor, being greatest at the inlet where substrate concentration and reaction rate are greater.

$$r_{ox, in} = \left[\frac{a\mu s_{in}}{b(K + s_{in})} + a'k_e\right]x_{in} \tag{7.75}$$

$$r_{ox, out} = \left[\frac{a\mu s_{out}}{b(K + s_{out})} + a'k_e\right]x_{out} \tag{7.76}$$

with s_{in}, s_{out}, x_{in} and x_{out} all calculable from previous equations.

Example 7.5. Repeat Example 7.3 for the plug flow aerator

Solution
From eqn. (7.65):

$$\frac{40(1+0.3)}{250-25}\ln\left(\frac{250/25 + 0.3}{1 + 0.3}\right) = \frac{0.1\theta_c}{1 + 0.012\theta_c} - 1$$

whence $\theta_c = 18.0\,h$

As expected this is less than the value calculated for the CSTR (37.8), but as explained in Example 7.3, we must have a value of at least 72 h to get a well settled sludge. Thus re-using eqn. (7.65):

$$\frac{40(1 + 0.3)}{250 - s_{out}} \ln\left(\frac{250/s_{out} + 0.3}{1 + 0.3}\right) = \frac{0.1 \times 72}{1 + 0.012 \times 72} - 1$$

whence $s_{out} = 2 \times 10^{-4}$ mg/litre

Equation (7.69):

$$\alpha = \frac{\dfrac{1 + 0.25 \times 0.012 \times 72}{1 + 0.012 \times 72} \times 0.58(250 - 0.0002) - 10}{(8000 - 10)}$$

$$= 0.0106$$

Equation (7.73):

$$\theta_h = 2(1 + 0.3) \times 72 \times \frac{0.0106(8000 - 10) + 10}{0.0106(8000 - 10) + 10 + 2 \times 0.3 \times 8000}$$

$$= 3.62\,h$$

Equation (7.64):

$$s_{in} = \frac{0.3}{1 + 0.3} \times 2 \times 10^{-4} + \frac{1}{1 + 0.3} \times 250 = 192.3\,\text{mg/litre}$$

Equation (7.68):

$$x_u = 8000/(1 + 0.25 \times 0.012 \times 72) = 6578.95\,\text{mg/litre}$$

and

$$x_e = 10/(1 + 0.25 \times 0.012 \times 72) \quad = 8.22\,\text{mg/litre}$$

Equation (7.71):

$$x_{in} = 0.3 \times 6578.95/1.3 = 1518.22\,\text{mg/litre}$$

Equation (7.72):

$$x_{out} = [(0.0106 + 0.3) \times 6578.95 + (1 - 0.0106) \times 8.22]/1.3$$
$$= 1578.12\,\text{mg/litre}$$

Equation (7.74):

$$\bar{r}_{ox} = \frac{250 - 0.0002}{3.62}\left(0.38 + \frac{1.06 \times 0.58 \times 0.012 \times 72}{1 + 0.012 \times 72}\right)$$

$$= 45.9\,\text{mg/litre h}$$

Equation (7.75):

$$\bar{r}_{ox,\,in} = \left[\frac{0.38 \times 0.1 \times 192.3}{0.58(40 + 192.3)} + (1.06 \times 0.012) \right] \times 1518.22$$

$$= 101.7 \, \text{mg/litre h}$$

Equation (7.76):

$$\bar{r}_{ox,\,out} = \left[\frac{0.38 \times 0.1 \times 0.0002}{0.58(40 + 0.0002)} + (1.06 \times 0.012) \right] \times 1578.12$$

$$= 20.1 \, \text{mg/litre h}$$

Thus, while the overall oxygen consumption $\bar{r}_{ox}$ is very similar to that for the CSTR, there is a factor of five between inlet and exit rates and the former is above the 80 mg/litre h maximum permissible. However, pure plug flow does not occur, and the degree of backmixing will probably reduce oxygen consumption in the inlet region to a more acceptable value. In extreme cases the first section of the reactor should be designed as a CSTR to prevent anaerobic conditions, or a portion of the effluent may be recycled to the inlet to dilute it and even out oxygen usage.

To cope with the higher oxygen demand at the inlet end, it is usual to arrange a larger number of, or more powerful, aerators in that region, a system called 'tapered aeration'. For example, at the Stoke Bardolph plant of the Severn–Trent Water Authority, each aerator consists of a series of 10 pockets each with one agitator (10 CSTRs in series approximate to plug flow). The first five pockets have large 15-kW agitators, while the last five have smaller, 6-kW devices.

The final design data for Example 7.5 are thus

$$A = 1000(1 - 0.0106)/0.9 = 1099 \, \text{m}^2$$

As in Example 7.3 some overdesign should be allowed for.

$$V = 1000 \times 3.62 = 3620 \, \text{m}^3$$

Total oxygen consumption $= 3620 \times 45.9 \times 10^{-3} = 166.2 \, \text{kg/h}$
Aerator power $= 166.2/2 = 83.1 \, \text{kW}$
Net purge flow $= 1000 \times 0.0106 = 10.6 \, \text{m}^3/\text{h}$
Net solids in purge $= 10.6 \times 8 = 84.8 \, \text{kg/h}$

Opinion is divided as to whether a new plant should be designed as a CSTR (short wide tank) or plug flow (long narrow tank or series of pockets).

The latter may give better effluent during steady state operation, and possibly a better settling sludge, while the former is less susceptible to shock loads of toxins or BOD.

7.7.5. Recent Developments

A number of recent commercial processes have been developed using oxygen or oxygen-enriched air in the activated-sludge process.[12,13] The tanks must be covered to allow recirculation of the oxygen, but higher MLSS concentration and greatly improved settling have been claimed. Some systems, e.g., Union Carbide's '*UNOX*' process[12] are virtually indistinguishable from conventional activated sludge, while others, such as the '*VITOX*' and '*MEGOX*' systems of BOC Ltd[13] use oxygen injection into a pumped external recycle. '*VITOX*' is essentially a means of uprating an existing plant, whereas '*MEGOX*' is a new concept in which reactor and clarifier are combined in a single unit. These oxygen systems are ideal for small-volume installations with high BOD, such as food processing, abattoir wastes, etc.

Another recent development of the activated-sludge process is the '*Deep Shaft*' of ICI Ltd.[6,14] As shown in Fig. 7.16, two parallel or concentric shafts are sunk to around 100-m depth with a diameter of 1–6 m. Air is injected to

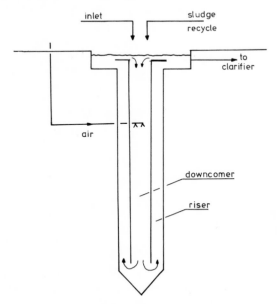

FIG. 7.16 The *Deep Shaft* system.

a depth of 20–40 m in the downcomer, and is swept down by the liquid, which flows at 1–2 m/s. Because of the greater aerated height in the riser, the mean density there is less than in the downcomer, which provides a driving force to maintain liquid circulation. At the foot of the shaft the high pressure causes almost complete dissolution of the air and yet the compressor need only overcome a hydrostatic head of 20–40 m; the riser effectively acts as a pressure recovery device, permitting oxygen transfer efficiencies of up to 6 kg/kWh.

Primary settlers are unnecessary, thus reducing land area requirements, and excellent sludge settling characteristics are claimed, even with difficult carbohydrate wastes, with a very low sludge yield. Desorbed air bubbles attached to the sludge make it necessary to include a vacuum degasser between the shaft and the clarifier.

The system is still under development, but promises substantial improvements in areas where land is scarce and geological formations suitable.

7.7.6. The Trickling Filter

Apart from simple lagooning on farmland, the oldest treatment method is the so called trickling filter, in which liquid flows over some form of solid support covered with a film of biological slime. The slime thickness is normally so great that mass transfer is limiting, giving an overall reaction order between $\frac{1}{2}$ and 1 as shown in Section 7.5.2. It is normally safe to assume a first-order reaction:

$$R_A = \beta s \tag{7.77}$$

where R_A is the rate of substrate usage per unit area. In the absence of liquid film resistance, we can set up a differential mass balance (Fig. 7.17) on an element of width w and height dh.

$$-Q\frac{ds}{dh} = \beta s w$$

whence

$$\frac{s_{out}}{s_{in}} = \exp\left(-\frac{\beta w h}{Q}\right) \tag{7.78}$$

In the presence of liquid film resistance, with mass transfer coefficient k_L, we have

$$R_A = k_L(s - s^*) = \beta s^*$$

whence

$$s^* = \frac{k_L}{\beta + k_L} \cdot s$$

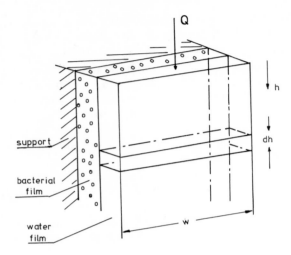

FIG. 7.17 Detail of the bacterial film in a trickling filter.

and

$$\frac{S_{out}}{S_{in}} = \exp\left(-\frac{\beta k_L}{\beta + k_L} \cdot \frac{wh}{Q}\right) \qquad (7.79)$$

Evidence as to the behaviour of k_L with Q is conflicting, even as to whether it increases[15] or decreases.[4] The effect is complicated by incomplete wetting of the packing so that w may also vary with Q, and the only reasonable approach seems to be to fall back on empirical relationships between the apparent value of β in eqn. (7.78) and Q. In many cases it seems that for a given packing and effluent, β may be taken as a constant of order 5×10^{-3} m/h, and eqn. (7.78) used directly.

An extensive series of trials at the WRC[16] on a variety of different filters has led to the following empirical equation:

$$\frac{S_{in}}{S_{out}} = 1 + k\Theta^{(T - 15)}\sigma^p/Q_h^q \qquad (7.80)$$

where Q_h is the hydraulic loading (m³/m³ day)
  σ is the specific surface (m²/m³)
  T is the temperature (°C)
  k, Θ, p and q are constants

TABLE 7.5
WRC VALUES FOR EQN. (7.80)

Coefficient	Stone packing	Plastic (modular)	All data
k	0.0204	0.4000	0.2101
Θ	1.111	1.089	1.094
p	1.407	0.7324	0.796
q	1.249	1.396	1.252

This equation can be regarded as a modified form of eqn. (7.78):

$$\frac{S_{in}}{S_{out}} = \exp\frac{\beta wh}{Q} = 1 + \frac{\beta wh}{Q} + \ldots$$

$$\approx 1 + k\sigma/Q_h$$

which is equivalent to eqn. (7.80) when $p = q = 1$.

Values of the four constants in eqn. (7.80) must be determined for individual cases by pilot-plant studies; the WRC data, for Stevenage sewage, gave the values in Table 7.5.

Specific surface area, σ, varies with the packing medium. For crushed gravel, it is inversely proportional to the packing size, and of order 100 m^2/m^3 for 50-mm pieces. For modular plastics, it can range from 80 to over 200 m^2/m^3

Hydraulic loading, Q_h, is mainly determined by a maximum allowable organic loading, beyond which the slime grows faster than it can be removed by predation and sloughing, and the filter chokes up ('ponding'). For a single-pass filter with 50-mm rock medium, this upper limit is taken as 0.10 to 0.12 kg BOD/m^3 day in British practice. Typical sewage, with a BOD of 200 mg/litre can thus be loaded at 0.5 to 0.6 m^3/m^3 day. Highly concentrated effluents would have to be loaded at ridiculously low levels, leading to incomplete wetting of the medium, and possible anaerobic conditions.

The problem can be overcome by recirculating some of the effluent. This increases the irrigation rate Q/A and the amount of sloughing, and permits organic loadings of up to 0.2 kg BOD/m^3 day. Equation (7.80) must then be modified to:

$$\frac{S_o/S_{out} + \varepsilon}{1 + \varepsilon} = 1 + k\Theta^{(T-15)}\sigma^p/[Q_h^q(1 + \varepsilon)^q] \qquad (7.81)$$

Rock should not be stacked more than 1.8 m deep, because of its great weight. The newer plastic media, being lighter, may be stacked up to 8 m, which for a given hydraulic loading increases the irrigation rate. This, together with the greater voidage of such packing, reduces the problem of ponding and allows BOD loadings of up to 8 kg/m³ day. Because a minimum irrigation rate of around 1.5 m/day is needed to wet the packing, recycle is normal in such high rate filters, which find their major use in preliminary treatment of very high BOD wastes, such as are produced in food processing.

Example 7.6. Design a trickling filter to treat 100 m³/h of liquid reducing the BOD from 250 to 25 mg/litre. Stone packing of specific surface 89 m²/m³ may be stacked up to a depth of 1.8 m and the irrigation rate should not fall below 1.5 m/day. Use data from Table 7.5 at a temperature of 15°C.

If the flow rate falls by half and the inlet BOD rises to 400 mg/litre what recycle fraction would be needed to maintain operation within the required limits?

Solution

Equation (7.80):

$$\frac{250}{25} = 1 + 0.0204 \times 1 \times 89^{1.407} Q_h^{-1.249}$$

$$\therefore \quad Q_h = 1.1984 \text{ m}^3/\text{m}^3 \text{ day}$$

Taking a height of 1.8 m, $1.1984 = \dfrac{24 \times 100}{1.8A}$

$$\therefore \quad A = 1113 \text{ m}^2$$

This is a circular bed 37.6 m in diameter
Irrigation rate $= Q/A = 2.15$ m/day
Halving Q drops the irrigation rate below 1.5 m/day, so some recycle will be needed. To meet the minimum irrigation,

$$1200(1 + \varepsilon)/1113 = 1.5$$

$$\therefore \quad \varepsilon = 0.39$$

Equation (7.81):

$$\frac{s_0/s_{out} + 0.39}{1.39} = 1 + \frac{0.0204 \times 1 \times 89^{1.407}}{(\frac{1}{2} \times 1.1984 \times 1.39)^{1.249}}$$

$$\therefore \quad \frac{S_o}{S_{out}} = 20.71$$

$$S_{out} = \frac{400}{20.71} = 19.3 \, \text{mg/litre}$$

Thus the system will meet the required BOD limit.

7.7.7. Rotating Biological Contactor

These units (Fig. 7.18) consist of plastic discs ranging in diameter from 0.7 to 3 m rotating at from 0.5 to 3 rev/min. They are mounted in units, 5–20 cm apart on a common axis, with about 40% of the disc submerged. Biomass attached to the discs is exposed alternately to liquid and air, allowing very high organic loadings of 5–10 g BOD/m² day (compare trickle filters ~ 1 g/m² day). Design data from pilot plant units is scaled up on the basis of a constant peripheral speed of disc provided this speed is fast enough to maintain about 2 mg/litre of dissolved oxygen in the trough.[17]

Equation (7.78) may be used for design purposes, with hw equal to the disc area, and β determined from pilot plant studies. The RBC is normally considered for small communities, or to treat industrial wastes high in BOD. Its capital cost is relatively high, but running costs are low, and recovery from shock loadings is rapid, so that skilled operators are not needed.

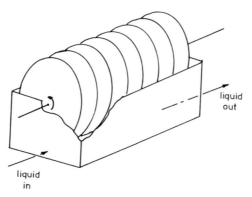

liquid out

liquid in

FIG. 7.18 The rotating biological contactor.

7.7.8. Anaerobic Digestion

Compared with aerobic reactions, anaerobic digestion is very slow, with μ typically of order 0.1 to 0.2 day^{-1}. Since the feed is a solid, the reaction rates are very low and the quality of the 'effluent' (digested sludge) is determined mainly in non-quantitative terms such as lack of offensive odour, good settling and dewatering characteristics, etc.; it is very difficult to obtain numerical data for design. Instead, pilot-plant studies are used to determine the residence time needed for 'complete digestion' (as defined by whatever criteria are used) and this is used for full-scale design. Twenty to thirty days at 30°C is a typical value and, although feed is in fact intermittent, (once or twice a day) the system can be regarded as a CSTR.

Mixing and heating are usually provided by pumping the slurry through an external heat exchanger. From eqn. (7.7), about $0.3 \, m^3$ of CH_4 (0.21 kg) are produced per kg of BOD removed; in terms of solids fed this is equivalent to 0.10 to $0.20 \, m^3/kg$. Considerable quantities of CO_2 and small amounts of H_2S and H_2 are also generated, giving a final gas mixture containing 65–70% CH_4. This gas may be used to run a gas engine to power the sewage works, with the waste heat going to heat the digester. A large works can be practically self-sufficient in energy.

Acetic acid is an intermediate in the complex chain of reactions occurring, but as the methane forming bacteria are sensitive to pH, careful control is needed to prevent the reactor from 'going sour', and the 20–30 day typical residence time represents a considerable overdesign to allow for this problem.

Example 7.7. Pilot-plant studies on a sludge digester showed that with an inlet slurry of mixed primary and secondary sludge containing 50 kg solids per m^3 satisfactory digestion was complete in 20 days. One third of the mass of inlet solids was consumed, yielding $0.35 \, m^3$ of methane per kg of solids consumed. Design a full-scale digester to handle $400 \, m^3/day$ of the mixed sludge.

Solution
Volume of slurry in digester $= 400 \times 20 = 8000 \, m^3$
This suggests the use of two tanks, each $4000 \, m^3$ capacity. A depth of 10 m and diameter of 25 m give $4909 \, m^3$, allowing a free space at the top for gas collection, foaming, etc.

Solids loading rate $= 50 \times 400 = 20 \, 000 \, kg/day$
Methane generation rate $= 20 \, 000 \times \frac{1}{3} \times 0.35 = 2333 \, m^3/day$

With an average calorific value of $37 \, MJ/m^3$ this gives a fuel value of $86 \, GJ/day$ or around 1 MW.

7.8. CONCLUSION

Most plants have been designed on an empirical basis in the absence of effective understanding of mechanisms or detailed design data. While the methods outlined above are a real improvement on pure empiricism, there are still too many uncertainties to allow design without large safety factors.

One area where much remains to be done is in the control of sewage plants, whether manual or automatic. For this dynamic models are needed and, while some such models have been proposed recently, they are incompletely tested. Andrews and his co-workers have developed one for anaerobic digestion[18] which has successfully been applied to a laboratory reactor[19] and one for activated sludge[20] which includes a term for absorption of substrate on the sludge prior to reaction. Apart from its use in the contact stabilisation process, which relies on this absorption to give a rapid lowering of BOD in the effluent, the model appears to explain the behaviour of a conventional CSTR to transients in the feed concentration, for which the Monod equation is inadequate.[21]

BIBLIOGRAPHY

1. Schroeder, E.D., *Water and Wastewater Treatment*. McGraw-Hill, New York, 1977.
2. Bailey, J.E., and Ollis, D.F., *Biochemical Engineering Fundamentals*. McGraw-Hill, New York, 1977.
3. Eckenfelder, W.W., Jr., *Industrial Water Pollution Control*. McGraw-Hill, New York, 1966.
4. Atkinson, B., *Biochemical Reactors*. Pion, London, 1974.
5. Atkinson, B., In *Chemical Engineering*, Vol. 3. (eds. J.M. Coulson and J.F. Richardson). Pergamon, Oxford, 1971.
6. Bolton, D.H., and Ousby, J.C., The ICI deep shaft effluent treatment process and its potential for large sewage works, *Prog. Water. Tech.*, **8**(6) (1977), 265.
7. Helmers, E.N., Frame, J.D., Greenburg, A.F. and Sawyer, C.N., *Sewage Ind. Wastes*, **23** (7) (1951), 834.
8. Garret, M.T., and Sawyer, C.N., *Proc. 7th Ind. Waste Conf. Purdue Univ. Ext. Ser.* 51, 1952.
9. Kornegay, B.H., and Andrews, J.F., Kinetics of fixed filter biological reactors, *J. Water Pollut. Control Fed.*, **40** (1968), 460.
10. Grady, C.P.L., Jr. and Roper, R.E., Jr, A model for the bio-oxidation process which incorporates the viability concept, *Water Research*, **8** (1974), 471.
11. Chiu, S.Y., Erickson, L.E., Fan, L.T. and Kao, I.C., Kinetic model identification in mixed populations using continuous culture data *Biotech. and Bioeng.*, **14** (1972), 207.

12. Lewandowski, T.P., The use of high purity oxygen in sewage treatment, *Water Pollut. Control*, **73** (6) (1974), 647.
13. British Oxygen Company Ltd, *Oxygen in Wastewater Treatment*, Document Ref. J7943/M3/PPP (1978).
14. Hemming, M.L., Ousby, J.C., Plowright, D.R. and Walker, J., Deep shaft — latest position, *Water Pollut. Control*, **76** (4) (1977), 441.
15. Perry, R.H. (Ed.) *Chemical Engineers Handbook*, 4th edition, pp. 10–24. McGraw-Hill, New York, 1963.
16. Pike, E.B., *The Design of Percolating Filters and Rotary Biological Contactors, Including Details of International Practice*, WRC Technical Report TR93 (1978).
17. Chesner, W.H. and Molof, A.H., Biological rotating disk scale-up design: dissolved oxygen effects, *Prog. Water Tech.*, **9** (4) (1978), 811.
18. Graef, S.P. and Andrews, J.F., Mathematical modelling and control of anaerobic digestion, *CEP Symp.*, Series 136 **70** (1974), 101.
19. Carr, A.D. and O'Donnell, R.C., The dynamic behaviour of an anaerobic digester, *Prog. Water Tech.*, **9** (3)(1977), 727.
20. Busby, J.B. and Andrews, J.F., A dynamic model and control strategies for the activated sludge process *J. Water Pollut. Control Fed.*, **47** (1975), 1055.
21. Selna, M.W. and Schroeder, E.D., Response of activated sludge processes to organic transients — kinetics, *J. Water Pollut. Control Fed.*, **50** (5) (1978), 944.

8

Practical Considerations

B.J. BORNE

Formerly Head, Industrial Wastes Section, Water Research Centre, Stevenage, UK

8.1. THE APPROACH TO THE PROBLEM

Industrialists are becoming increasingly aware of the importance of controlling the use of water on their premises because of the need to maintain an adequate supply of water suitable for their processes and to minimise expenditure on fresh water and the problems and costs of treatment and disposal of waste water. There are therefore incentives to industry to reduce both the volume of water used and the polluting character of water discharged.

Because of the rising cost of potable water, industry would be unlikely to use water of a higher quality than was needed for a particular process if a cheaper supply of non-potable water and an appropriate distribution system were available; in the UK there are many private supplies of non-potable water through special mains. Water reclaimed from sewage effluents is likely to be used by industry to an increasing extent as a low-cost supply for some purposes. However, in many factories there is the possibility that water can be re-used either for a process which can tolerate a quality of water lower than 'potable' or, after treatment, as a proportion of the main supply. Industry may use water for cooling, boiler-feed, processing, cleaning, and domestic purposes. Variations in efficiency of water use are apparent because manufacturers of similar products use different volumes of water per tonne of product.

8.1.1. Minimising the Use of Water

In situations where large amounts of cooling water are required the water is used on a 'once-through' system. Most commonly, cooling water is recirculated through towers or spray ponds and cooled by evaporation.

These systems require make-up of less than 10% of the total volume recirculated. Air-cooled heat exchangers, which are particularly applicable for reducing high temperatures, have advantages over more conventional systems because water can be used in a completely closed system and the high cost of distribution mains for cooling water is avoided. A very high quality of feed water is needed for high-pressure boilers and condensate is normally re-used to minimise costs.

In processing most water is used for transporting chemicals or materials to and carrying dirt and by-products away from machinery and equipment. A change from water carriage of solids to conveyance of dry or semi-dry material and mechanical methods of cleaning can reduce the volume of water used and the weight of polluting matter discharged in waste waters. Economy is possible when the washing process can be split into stages and the movement of product and water are in opposite directions so that contaminated water is discharged only from the 'dirty' end of the system.

Large volumes of water are used for cleaning between stages of production and towards the end of work shifts. However, cleaning can often be accomplished successfully by using less water at high pressure in sprays or jets and limiting the flow by automatic or manual control valves. Steam or hot water may be more effective than cold water under pressure. Management is often unaware of the volumes of water used for particular purposes and metering of flow and continuous monitoring of other parameters such as conductivity assist water saving.

8.1.2. Minimising the Problem of Effluent Disposal

The segregation of effluents into different drainage systems is clearly advantageous and a first priority should be to drain surface water and clean cooling water either into a separate surface-water drain or direct to a watercourse.

Areas where raw materials are received and the products despatched should be designed to avoid contamination of surface water drains and to facilitate sweeping up of accidental spillages of dry materials; this may require sheltered loading of raw materials or products. Accidental pollution by spillage of liquid chemicals can be prevented by adequate bunding of tanks installed above ground level and by provision of catch-pits for areas where there is a risk of spillages.

Segregation of 'strong' and 'weak' effluents can reduce overall treatment costs if it is possible to discharge weak effluents directly to a sewer and to treat partially the strong effluents. Mixing of some effluent streams before pretreatment can be detrimental to the treatment process and segregation is then essential.

Dry solids and slurries of more than a few per cent dry weight of solids in water could be collected separately from one or more process plants for recovery of product or disposal to a suitable landfill site. 'In-place cleaning' of equipment at the end of a production run can reduce the amount of raw material or product lost in the effluent. Storage vessels should be installed so that they can be drained to leave only a very small residue. The first rinse water can often be used in the manufacturing process. Overflows, leaks and spills from process equipment can often be reduced by provision of alarm systems and modifications to the equipment. If arrangements are made to collect spillages these may be re-used or separately processed or disposed of at a lower cost than when diluted with other effluents.

8.1.3. General Considerations in Regard to Discharge of Effluents

Assuming that measures have been taken to reduce to a minimum the volume and strength of the waste waters which have to be discharged, consideration can be given to planning the treatment process so that effluent to be discharged will comply with the requirements of the Water Authority. These will be based on a number of factors which will include:

(1) the effects of the industrial waste water on the fabric of sewers and on men working in them,
(2) the capacity of the Water Authority's sewage treatment works and the volume of similar industrial discharges treated there,
(3) the effect of constituents of the factory effluent on aerobic biological treatment processes and anaerobic digestion of sludge,
(4) the industrial residues likely to be present in treated primary and secondary sludges which may make disposal difficult or costly,
(5) the possible presence of chemicals that may pass through the sewage works into watercourses and adversely affect fish and other river life or the use of the river water for agriculture or as a source of potable supply.

To satisfy these requirements it may be necessary to:

(1) segregate process effluents and pretreat them by chemical and physical processes;
(2) balance the flow and composition of the waste waters;
(3) remove excess suspended matter;
(4) reduce the concentration of inorganic and organic pollutants by chemical or biological methods;
(5) reduce the temperature of the waste waters.

Provided adequate sewerage and sewage treatment facilities are available, firms are encouraged to discharge waste waters to sewers. The advantages are that

(1) the firm is relieved of the responsibility of attaining the high standards required for direct discharge of effluent to a watercourse;
(2) constituents of the waste water may be more easily treated after dilution by sewage;
(3) sewage contains an excess of the nutrient elements, nitrogen, phosphorus and potassium required for biological growth, which may be lacking in the industrial waste waters;
(4) the treatment process is supervised by skilled personnel.

However, in some cases, because of the prohibitive cost of provision of adequate sewerage and sewage-treatment capacity, or for technical reasons associated with the concentration and/or toxicity of constituents of the waste waters, it is necessary to provide treatment facilities at the factory. In other cases there may be a cost incentive to provide partial biological treatment before discharge of waste waters to a Water Authority sewer, but careful assessment should first be made of the costs of dewatering and disposal of the sludge produced and of the possibility of production of odour during high-rate treatment.

8.2. PRETREATMENT

Some pretreatment of segregated effluent streams is often advisable before discharge of waste water to the main factory treatment plant or to a local authority sewer. Examples include the removal of fats, oils, solvents, etc., in simple traps sited close to the source of the material and separate pretreatment of waste waters containing cyanide from acidic rinse waters containing chromate or nickel.

It may be advantageous to store concentrated solutions in separate tanks and discharge these slowly into the bulk of the waste waters. This is particularly true when strong acids and alkalis have to be disposed of. Controlled discharge of these liquids may reduce or eliminate the need for further adjustment of the pH value of the mixed effluent.

Balancing tanks may be required to regulate the flow or composition of factory effluent, for example, when biological treatment on site is necessary for waste waters from a factory working a five-day week. The cost effectiveness of treatment is improved if sufficient feed can be stored to operate the plant during the weekend.

8.3. PHYSICAL PROCESSES

Some of the wide variety of treatment processes available for the recovery or removal of material in solution or suspension in waste waters are listed in Table 8.1 and have been discussed in detail in earlier chapters. The objective of much of the physical treatment applied to effluents is the separation of a high proportion of the dissolved or suspended matter. The result is therefore a partially treated water and a concentrate, which may be a sludge, scum or liquor, containing the original pollutants but in much greater concentration. There may be appreciable difficulties and costs associated with the disposal of this concentrate and these must be considered in relation to the overall cost of treatment. It is at this stage that careful choice of physical treatment of a segregated process stream may result in the recovery of a valuable concentrate which can be re-used in the factory or disposed of to a contractor for further processing.

TABLE 8.1

EXAMPLES OF PHYSICAL PROCESSES FOR THE TREATMENT OF INDUSTRIAL WASTE WATERS

Process	Types of industry using process	Examples of material removed or reduced
Screening	Vegetable processing	Peas
Microstraining	Water industry	Humus
Filtration (including ultra-filtration)	Dairy	Protein
Reverse osmosis	Dairy	Lactose
Sedimentation	Wide application	Wide application
Flotation	Automobile	Paint residues
Adsorption on activated charcoal	Agricultural chemicals	Pesticides
Centrifuging	Cheese making	Cheese fines
Distillation	Formaldehyde	Formaldehyde
Evaporation	Sugar	Sugar
Incineration	Chemical synthesis	Amines, acrylates

8.3.1. Screening

Separation of large particles on grids or meshes is not costly to provide and consumes little power. The screenings tend to be low in water content and can be dried and, if necessary, incinerated. Screenings from the food processing industries may be suitable for animal feeds.

8.3.2. Filtration

For small particles the nature of the solids as well as their size will determine the best filtration medium. As the mesh or pore size for filtration is decreased, the cost and power required to operate the process increases so that, to justify the process, either the filtered water or filter cake must be of value or overall treatment costs must be reduced as a result. To give an example, it is technically possible, by reverse osmosis, to produce a water of high quality from 'polished' sewage effluent, but in practice this water is far more expensive than potable water from other sources. However it is economically feasible to use a membrane filtration process to recover valuable protein and lactose from whey. Other examples of the use of reverse osmosis include concentration of plating bath drag-out for return to the plating bath and concentration of coffee extraction residues in wash water and pressings from grounds used in the manufacture of instant coffee. In the latter concentration to a solids content of 25% enables the concentrate to be recycled to the coffee extract at the feed to the spray drier.

As an example of the use of ultrafiltration, a high proportion of the organic matter in cutting fluids used in engineering can be separated from the emulsion without addition of chemicals. The oil-enriched stream is said to contain oil at a concentration of about 50% and this could be incinerated with dry refuse on the site. The recovered water, after further treatment, may be re-used for purposes such as floor-washing. Ultrafiltration is also used to recover valuable pigments in effluents from some painting systems, e.g., electrophoretic painting of car bodies.

8.3.3. Sedimentation

As mentioned in Chapter 6, suspended matter of greater density than water can be removed by gravitational settlement under relatively quiescent conditions in large tanks or lagoons. The period of retention required to remove the majority of the solids (say 70%) is usually in excess of 2 h, but can sometimes be reduced if the water is induced to flow between inclined plates or tubes which can be provided within the settlement tank.

8.3.4. Centrifugation

If space for solids removal is at a premium and the concentration of solids is high, centrifugation might be considered.

8.3.5. Flotation

Solids with a density less than or close to that of water may be removed by flotation. Fats and oily materials rise naturally to the surface of quiescent

TABLE 8.2
PERFORMANCE OF FLOTATION PLANTS

Industry	Pollutant	Suspended solids			COD		
		Before	After	Removal	Before	After	Removal
		(mg/litre)		%	(mg/litre)		%
Steel (rolling mill)	Oil and metallic oxides	1 420	40	97	1 115	70	94
Steel (rolling mill)	Soluble oil	2 800	30	99	52 000	1 000	98
Paper	Fibre	1 800	30	98	2 425	18	99
Wool	Scourings	6 590	730	87	15 290	2 140	86
Chemical	Latex PVC	300	30	90	1 060	520	50
Paint	Paint	2 000	30	98	1 500	350	77
Food	Renderings	5 270	60	98	14 100	5 490	61
Food (abattoir)	Fat, protein, etc.	5 440	30	99	6 200	1 570	75
Cosmetics	Various	480	3	99	6 150	1 150	81
Pharmaceutical	Various	85	1	99	10 000	2 840	72

water, but more positive separation of such solids can be achieved by artificially increasing their buoyancy by causing bubbles of gas to adhere to the particles or become entrained in floc. Two methods are currently available: (1) electro-flotation, i.e. electrolysis of the waste water to produce small bubbles of oxygen and hydrogen which become attached to the suspended matter, and (2) diffused-air flotation, in which water or effluent, saturated with air under pressure, is mixed with the waste waters as they enter the flotation tank. In the latter method, air comes out of solution and forms small bubbles on particles of suspended matter or within flocs, so buoying them to the surface. If scum is allowed to accumulate and thicken at the surface of the tank the solids content is often higher than could be achieved by a process of settlement. Careful control of the processes is essential to ensure that only ultrafine bubbles are produced; coarse bubbles are not only ineffective for flotation of solids but tend to break up the scum. Much greater separation of solid material can often be achieved if colloidal solids are first coagulated and emulsions of fat and oil broken by addition of coagulating chemicals. Studies by Pearson at the Warren Spring Laboratory have shown that both metal hydroxides and basic carbonates can be floated successfully using cationic collectors such as Duomac T — an acetate of a high-molecular-weight tallow, which behaves as a cationic collector. The performance of flotation plants treating a variety of industrial waste waters is shown in Table 8.2.

8.3.6. Distillation
Steam distillation, 'dry' distillation or distillation under reduced pressure, as appropriate, can be used to separate volatile organic matter from waste waters and the organic matter can then be reused or oxidised — usually by incineration.

8.3.7. Evaporation
Evaporation of concentrated waste waters before incineration or crystallisation might be considered, especially when waste heat is available.

8.4. CHEMICAL TREATMENT PROCESSES

8.4.1. Neutralisation
Neutralisation of alkaline or acidic waste waters is necessary to protect sewerage systems and treatment plant. Waste waters discharged to sewers are generally required to have a pH value not less than 5 nor greater than

10, though a range of values from 6 to 9 may often be imposed (see Chapter 2). For efficient biological treatment the pH value of waste waters in the treatment plant should normally be within the range 7 to 8, although satisfactory treatment is usually possible within the wider pH range of 6.5 to 8.5. The choice of neutralising chemicals is usually based on cost and on convenience of handling, but other factors should also be considered. Sulphuric acid may be the least costly acid, but its use can result in unacceptable concentrations of sulphates in effluents discharged to sewers (typical maximum permissible concentration 1000 mg SO_4/litre). The alternatives are hydrochloric acid, nitric acid and carbonic acid. Carbon dioxide gas can be produced by submerged combustion of natural gas or butane. If a reliable source of boiler-flue gas (approximately 14% CO_2) is available near the treatment plant this would be cheaper. A proportion of the calcium in the waste waters will be removed as insoluble calcium carbonate. Of the alkalis, sodium hydroxide or sodium carbonate are often preferred to lime despite their higher cost, because they react more quickly and because control of the neutralisation process can be more precise as solutions can be used instead of slurries. However, the use of lime has advantages in that sulphates from sulphuric acid present in excess of 2000 mg/litre are precipitated and can be removed from the waste waters. It is apparent from the foregoing that waste waters containing much sulphuric acid, even if neutralised by lime, require dilution by other waste waters low in sulphate before they can be discharged to sewers. A case study is given in Chapter 9. In the absence of high concentrations of sulphuric acid, passage of the waste water upwards through an expanded or fluidised bed of limestone grit is probably the least costly method of neutralisation. Beds of calcined magnesite might be used in some cases for neutralisation of acidic waste waters which are largely free from dissolved metals liable to precipitate insoluble hydroxides on the surface of the bed material.

8.4.2. Precipitation

Precipitation can be linked with neutralisation because adjustment of pH value reduces the solubility of many inorganic and organic compounds. Probably the best known reaction is that of the precipitation of heavy metals as their hydroxides or basic carbonates after addition of alkali to acidic solutions of metal salts. The pH values which must be reached are indicated in Table 8.3. In practice, precipitation at pH values in the range 9–10, suitable for discharge to most sewerage systems, is effective for a mixture of metal ions. Increasingly, valuable metal salts are being recovered from the waste waters from metal-finishing processes by integral treatment of

B.J. Borne

TABLE 8.3
pH VALUES REQUIRED FOR PRECIPITATION OF THE
COMMON METALS. VALUES ARE BASED ON
COAGULATION AND SETTLEMENT TESTS IN
PREFERENCE TO CALCULATED VALUES.

Metal	Optimal pH value or range
Fe^{2+}	10
Fe^{3+}	4.3
Al^{3+}	5.2
Cr^{3+}	6.5–7.3
Cu^{2+}	7.1–7.3
Zn^{2+}	9–10
Ni^{2+}	9.2–9.4
[a]Cd^{2+}	ca 9.7
Sn^{2+}	4.0–4.5
Pb^{2+}	ca 6.3

[a]Best precipitated as the carbonate.

rinse waters. The treatment units need to be small and techniques such as flotation and those which produce coarse-grained precipitates are helpful in minimising the size of the separation tanks needed. Organic surfactants in low concentrations can be used to facilitate separation of metal hydroxides by flotation. Alternatives to alkalis for the precipitation of metals are being investigated. These include naturally occurring polyelectrolytes like alginic acid (AC) and polygalacturonic acid (PGA) and starch xanthates. Economical treatment using these compounds depends on recovery of a high percentage of the reagent.

Addition of ferrous sulphate to a solution of a simple cyanide causes precipitation of a mixture of the complex cyanides of iron. The process not only produces large volumes of a watery sludge, but also may not reduce the concentration of cyanide below 5 mg/litre. This process in now rarely used, having been superseded by the more efficient alkaline chlorination. Reference has already been made to the precipitation of sulphates by calcium ions and of carbonates by carbon dioxide. The protein in waste waters such as those from slaughterhouses can be precipitated and coagulated by addition of sodium lignosulphonate and sufficient sulphuric acid to reduce the pH of the waste waters to 3. At this pH value, emulsions of fatty material are broken and fat is released which can be recovered with the precipitated protein by flotation. This is the basis of the Alwatech process which is reported to reduce the BOD of screened abattoir waste water by 70 to 80%. An alternative precipitant for protein suggested by Jørgensen is a mixture of glucose trisulphate and azoprotein.

8.4.3. Coagulation

A variety of chemicals is used in waste treatment to coagulate colloidal suspended matter and facilitate its removal by the processes of sediment-ation, centrifuging and flotation already described. A short period of flocculation before sedimentation is generally helpful. The chemicals most commonly used include aluminium sulphate, aluminium chlorohydrate, ferric chloride, chlorinated copperas (a mixture of ferric sulphate and ferric chloride), a combination of ferrous sulphate and lime, and a range of proprietary organic polyelectrolytes (typically long-chain molecules such as polyacrylamide). Often a combination of an inorganic coagulant and a 'coagulant aid', which may be a polyelectrolyte or activated silica, is the most effective.

8.4.4. Ion Exchange

Ion exchange may be used for the production of high-quality water from water contaminated by inorganic salts and, when needed, is usually most economically employed in conjunction with a water treatment and recirculation system. Chloride is not removed during the treatment of water for potable supplies and in situations where the raw water contains a proportion of treated sewage effluent it is therefore important to restrict the discharge of chlorides to the sewers. One important source of chloride is regenerant liquor from water softening. A possible method of recovering the chloride involves the addition of sodium carbonate to precipitate calcium and magnesium carbonates, the removal of which leaves a solution of sodium chloride which can be concentrated and re-used for regeneration of the ion-exchange resin. Resins are available for particular applications, for example, to remove contaminating metals from rinse waters containing chromic acid in plating shops, permitting the concentration and recycle of pure chromic acid solution to the plating process. The unwanted regenerant liquors contain high concentrations of dissolved solids which may include heavy metals, sulphates and cyanides, and some chromate, and require treatment to minimise the costs of final disposal. Jørgensen has proposed the use of ion-exchange in two stages for the removal and recovery of residual organic matter after pretreatment of food-industry waste waters by precipitation of protein. The waste waters are first passed through a cationic exchanger containing cellulose sulphate, which removes polypep-tides, and subsequently through a chelated anionic exchanger (IRA-400) in which carbohydrates are removed. This type of process is now offered commercially.

8.4.5. Solvent Extraction

Solvent extraction in waste-water treatment has in the past been mainly associated with the extraction of phenol from waste waters from carbonisation of coal. Solvents used have included benzol and phenosolvan (a mixture of aliphatic esters with butyl acetate as chief component), from which the phenol can be recovered by stream stripping after the addition of alkali. The method can be used to recover the bulk of the phenol from concentrated solutions (above 2%). Residual phenol is probably most economically destroyed by a biological process. Solvent extraction can also be used to regenerate beds of activated carbon, thus recovering valuable materials. More recently, solvent extraction from waste waters of heavy metal complexes such as that of nickel and di(2-ethylhexyl) phosphoric acid (DEHPA) in kerosene has been investigated. The economy and success of solvent extraction will often depend on the amount of solvent and complexing agent lost in the effluent and on whether the raffinate is suitable for re-use.

8.4.6. Chemical Oxidation and Reduction

Chlorination and ozonation are established methods for disinfecting potable water and water for recycling, particularly in food factories. Ozone is useful for destroying the colour of effluents. In particular circumstances hydrogen peroxide and possibly potassium permanganate might be used as oxidants for low concentrations of polluting matter, for example phenol. These oxidising agents are not generally employed in treating waste streams containing high concentrations of organic matter, although there are specific applications, such as the destruction of cyanide by chlorine. Chlorination in alkaline solution at a pH value of about 11 destroys simple cyanides and the complex cyanides of copper, zinc and cadmium. The complex cyanide of nickel is only slowly attacked and those of iron not at all. When chlorine is added to a solution of an alkali cyanide the first product of the reaction is cyanogen chloride. This then hydrolyses at a rate given by the equation

$$- d[CNCl]/dt = k[CNCl][OH]$$

initially with the formation of cyanate. The value of k ranges from 80 litre/mole min at 0°C to 530 litre/mole min at 25°C. In alkaline solution an excess of chlorine appears to catalyse the hydrolysis of cyanogen chloride to cyanate. In solutions of lower pH value the excess of hypochlorite reacts to liberate nitrogen and traces of oxides of nitrogen. At pH 11 the overall reaction requires 2 atoms of chlorine per molecule of cyanide, while at pH 8.5 rather more than 5 atoms of chlorine per molecule of cyanide are required. The rate of hydrolysis of cyanogen chloride to cyanate is such that a period of contact of the waste water with chlorine of 30 min is sufficient. Alkaline chlorination should be confined to dilute solutions of cyanide (less than 100 mg/litre) because of the volatility and toxicity of cyanogen chloride.

At pH 11, the equations for the oxidation of cyanide by chlorine are:

$$NaCN + NaOCl + H_2O \rightarrow CNCl + 2NaOH$$

$$CNCl + 2NaOH \rightarrow NaCNO + NaCl + H_2O$$

If the solution is then neutralised the cyanate hydrolyses to ammonium bicarbonate:

$$HCNO + 2H_2O \rightarrow NH_4 HCO_3$$

In neutral solution and in the presence of excess chlorine elimination of nitrogen occurs and traces of nitrate may be formed:

$$2HCN + 5Cl_2 + 5H_2O \rightarrow 2CO_2 + N_2 + H_2O + 10HCl.$$

Cyanide may also be oxidised by substances releasing hydrogen peroxide. Caro's acid (permonosulphuric acid), for example, in the presence of traces of copper ion as catalyst oxidises cyanide to cyanate:

$$HCN + H_2SO_5 \rightarrow HCNO + H_2SO_4.$$

Chemical oxidation and reduction are also used in the treatment of electroplating rinse waters. Rinse waters containing hexavalent chromium are generally treated with sulphur dioxide or a solution of a soluble sulphite at a pH value of less than 3 to reduce the hexavalent chromium to the trivalent state in which it can be precipitated by addition of alkali. Ferrous sulphate can be used for reduction of chromates to the trivalent state but, as already mentioned, is rarely employed because of the large volumes of watery sludge which are produced when the iron is subsequently precipitated as the hydroxide. The equations for the reduction of hexavalent chromium are: (a) with ferrous sulphate:

$$2H_2CrO_4 + 6FeSO_4 \cdot 7H_2O + 6H_2SO_4 \rightarrow Cr_2(SO_4)_3 + 3Fe_2(SO_4)_3 + 15H_2O$$

(b) with sulphur dioxide:

$$2H_2CrO_4 + 3SO_2 \rightarrow Cr_2(SO_4)_3 + 2H_2O$$

(c) with a soluble sulphite, e.g., sodium metabisulphite:

$$4H_2CrO_4 + 3Na_2S_2O_5 + 3H_2SO_4 \rightarrow 2Cr_2(SO_4)_3 + 3Na_2SO_4 + 7H_2O$$

Borohydride solutions are reported to reduce mercury, lead and silver salts to their corresponding metals, which readily precipitate and can be recovered.

8.4.7. Electrolysis

Relatively concentrated solutions of sodium cyanide and of the complex cyanides of copper, cadmium and zinc, such as spent plating baths and cyanide-containing stripping solutions, can be treated by electrolytic oxidation at a graphite or platinised titanium electrode. The amount of cyanide destroyed increases with temperature from about 0.5 moles cyanide/Faraday at 50°C to 0.59 moles/Faraday at 90°C. The cost of electrical energy for electrolytic oxidation of cyanide appears to be about one third of the cost of chlorine for alkaline chlorination. The process, however, can only be used to reduce the concentration of cyanide to about 1000 mg/litre and any further reduction must be by a chemical process. This is because the efficiency of oxidation of the cyanide decreases in dilute solution and the graphite anode becomes subject to attack. Electrolysis can also be used for the recovery of copper, gold, silver and tin from pickling or plating liquors. Other examples concern the use of electrolysis for the regeneration of spent caustic solutions containing mercaptans produced during removal of sulphur compounds from petroleum, the production of hypochlorite from chloride solutions and electroflotation.

8.4.8. Electrodialysis

Electrodialysis can be used either for reducing the ionic content of effluents (making them more suitable for re-use or for discharge) or for concentrating the ionic substances before further dewatering by evaporation or in-cineration. The process can be used for separating selected ions from solutions and especially for separating small ions from large ones.

8.4.9. Adsorption on Activated Carbon

Adsorption on activated carbon has been used to remove chemicals toxic to bacteria before biological treatment and, after biological treatment, to remove residual colour or residues of materials which are unacceptable in watercourses or in water for re-use. Examples are the treatment of waste waters from the production of pesticides, described by Sharpe, and the removal of residual colour and phenols from plastics manufacture. The following classes of compounds are readily adsorbed on carbon: aromatic substances, phenols, chlorinated hydrocarbons, surfactants, soluble organic dyes, organic acids, branched-chain aliphatic substances, and amines of high molecular weight. Before adsorption on activated carbon some pretreatment of the waste waters is normally necessary to remove all but small amounts of suspended matter and oil (< 10 mg/litre). Beds of activated carbon can be designed to remove small amounts of suspended matter by provision of facilities for backwashing, surface wash or air scour of the first stage. Some adjustment of the pH value of the waste waters to minimise the polarity of the molecules to be adsorbed can improve the efficiency of removal.

8.5. BIOLOGICAL TREATMENT

Biological processes (Table 8.4) may be broadly classified as either aerobic or anaerobic; they are widely used for the treatment of sewage and sewage sludge and, although much of the associated technology can be applied to the treatment of industrial waste waters containing organic matter, certain differences must be taken into account.

One of the factors to be considered is the biodegradability of the substances present in the waste waters. In the broadest sense biodegradability can be taken to be the extent to which the structure of a substance can be changed by biochemical activity in such a way as to alter substantially its chemical and physical properties, especially properties which are undesirable in the natural environment. If organic compounds are not biodegradable, they will probably not be removed by conventional sewage treatment and will be present in the receiving stream. If they are lyophilic and also toxic, they will then tend to be concentrated in aquatic organisms and be harmful to aquatic and other life. Whether toxic or not, they may also impart undesirable characteristics to the receiving water, such as colour, turbidity, taste, odour or tendency to foam. Some non-biodegradable substances which become associated with the various sludges produced during treatment of waste waters may, if toxic, present a special problem if the sludges are disposed of on land since this toxicity may affect soil micro-organisms or plants. Thus it is desirable to consider carefully the case for the use of non-biodegradable substances and to balance potential disadvantages against benefits.

TABLE 8.4

EXAMPLES OF BIOLOGICAL PROCESSES FOR THE TREATMENT OF INDUSTRIAL WASTE
WATERS

Process	Types of industry using process	Examples of material removed or reduced
Anaerobic digestion		
Conventional	Food	Sludge
'Anaerobic contact'	Meat processing, wine production	Fats, protein and cellulose
'Anaerobic filter'	Starch	Starch
Aerobic processes		
Activated sludge		
Conventional	Food and organic chemicals	Oxidisable organic matter
Contact stabilisation	Food and organic chemicals	Oxidisable organic matter
Extended aeration	Food and organic chemicals	Oxidisable organic matter
Biological filtration		
Conventional	Food and organic chemicals	Oxidisable organic matter
'Alternating-double'	Food and organic chemicals	Oxidisable organic matter
'High-rate'	Food and organic chemicals	Oxidisable organic matter

Besides some synthetic compounds like certain pesticides, some naturally occurring substances are also resistant to biological attack, e.g., some fractions of soil humus, lignins and tannins. Some of the factors which increase resistance to degradation are molecular size; insolubility; tertiary branching; the nature, position, and number of substituents in the molecule; and the presence of heterocyclic atoms. Before a new compound is allowed to be discharged to the sewer — and this now usually means before it is produced in bulk for marketing — it is desirable to establish its biodegradability. One may then predict whether it will be degraded in the usual treatment plants at conventional loadings or whether extra steps would need to be taken to ensure its degradation. Some compounds will be readily degraded within the normal conditions of treatment of sewage and these will not cause subsequent pollution of the river or estuary, but problems could arise in the treatment plant. For example, more oxygen could be required so that the aeration capacity might have to be increased; larger amounts of surplus sludge might be produced making sludge disposal more costly; higher concentrations of suspended solids might have to be carried in the mixed liquor; the physical properties of the activated sludge might change to make it more difficult to settle or to dewater or both; the coagulant demand of the sludge might be increased; and the growth of fungi in filters might be encouraged, giving rise to ponding. Other, less readily degradable, compounds will either be only partially degraded, especially if they are 'co-metabolised' at low rates with other substances, or will not be removed at all in conventional treatment systems. They will need special consideration; for example, a lower rate or a different method of treatment might be needed, such as specific treatment to destroy the pollutant (e.g., cyanide) before discharge to the sewer. In the case of some industrial waste waters which are otherwise treatable biologically, the addition of essential nutrients, such as ammoniacal nitrogen and phosphate, may be necessary.

Biodegradable compounds which require the activated sludge or the biological film in a filter to become acclimatised, for whatever reason, may not be broken down adequately if discharged intermittently to the sewer; it may therefore be necessary to arrange for waste waters containing such compounds to be collected for continuous slow release to the sewer. Also, upper limits may have to be set on the concentration of compounds which, though degradable by some organisms, are toxic to species which are essential for degrading other compounds in the waste water (e.g., nitrifying bacteria).

Inhibition of the microbial degradation of organic matter can occur in various ways and must be avoided in treatment plants, as well as in any test for biodegradability. Metals such as mercury and copper form complexes with enzymes and other metabolic agents connected with respiration, thus rendering the enzymes inactive. Some organic compounds can themselves react with the enzyme, preventing further action on the substrate under test; other inhibitors, usually containing nitrogen and sometimes sulphur as well, compete with enzymes for essential trace metals which act as co-enzymes and catalysts; yet others act by denaturing or disintegrating the cell wall. However, mixed cultures, such as activated sludge or filter film, treating mixed wastes are much less susceptible to toxic agents than individual populations, since chemical reactions, such as chelation and precipitation, between the inhibitor and other constituents of the waste water or with a component of the biomass itself, make the inhibitor less effective.

Several tests of biodegradability of varying degrees of complexity and usefulness are available. Probably the simplest of such tests consists of comparing the biochemical oxygen demand exerted by the substance in the standard five-day BOD determination, in which the inoculum of organisms is usually derived from sewage or sewage effluent, with the chemical oxygen demand (COD). Generally, with readily degradable organic substances, the oxygen demand in the BOD test is about two-thirds of the total required for complete oxidation, of which the COD provides a measure. This statement is an oversimplification, but a BOD to COD ratio of around 2 : 3 will be a fair preliminary indication that the substance tested is completely biodegradable. A substantially lower ratio would indicate, in the case of a pure substance, either that biodegradation was slow or that the molecule was only partially degradable; in the case of a mixture of substances it could indicate, in addition, that at least one component was non-degradable under the conditions of the test. However, the possibility could not be excluded that, given greater opportunites for adaptation of the population or exposure to a wider range of organisms, biodegradation could be achieved.

A slightly more elaborate method, but one that eliminates some of the ambiguity of the former approach, is the 'die-away' test in which the concentration of the substance in sewage effluent, river water, or BOD dilution water maintained at a constant temperature is measured at intervals over a suitable period of incubation. This form of test can also be conducted in a respirometer; any oxygen demand associated with changes in concentration of the substance can then be measured simultaneously.

Conditions in these screening tests bear little relation to conditions in treatment processes and so further tests simulating biological treatment in model percolating-filter or activated-sludge plant are usually carried out. The most promising method and conditions of treatment can then be investigated on a pilot scale on-line at the factory.

8.5.1. Anaerobic Processes

These processes tend to be used for waste waters and sludges containing high concentrations of organic material (generally more than 0.2%) and traditionally needed more tank volume than aerobic processes because the rate of growth of the essential methanogenic bacteria is lower than that of aerobic types. Modifications to the process, described later, are designed to overcome this weakness and can provide at least as high a rate of removal of BOD per unit tank volume as can aerobic processes. Unlike some aerobic processes, anaerobic treatment methods require little energy and produce relatively little sludge and, under favourable conditions, permit recovery of energy in the form of combustible gas containing up to 80% methane. The process might be considered as an avenue by which 'low-grade' waste heat might be converted to a primary fuel. Three types of anaerobic plant are now available for the treatment of liquid waste—the conventional digester, the anaerobic contact plant and the anaerobic filter.

In the conventional digestion process, the mean retention period of the biological solids within the digester is roughly equivalent to the hydraulic retention period. Because the doubling time of methanogenic bacteria is about 4–6 days, the retention period must be at least as long as this and in order to achieve an economic rate of removal of BOD per unit volume of tank the method is usually restricted to very strong wastes which are usually sludges. The heat balance is another important consideration because, if operation is required in the mesophilic temperature range (25° to 40°C), only a strong waste can provide enough methane for heating. After digestion and solid/liquid separation further treatment of the liquid may be required before discharge to a watercourse.

In the 'anaerobic contact' process the hydraulic retention time can be reduced, without reducing the critical solids retention time, by recycling solids (bacteria) recovered from the effluent. This enables less strong wastes to be treated while still maintaining high levels of BOD removal per unit tank volume. Recovery of the solids from a settlement tank for recycling poses problems because of flotation of solids as a result of continued gasification. Solutions to the problem include vacuum de-gassing of the sludge before settlement or separation of the solids by centrifuging or flotation.

Retention of solids is taken a stage further with the 'anaerobic filter', which consists of a submerged bed of medium through which the waste water flows in an upward direction. The medium does not appear to support a biological film as it does in the aerobic biological filter, but instead functions more like a pebble-bed clarifier by retaining suspended solids in the filter and also by detaching gas bubbles which would otherwise buoy up suspended solids and cause them to be removed with the effluent. In this way the hydraulic retention time can be reduced to a few hours without loss of stability. Although the process is still largely in the experimental stage, there clearly exist interesting possibilities for treating much more dilute wastes than hitherto, either at very high rates if the heat balance permits operation at mesophilic temperatures or at somewhat lower rates at ambient temperatures. Further treatment of the effluent would be required in most cases before discharge to a watercourse. Very high removals of BOD can, however, be achieved in the anaerobic stage and, using small-scale anaerobic filters at the Water Research Centre the

BOD of a starch waste (initially about 7000 mg/litre) was reduced by 99% at 35°C.

8.5.2. Aerobic Processes
The processes available for treating waste waters include biological filtration and the activated-sludge process. Both systems can be operated at so-called 'high' and 'conventional' rates or loadings, depending on the quality of effluent required.

8.5.3. 'High-rate' Biological Filtration
This term is used to describe filtration at loadings in excess of 2.0 kg BOD/m^3 medium per day. Because at high loadings the growth of bacterial slime is considerable, a medium is required which provides voids of a size which will not readily become blocked. Suitable materials include large rock (10–15 cm), fabricated sheets of plastics or large loose-fill plastics formulations. The rate of application of waste water to the filter is adjusted, if necessary, by recirculation of effluent, so that all parts of the filter bed are completely wetted. Treatment on this type of medium at this loading will produce only a partially purified effluent and the process is used as a first stage before secondary biological treatment or before discharge of waste waters to a sewer.

8.5.4. Conventional Biological Filtration
Conventional biological filtration is carried out at loadings in the range 0.1 to 0.3 kg BOD/m^3 medium per day through beds of medium, normally of 3–6 cm granite, gravel or hard limestone. More recently, loose-fill plastics media of these dimensions have become available. The choice of medium is usually based on the cost of providing filter beds with medium of sufficient intrinsic surface area to provide satisfactory treatment. Conventional biological filters may be operated with recirculation of effluent, as two stages in series, and with alternating double filtration. These plants are capable of producing effluents of good quality 'Royal Commission' standard suitable for discharge to most watercourses. If necessary, the effluent can be further improved by adding a 'polishing' stage of treatment (e.g., sand filtration, grass plots, microstrainers, lagoons, pebble-bed clarifiers) to reduce further the amount of residual suspended matter present.

8.5.5. The Activated-sludge Process
This may also be operated in a number of ways such as plug flow, complete

mixing, extended aeration, or contact stabilisation, among others. The differences refer to the methods of mixing the waste waters with the activated sludge and to the hydraulic loading of the plant. Aeration can be by diffused air or by mechanical agitation at the surface. Conventional BOD loadings are in the range 0.2–0.3 kg BOD/kg solids per day and plant loaded in this way should produce a 'Royal Commission' effluent. Extended-aeration plants are designed to operate at a lower loading (0.05–0.1 kg BOD/kg per day), so that their performance is maintained with the minimum of supervision and with feed stock of variable strength. The activated-sludge process can be operated to give partial treatment by reducing the period of aeration to such an extent that full treatment does not occur. This is probably best arranged in a contact-stabilisation plant in which the activated sludge in contact with the waste waters assimilates or removes by adsorption a significant proportion of the organic matter, particularly that in colloidal suspension. After settlement of the partially treated waste waters, the activated sludge is aerated in a separate tank without addition of fresh material, during which period the adsorbed organic material is stabilised, i.e. broken down and oxidised to new cells and carbon dioxide. This method has been shown to be satisfactory on a pilot-scale for the partial treatment of waste waters from the dairy and pharmaceutical industries. The partially treated liquor would generally be acceptable for discharge to sewers.

8.5.6. Other Biological Processes
These include rotary-biological contactors. A series of discs or a horizontal cylinder of wire mesh containing random-fill medium rotates on a horizontal axis in a close-fitting hemi-cylindrical trough through which the waste water flows. For the production of high-quality effluents the BOD loading applied should be less than 6 g/m^2 disc surface, although it has been shown that dairy effluents and waste waters from the processing of vegetables can be partially treated at loadings which may be in the range 20 to 300 g/m^2.

8.5.7. Combinations of Processes
The solution to a particular problem may require a combination of several of the processes described. For example, a steel works which consulted the Water Research Centre was using a large volume of water on a once-through basis for washing blast-furnace gas. The company accepted the recommendation to recirculate this water and the Centre investigated treatment of the purge water arising from this procedure. The method

developed involved precipitation of metals (mainly zinc) with calcium hydroxide followed by removal of the floc by sedimentation. The addition of an anionic polyelectrolyte was also found to improve this removal and the sludge obtained could be dewatered, for example by filter pressing without further treatment. After removal of the toxic metal the liquor could be treated biologically and, because there was a tendency for delayed precipitation of calcium carbonate following the chemical treatment, the activated-sludge process was preferred. There was also further removal of zinc on the activated sludge and, because it was not necessary to produce a nitrified effluent, any depression of pH value which would have tended to redissolve zinc was avoided. Phenol was adequately degraded and on the basis of separate work at the laboratory it was expected that, after an adequate period of acclimatisation, cyanide would also be removed successfully.

8.6. SLUDGE TECHNOLOGY

Most of the processes already discussed produce sludges and their successful disposal may depend on careful consideration of a number of aspects, which may fundamentally influence the choice of the original processes leading to the sludge production. For example, in sewage treatment the volume of sludge produced is only about 0.6% of the volume of sewage treated and probably mainly for this reason its disposal has frequently been neglected in the past. Sludge treatment and disposal, however, generally account for about 40% of the total cost of sewage treatment, and this disproportionate cost is related more closely to the pollution load of the sludge than to its volume. In this situation the choice of high-rate sewage-treatment processes, which tend to produce large amounts of unstable sludge which are very difficult to dewater, can be justified only after a careful balancing of all the costs involved, for sludge disposal as well as for sewage treatment. The same considerations apply to waste water of industrial origin and in some cases very costly methods have had to be adopted for sludge disposal, because this was neglected at the design stage, when high-rate processes were chosen solely because of their apparent economy in reducing BOD.

The high cost of sludge disposal does at least serve to direct attention to the possibilities for recovery of valuable materials from sludge, and examples include the recovery of metals from certain industrial sludges, the utilisation of many organic sludges for animal feeding or the separate recovery of protein and even the recovery of methane as an energy source by anaerobic digestion. This process also conserves nitrogen in the liquid phase, providing further opportunities for recovery if the digested material is ultimately used on agricultural land. The nitrogen may well have been added to an industrial effluent in the first place in order to satisfy microbial requirements during treatment and, even if payment is not made for the digested material when applied to land, its nitrogen content may well secure an inexpensive outlet for disposal as liquid, thus eliminating the need for expensive procedures for both dewatering and disposal.

8.6.1. Processes for Sludge Treatment

Table 8.5 lists individual processes for dealing with sludge. Additional methods of limited application could still be added and the general picture is clearly one of very wide diversity. Although for convenience the methods have been listed under four general headings it is essential to remember that there may be appreciable overlap between them. For example, anaerobic

TABLE 8.5
UNIT PROCESSES FOR DEALING WITH SLUDGE

Treatment	*Dewatering*
Biological	Drying beds
(i) aerobic digestion	
(ii) anaerobic digestion	Lagoons
(iii) composting	
	Vacuum filters
	(i) disc filters
Chemical conditioning	(ii) drum filters
Thermal[a]	Pressure filters
(i) heat treatment	(i) filter presses
(ii) wet oxidation	(ii) belt presses
	(iii) tube presses
Elutriation[a]	
	Centrifuges
	(i) solid bowl with scroll discharge
Thickening	(ii) disc
	(iii) various filtration and other types
Gentle stirring	
	Disposal
Flotation	
(i) dissolved air	Landfill
(ii) electrolytic	Use as agricultural fertiliser
(iii) froth	Discharge to sea
(iv) biological	Incineration

[a]In special situations.

digestion may be used primarily for treatment to reduce BOD and smell from unstable sludges, but if operated in two stages, as is common in sewage-sludge digestion, it also provides a method for thickening and, because of the conversion of a substantial proportion of the organic matter to gas, it also achieves partial disposal.

Aerobic digestion may be regarded as an extension of the activated-sludge process to organic sludges. It shares some of the advantages of anaerobic treatment, namely elimination of offensive smell and stabilisation of putrescible organic material, but has an advantage over the anaerobic process in that the liquor which subsequently separates on standing is of far higher quality and can even be of Royal Commission standard. One major disadvantage appears to be that it has high energy requirements for supplying compressed air for aeration, although part of the energy so consumed is converted to heat, resulting in an appreciable temperature rise and therefore also a higher rate of biological activity.

The rôle of composting in the present context is likely to be restricted to that in heaps of dewatered material or possibly to the treatment of organic material in municipal composting plants, but because the amount of sewage sludge that can be treated in such plants is limited by a maximum acceptable water content any other added material would be subject to the same constraint.

Elutriation may be used to reduce the proportion of fine particles which are commonly the cause of difficulty in dewatering of sludges, and it can likewise remove soluble constituents which otherwise reduce the effectiveness of chemicals used for improving filtrability. Evaluation of the potential benefits of elutriation must include the problem of dealing with the elutriate, which often means that elutriation can only be suggested as a temporary remedy.

The thermal treatments provide the most effective methods available for improving filtrability of certain organic sludges, but by converting a proportion of suspended material into soluble matter they can lead to a major recycling of the polluting load. Furthermore, a proportion of the soluble matter in the liquors is resistant to biodegradation and results in an increase of COD in the final effluent. This drawback together with poor operational reliability of equipment has caused the closure of most of the thermal treatment plants. However, where sterilisation of the sludge before disposal is essential, thermal treatment of sludge is still practised.

A wide choice of methods is available for dewatering and the selection of the best method for a particular sludge can be difficult. Much depends on the dewatering characteristics of the sludge, which are dealt with later in this chapter. Drying beds have been used extensively and require relatively unskilled labour for operation. They do, however, require large areas of land which may limit their current suitability. The Stevenage Laboratory of the Water Research Centre (formerly the Water Pollution Research Laboratory) has studied them in detail for dewatering sewage sludges, but also, with particular reference to sludges derived from industrial operations, has developed a method for predicting the area of beds required for any given situation. One conclusion from this work was that, although many industrial sludges drain more rapidly on beds than does sewage sludge, this advantage can be largely lost where the sludge characteristics are such that an appreciable proportion of the water still remains to be removed by evaporation. The other methods of dewatering also depend ultimately on sludge characteristics, although certain other considerations also apply. For example, an important factor distinguishing filter pressing is its ability to dewater sludge to a higher solids content than other mechanical methods. This may be an important consideration if the sludge is to be incinerated, although the necessity then to break up the press cakes can introduce severe difficulties. The filter press may well be the most widely applied method for dealing with relatively small quantities of a wide range of sludges. Modern mechanically assisted presses eliminate the manual effort required to move heavy press plates, although there is still a considerable manpower requirement to assist the clean dropping of cakes and to ensure the correct placement and cleanliness of cloths before press closure.

Where sludge is amenable to centrifugation the method has the great advantage, especially for large installations, of compactness. It also allows clean operation and relative freedom from smell because the sludge and liquor are enclosed. However, careful attention to the operation of the centrifuge is essential as a low efficiency of recovery of solids can have deleterious consequences on the secondary stage of treatment.

8.6.2. Sludge Characteristics

In considering sludge characteristics it is important not to overlook the potential value of very simple properties such as solids content and the volatile content or loss on ignition of dry solids. For sewage sludge the volatile content gives an invaluable initial indication, not only of the potential amenability of the sludge to biological treatment, but also of difficulties likely to be encountered in dewatering it. For example, particularly with secondary sludges which vary over a wide range of dewaterability, high contents of volatile matter generally indicate great difficulty in dewatering. The characteristic is less useful for other types of sludge which may contain an appreciable amount of volatile matter other than organic material, although low volatile contents would in most cases indicate a low potential benefit from biological treatment. The wide choice of methods available for the filtration of sludge confirms the importance of the laboratory measurement of filtrability. The method developed and extensively used at the Stevenage Laboratory over many years is in terms of specific resistance to filtration, which theoretically is independent of such important variables as the area of filtration, solids content, viscosity and temperature. Coakley first showed in 1956 that the concept of specific resistance could be applied to sewage sludges, although subsequent work at the laboratory showed that it was not independent of solids content, particularly in the case of activated sludge, and this would also need to be checked for certain sludges, other than sewage sludge, of light flocculant nature. Extensive work at the laboratory has shown that this characteristic can be reliably used to predict performance of full-scale vacuum filters and it has proved an invaluable tool in investigations of full-scale installations, resulting in marked improvements in performance.

It has also been shown that specific resistance to filtration can be used for the empirical prediction of filter-press performance, and again it has been invaluable in investigations, resulting in marked improvements in the performance of full-scale plant.

The introduction and development of capillary-suction time (CST) measurement has greatly extended the scope of filtrability determinations and, in particular, can greatly expedite such determinations. Although it is frequently necessary, for instance in applying filtration theory, to relate the CST values back to specific resistance by means of calibration, for many purposes where the solids content is constant the measurement of CST alone is sufficient. It is essential to remember, however, that CST is dependent on solids content. CST and specific resistance to filtration have been used regularly for the control of filter pressing operations at the largest plant of its kind (Sheffield) in this country dewatering sewage sludge.

Of probably equal importance in studies of filtration procedures is the laboratory's introduction of a standard stirrer to be used when measuring the effect of chemical conditioners. In any full-scale operation sludge flocs are damaged to some extent during chemical conditioning procedures, by pumping, and even by introduction into dewatering plant. This damage can be simultated in the laboratory test and, if the increase in CST during full-scale handling is measured, it can then be related to a given period of standard stirring. By the use of simple equipment, recently introduced, sludge can be sampled from within a filter press during operation, with minimum subjection to further shear. This permits monitoring of the shearing effect at all stages of filter press operation.

Filtrability and standard stirring tests are also invaluable in choosing the most suitable chemicals for conditioning sludges. Not only can assessment be made of the ability of a chemical or other method of conditioning to reduce specific resistance, but the strength of the conditioned floc can also be assessed. For example, these techniques have been used at the laboratory to show how freezing and thawing can greatly improve the filtrability of sludges; when this method is applied to waterworks alum sludge, a very stable floc results, whereas with sewage sludge the floc is very fragile and unless handled with extreme gentleness the filtrability can easily deteriorate to its initial value. Returning to the problem of secondary sludges in biological treatment, and particularly to the high-rate sludges referred to earlier, the same test methods have been used to show that high-rate sludges not only exhibit poorer filtrability initially than those from conventional treatment, but also have much weaker flocs.

Cloth-blinding is an important phenomenon which can conveniently be investigated with a filter leaf and at the laboratory such a leaf has been attached to a simple jig above a trough of sludge so that it can be taken through repeated filtration cycles, faithfully simulating a vacuum-filter cycle. By testing the cake after various cycles any deterioration in the porosity of the cloth can be assessed.

A new method for assessing the thickenability of sludge has been developed in which the effect of sludge blanket height can be determined. Samples of sludge, 1 litre in volume, are subjected to a range of centrifugal accelerations, between 10 and 100 times that of gravity, in a low-speed centrifuge. The centrifugal acceleration increases the compressive effect of the upper layers of particles on the lower layers in the same way as in a thickener. The fall of the interface between the sludge and the supernatant liquor is observed with time. The maximum concentration that can be achieved in a thickener of any height can be predicted.

Drainage tests have also been used at the Stevenage Laboratory utilising vertical glass tubes of about 40-mm bore with a layer of sand or other drainage material in the bottom and sufficiently long to accommodate a typical application of sludge to a bed. In this way it has been shown that values of specific resistance determined from the observed rate of drainage are consistent with those measured in a Buchner funnel and also that, by observing the total removal of water by drainage, the time required for further removal by evaporation to give a cake of any required solids content could be calculated.

When organic sludges are treated by biological methods measurements of BOD and COD are essential. Especially in the case of anaerobic treatment it is important to know whether the raw material contains any toxic constituent and also to know the extent of biodegradation that can be expected. Techniques have been developed at the laboratory for assessing these sludge characteristics using batch digesters of about 400-ml capacity.

Where incineration may be used, calorific value is of obvious significance and work at Stevenage has served to focus attention on the importance of the organic fraction of the sludge solids. For example, a single figure is often quoted for the solids content of sewage sludge necessary to permit autothermic combustion. When different furnace operating conditions and different types of sewage sludge are taken into account it has been shown, however, that the solids content necessary for autothermic combustion can be as low as about 17% at one extreme and that, at the other, such combustion would not be achieved even with bone-dry material.

8.6.3. Choice of Methods of Treatment

An attempt has been made to outline some of the most useful sludge characteristics that can be measured and this permits a selection of compatible unit processes from Table 8.5. The options open for final disposal of sludge or its residues can frequently be the overriding consideration and in many cases justification can be found in plant design for starting at this end of the system. If the opportunities for final disposal are very restricted, the selection of unit stages of treatment and dewatering can then logically be limited to those providing the most economical way of modifying the sludge into a form acceptable for disposal. Such a choice of processes will generally also be the simplest and most direct route to disposal.

8.7. CONCLUSION

Careful consideration of water use and effluent treatment at the design stage of process or factory planning can substantially reduce the costs and problems of disposal. Similarly, modifications of existing manufacturing processes and clean-up procedures can produce worthwhile savings.

There is a wide range of processes for the treatment of waste waters and the scheme which is adopted for a particular factory will normally include a combination of processes which keeps the overall costs to a minimum and produces a discharge of the required standard. In assessing total costs the cost of treatment and disposal of any sludge or concentrate produced by the process should not be neglected. Recovery of products, raw materials and treated process water for re-use can help to reduce the cost of treatment of industrial effluents.

ACKNOWLEDGEMENT

This contribution is reproduced by permission of the Director of the Water Research Centre, Stevenage Laboratory.

BIBLIOGRAPHY

1. Berger, O., Solids separation from industrial waters and effuents, *Chemy Ind.* (1974), 50.
2. Boon, A.G. and Borne, B.J., Conference on Preventing Industrial Pollution, sponsored by the Journal *Pollution Control*, June 1971. Also, Minimising the problem of treatment and disposal of industrial effluent, In *Industrial Pollution Control Yearbook 1974*, 137–144. Fuel and Metallurgical Journals Ltd, London, 1974.
3. Special Publication 14, Methods for treating carbonisation effluents: a critical review. British Coke Research Association, 1973.
4. Chalmers, R.K., Some conservation problems in the metal-finishing industry, *Chemy Ind.* (1973), 554.
5. Committee of Directors of Textile Research Associations, Effluent treatment and water conservation. *Effluent and Water Conservation sub-committee, final report*, 1970.
6. Forbes, F., Role of ultrafiltration in industrial effluent problems, *Chemy Ind.* (1974), 56.
7. Franklin, J.S., Oil reclamation—an assessment of current techniques, *Effl. Wat. Treat. J.*, **13** (1973), 655 and 657.
8. Gale, R.S., Recent research on sludge dewatering, *Filtration and Separation*, **8** (1971), 531.
9. Gale, R.S., The sludge treatment and disposal problem. Paper presented at Symposium on Incineration of Refuse and Sludge, University of Southampton, Dept. of Civil Engineering, Jan. 1972.
10. Hager, D.G., Industrial wastewater treatment by granular activated carbon, *Ind. Wat. Eng.*, **11** (1) (1974), 14.
11. Hemming, M.L., Biofiltration of aqueous effluents from the food industry using synthetic media, *Pollution Monitor*, **22** (1974/75), 30–32.
12. Hewson, J.L., *Water in the Chemical and Allied Industries.* Monograph No. 34, Society of Chemical Industry, London, 1970.
13. Hillis, M.R., Electrolytic treatment of effluents, *Effl. Wat. Treat. J.*, **9** (1969), 647 and **10** (1970), 33.
14. Institute of Water Pollution Control and Newcastle upon Tyne University,

Proceedings of a Symposium on the Treatment of Wastes from the Food and Drink Industry. Newcastle upon Tyne, January, 1974.

15. Institution of Public Health Engineers, Proceedings of Symposium on the Engineering Aspects of the Use and Re-use of Water, June 1967.

16. Institute of Water Pollution Control, Proceedings of Symposium on Trade Waste Treatment and Water Conservation, Coventry, April 1967.

17. Institution of Chemical Engineers, *The Application of Chemical Engineering to the Treatment of Sewage and Industrial Liquid Effluents*. I.Chem. E. Symposium Series No. 41, 1975.

18. International Union of Pure and Applied Chemistry, *Re-use of Water in Industry*. Butterworths, London, 1963.

19. Jørgensen, S.E., The combination precipitation-ion exchange for waste water from the food industry, *Vatten*, 29 (1973), 40.

20. Landine, R.C., Cyclones: water and waste water applications, *Wat. Pollut. Control*, **113** (4) (1975), 28 and 74–78.

21. Mayhue, L.F., *Solvent Extraction Status Report*, US Environmental Protection Agency, Envir. Protect. Technol. Ser. EPA-R3–72–073. US Govt. Printing Office, Washington, DC, 1972.

22. Ministry of Agriculture Fisheries and Food, *Dairy Effluents*. HMSO, London, 1969.

23. Painter, H.A., Biodegradability, *Proc. R. Soc. Lond. B.*, **185** (1974), 149.

24. Pearson, D. and Shirley, J.M., Precipitation flotation in the treatment of metal bearing effluents, *J. Appl. Chem. Biotechnol.*, **23** (1973), 101.

25. Proceedings of a Symposium on Effects of Trade Waste on the Treatability of Sewage, London, 1966, *Wat. Pollut. Control*, **66** (1967), 140.

26. Proceedings of a Symposium on Toxic Wastes, *Wat. Pollut. Control*, **69** (1970), 269.

27. Proceedings of a Symposium on Discharge of Industrial Effluents to Municipal Sewerage Systems, London, 1971. Institute of Water Pollution Control, Maidstone, 1972.

28. Reinhardt, H., Solvent extraction for recovery of metal wastes. *Chemy Ind.* (1975), 210.

29. Shabi, F.A. and Cannon, M.C., Characteristics and treatment of dairy and meat effluents, *Effl. Wat. Treat. J.*, **15** (3) (1975), 130 and 138, and **15** (4) (1975), 172 and 176.

30. Sharp, D.H. and Lambden, A.E., Treatment of strongly bactericidal trade effluent by activated charcoal and biological means, *Chemy Ind.* (1955), 1207.

31. Solt, G.S., Waste treatment by ion exchange, *Effl. Wat. Treat. J.*, **13** (1973), 768.

32. Swanwick, J.D. and O'Gorman, J.V., Some effects of metals discharged in effluents and possibilities for their recovery, *Chemy Ind.* (1973), 573.

33. Swanwick, J.D., Fisher, W.J. and Foulkes, M., Some aspects of sludge technology, including new data on centrifugation. In *Water Pollution Manual* 1972, 141. Thunderbird Enterprises Ltd, Harrow, 1972.

9

Case Studies

A: FIBRE INTERMEDIATES

P.W.H. MOON

Division Environmental Adviser, ICI Petrochemicals Division, Middlesbrough, UK

9.1. SUMMARY

The manufacture of synthetic fibre intermediates gives rise to a number of aqueous effluents and poses problems in their segregation and treatment. Effluent flows and compositions are regularly monitored at a number of places within the Works, both as a check on materials discarded to drain and to gather information on the kinds of treatment processes which future discharge standards may require. Effluent samplers and flowmeters are described.

Water is used not only for cooling purposes but within processes for crystallisation, in countercurrent washing, hydrolysis, absorption and for steam raising. Water quality is critically important in many processes and there is a large demand for high purity water such as demineralised water and pure steam condensate. Other parts of the processes require less pure water, or can tolerate specific contaminants. One objective is to ensure the maximum utilisation of recovered water of all kinds, so that water unfit for direct recycle is used elsewhere for less critical uses and only water unfit for any process use or for cooling water make-up is put to drain. In addition to cost savings this action has postponed capital expenditure on new demineralising plant, reduced the overall water consumption and effluent volume and has reduced pollution because the demineralising operation is under 90% efficient and itself produces pollution from regenerants, etc.

9.2. INTRODUCTION

This paper describes the management of water resources and liquid effluent in a chemical works producing synthetic fibre intermediates. The effluent flow involved is of the order of 20 000 m³/day and forms part of the discharge from a large factory site into a river estuary. The Regional Water Authority has not yet fixed standards for liquid effluent, but the Works is progressively tightening its effluent control in anticipation of future requirements.

The effluent characteristics with which we are principally concerned are:

pH
Biochemical Oxygen Demand
Heavy Metals
Suspended Solids

9.3. EFFLUENT TREATMENT

The management of effluent starts with segregation for tipping or burning of those waste streams which can be dealt with in this way rather than by allowing them to go to drain. In this connection a very significant reduction in BOD was made recently by converting a steam distillation process, which discharged large quantities of dilute aqueous organic solution to drain, into a dry distillation producing a concentrated oily residue suitable as a boiler fuel.

Acid effluents arising principally in two locations are pumped to neutralising plants, together with weak alkaline effluent which assists the neutralisation. Chalk slurry is used as the neutralising agent. Spent acid and alkaline regenerants arising intermittently from an ion exchange plant are held in buffer tanks and released at a constant rate so as to even out the load on the neutralising system. Thus, only the portion of the Works' effluent which needs neutralisation is handled by the system, peak loads are buffered and maximum use is made of available alkaline effluent to effect neutralisation.

Most of the Suspended Solids in the effluent comes from the by-product chalk used in the neutralising plants. While the Suspended Solids concentration is not an embarrassment at present, it could be reduced, if it ever became necessary, by the use of hydrated lime instead of chalk.

9.4. EFFLUENT MANAGEMENT

The foregoing section outlines the system; to make effective use of it, it has to be managed:

(a) to keep it under control;
(b) to provide data for future improvements; and
(c) to monitor valuable materials in plant effluents.

In connection with (c) above, it may be noted that the cost of process raw materials amounts to roughly one-third of the plant cost of fibre intermediates and the maintenance of high yields at all stages assumes a correspondingly high importance. Plant yields are notoriously difficult to measure accurately over short periods, but effluent monitoring gives early warning of abnormal losses. Such losses can arise from diverse and insidious causes, such as poor liquid/liquid separation, entrainment from a condenser into a vacuum ejector on a still, or malfunction of equipment of almost any kind in consequence of instrument errors. To be of diagnostic assistance, information on such losses needs to be immediate rather than historical. An adequate effluent monitoring system provides this early warning in a form which periodic stocktaking and stock accounting can never achieve.

9.5. DRAIN FLOW MEASUREMENT

Analysis of an effluent sample, producing a result expressed as a concentration, is useless for materials monitoring purposes unless it is accompanied by a measurement of the flow rate, or at least a reliable presumption of the flow rate. Factory drains are seldom laid out to facilitate monitoring. As well as combining the effluent from functionally unrelated plants or splitting the discharge of single process entities, drains may be up to 5 m below ground level, rendering construction and access for maintenance very difficult for any flow measurement device which has to be located in such a pipe. Casual debris ranging from silt to plastic bags must be tolerated by the device without requiring unacceptably frequent maintenance.

Fortunately it is not imperative to measure all the flows at all the sampling points. Consideration of the discharges to each drain will show that in many cases the flow is constant within acceptable ($\pm 20\%$) limits, and it may be possible to establish a typical flow rate once and for all from design data or by radioactive or chemical tracer techniques. If there exists sufficiently far upstream in the drain network a stream whose flow can be measured and which contains a unique and analysable component, a large part of the problem can be solved. Provided that there is no other source of this component and that it does not precipitate, react or decompose, measurement of its concentration anywhere in the system will afford a measurement of the flow rate.

Flumes and weirs have been found to be the most suitable primary measuring devices for the conditions prevailing in drains and conduits in this particular Works. Other devices such as electromagnetic flowmeters will have application in special cases.

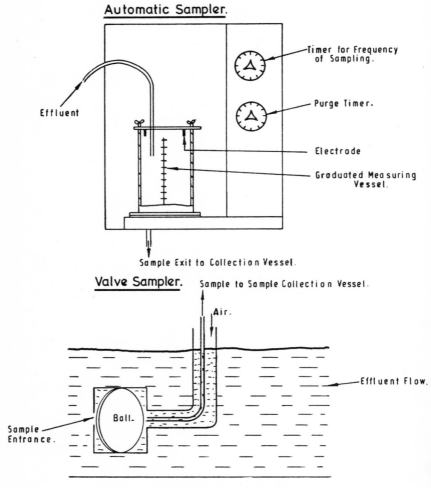

FIG. 9.1. Automatic sampler and valve sampler.

Pipeline Sampler.

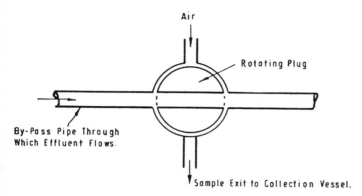

Dip & Tip Sampler.

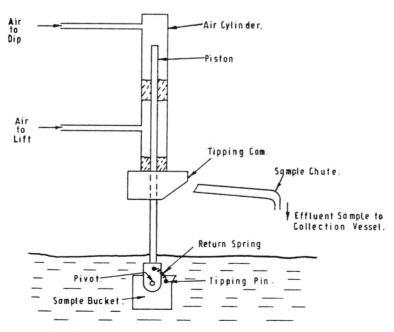

FIG. 9.2. Pipeline sampler and dip and tip sampler.

9.6. EFFLUENT SAMPLING

In a large Works operating 24 h/day automatic sampling is a *sine qua non*. The only decisions will be where to sample, how frequently to abstract material for a composite sample and whether the sampling frequency needs to be proportional to the flow rate. The latter is rarely mandatory unless the flow varies widely. The other questions must be answered by a careful appraisal of the most likely and most serious or costly sources of loss and by strategic selection of locations on a cost-effectiveness basis. Blanket coverage is unlikely to be justified in any practical situation, and if it were, the maintenance effort to keep the entire system in full working order would probably be insupportable.

Examples of three automatic samplers which have proved themselves over several years in fairly adverse environments are shown in Figs. 9.1 and 9.2. All these, being incremental rather than truly continuous samplers, can be operated at constant frequency to provide a composite sample of the required volume daily or shiftwise, or can have their frequency controlled from a flow measuring device so as to produce a composite sample proportional to flow and therefore truly representative of the effluent which has flowed past the sample point.

Use is made of Sieger detectors for flammable vapours, the presence of which in drains constitutes a serious hazard.

9.7. WATER RECYCLE

Effluent is 99% water and up to this point we have been concerned with the other 1%; now we turn to management of water itself as a periodically scarce resource of not inconsiderable cost. To put the matter into perspective, Table 9.1 shows the relative cost and quantities used of the four grades of water concerned.

TABLE 9.1
RELATIVE COSTS AND USAGES OF WATER

Grade	Relative unit cost C	Relative usage Q	Relative overall cost $C \times Q$
Raw water	1.0	50	50
Town's water	2.7	2.3	6.2
Steam condensate	—	11	—
Demineralised water	7.4	1	7.4

TABLE 9.2
WATER HIERARCHY

Demineralised water
Condensate
Town's water
Raw water
Cooling water
Effluent

Allowing full cost for steam, condensate is free and contains a bonus of thermal energy which is useful in numerous cases where there is a requirement for pure water which is heated in the process.

The way to conserve resources is of course to recycle water wherever possible. The principle on which the recycle is based is the water hierarchy, shown in Table 9.2. Used, surplus or unwanted water of any grade is recycled within the parent process if possible, or to the next lower level in the hierarchy which is able to accept it. Only as a last resort is water put to drain. Boiler feed water and water which goes directly into finished products have to be above suspicion. For this reason demineralised water is the service normally used, but clean condensate is equally suitable provided that its quality can be guaranteed. On-line analysers or conductivity meters are useful, operating alarms and automatically diverting the condensate if it becomes contaminated. For a variety of reasons connected with the integrity of process equipment, condensate does become contaminated from time to time with process materials even in the best run plants and it is wise to regard steam condensate as an aqueous solution of process materials, the concentration varying from high to undetectable.

For every source of water a critical examination has to be undertaken on the lines of Fig. 9.3, which illustrates the principle of recycle to the highest practicable level in the hierarchy. Before this critical attitude, there was a tendency for all the 'NO' branches on the decision boxes to lead straight to drain.

This critical examination needs to be performed for every source of water and every demand for water. Judgement enters into the decision whether to treat groups of producers and consumers together. Sometimes it pays to consider a single large plant item on its own if it produces a more reliable pure condensate than that of adjacent plant, or if its contaminants are less harmful than those in the condensate from nearby equipment. Often the demand is for pure *hot* water in which case condensate scores a bonus because it arises hot. If the demand be for cool water, the cost of cooling

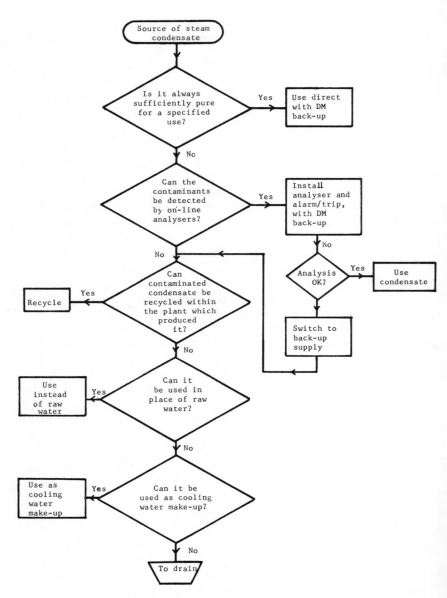

FIG. 9.3. Decision tree for water use and recycle.

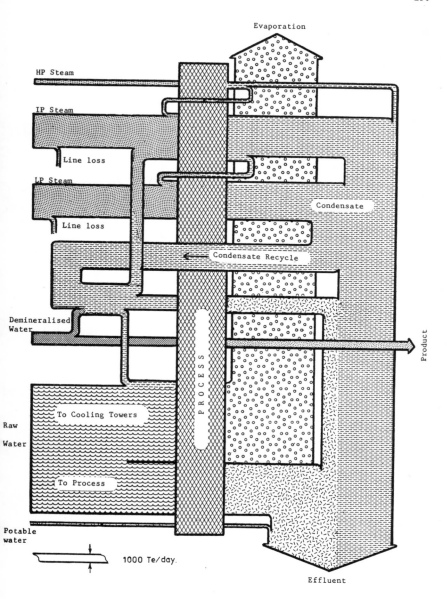

FIG. 9.4. Sankey diagram for water recycle.

condensate to 30–35°C will always be less than that of demineralised water to replace it. The spray condensers of vacuum ejectors can often be fed with the same grade of water used for cooling water make-up and, if entrainment into the vacuum system is minimal, the discharge from the ejector barometric legs can go directly into the cooling water return main.

The chief obstacle to water recycle in this way is the interruptible nature of the sources and the peaky character of some of the demands. Even if the water is available when wanted, the consumer and source may be some distance apart and each case must be treated on its merits as to the viability of pumping the condensate to where it is wanted.

The recycle of water of all grades over a dispersed factory site is a complicated problem and, before one can be sure that one has evaluated all the options, one needs to be sure that the whole situation is understood and quantified as well as possible. Unless one can draw a Sankey diagram on the lines of Fig. 9.4 one is never sure that the picture is well enough defined to justify spending money and effort on a particular recycle scheme, which may be surpassed in cost effectiveness by other less obvious ones.

If one does not have enough information to draw such a diagram, it shows that a better understanding is needed; conversely the availability of a diagram, no matter how crude or inaccurate, helps to show the relative importance of the various losses and puts a maximum to the amount which could be saved.

B: INDUSTRIAL TRADE EFFLUENT DISPOSAL

R.W. GRAFTON

Safety and Environment Officer, The Boots Company Ltd, Nottingham, UK

9.8. SUMMARY

The case study provides an interesting example of how government (local government) and industry can co-operate to the advantage of each other. With the recent change in operational responsibility for effluent treatment, co-operation has lost some of its old drive. The current climate of bureaucratic attitude is seen as being contrary to community effort and wasteful of resource. An optimum solution can only apply to today — tomorrow will be different.

9.9. INTRODUCTION

The period involved extends from 1930 to the present and into the future. It is an on-going involvement, being influenced all the time by political pressures, public opinion and the social conscience of industrial management in addition to response to technical innovation dictating the 'state of the art' and economic forces.

This case study is a striking example of the need and value of a total concept approach, an appreciation of the macro- as well as the micro-structure in which operations take place and provides a continuing awareness of the environment which requires respect. It will be seen that of paramount importance is a constructive understanding and common purpose by both industrial management and local and other government authorities.

Too often there appears a lack of appreciation by bureaucratic bodies of overall community benefit. Too often are decisions of expediency taken arising from the lack of tangible recognition by political groups of their and the community's livelihood being sustained by the success of industry. Whilst no socially conscious industrial management would wittingly act contrary to long-term community interest, it should be remembered that industry is part of the community — there are no separate funds and any extravagance or ill directed expenditure is borne by the community as a whole. The special place in the community occupied by industry is that of wealth creator — thus it is of utmost importance to the community to understand the problems of industry and to endeavour to establish an environment conducive to wealth creation.

The success story of this case study of the late 1960s was made possible as a result of the determined effort of the local authority, who at the time were responsible for the operation of the sewage works and for contributing to the wellbeing of the community. This in no way led to any soft attitudes, but rather to a commitment to co-operate fully in arriving at an acceptable solution of the difficulties without waste of resource. In no way were any economic concessions in terms of easement of charges made — nor were they sought, it always being recognised that charges should reflect cost incurred by the effort of the authority.

There have been many cases where local authorities, under earlier arrangements, have made concessions to industry in the belief that they have been to the advantage of the community they serve. This is no longer the case — the converse being so. This change in political attitude has nullified much of the fundamental advantage of this case study. It will also prove contrary to community effort as a result of waste of resource.

9.10. HISTORICAL SUMMARY

It was at the beginning of the 1930s that the industrial site was established on the outskirts of one of the country's larger inland cities which lies on a major river. A significant feature to become of later importance was the unusual situation of considerable industrial development in the upper reaches of this river which over the years led to a pollution load unmatched by natural restorative resource. The site, covering some 300 acres and currently employing 7000 people has over the years become extensively engaged in organic synthesis and the preparation of pharmaceutical, cosmetic and toilet preparations.

At the outset a cash contribution was made to the local urban authority to establish a sewage works on the perimeter of the industrial site. From then on this authority treated the industrial effluent along with the urban effluent, charging for its service based on the proportion of the oxidising load on the works, as measured by the McGowan formula. No further cash contributions were made—any capital extensions over the years being proportioned out as amortisation according to load.

Over the years both the urban and industrial activity increased. In the mid 1960s urban development had reached saturation whereas industrial activity on the site was continuing to increase. At this time this industrial activity amounted to 40% of the volumetric and 65% of the oxidation loads. A somewhat 'laissez-faire' attitude had existed over the 30 and more years. Whereas the discharge Consent had been revised in 1938, by the mid 1960s the discharge was at times five times the Consent of a then irrelevant 1100 m³/day (0.25 million gallons/day) limit. Very little restriction existed as to composition—save for a somewhat vague reference to '...the effluent shall be free of material (1) injurious to the structure of the sewers or works (2) prejudicial to normal and proper treatment'.

Little or no pre-treatment was effected—save for pH adjustment. Even this had taken the form of neutralisation with caustic soda for convenience. Thus unimaginably high dissolved sulphate concentrations from much of the chemical activity remained, resulting in massive deterioration of the concrete sewers.

A simple site drainage system had evolved over the years. Except for provision of 'acid' drains in one small area of the site, a common process and foul drainage had been adopted, making individual area monitoring and modification unattractive.

In 1966 the then River Authority became interested in improving the general river water quality with a long-term ambition of regarding the lower reaches of the river as a source of potable water. In consequence, attention was focused on the quality of the outfall of the urban sewage works. It was obvious that some massive improvement would be essential to meet the River Authority's target.

9.11. THE SITUATION IN 1966

Pressure by the River Authority and the method of charging by the sewage works had exacerbated an already poor situation by encouraging relatively clean water from the drains being included in the discharge to the sewage works. The industrial site was contributing not only a substantial volumetric load, but more than half the oxidation load on the works. Naturally the sewage works management looked to the industrial site for a solution of its problems. With financial support the urban works initiated an impartial assessment and pre-oxidation pilot investigation.

Contrary to the generally pronounced view that the industrial site effluent was basically difficult to treat and was inhibitory in the percolation filter bed oxidation of urban effluent, a number of interesting observations were made:

(1) the trade effluent significantly reduced biological treatability when diluted with less than an equal quantity of urban effluent;
(2) the above effect was insignificant when trade effluent was diluted with an equal quantity of urban effluent;
(3) both the trade and urban effluents were more readily bio-degraded when admixed with urban effluent in excess;
(4) 25–50% of the trade effluent was readily bio-degradable, but a considerable proportion of the remainder was highly intractable; and
(5) it was considered inadvisable to attempt full-scale biological treatment or pre-treatment of full-strength trade effluent.

The urban sewage works had a treatment capacity of 2700 kg (6000 lbs) BOD per day. The urban load was 1700 kg (3750 lbs) whilst the trade load was 3300 kg (7200 lbs) BOD per day. Thus, neglecting any allowance for future expansion, the sewage works was looking for an oxidation load reduction of the trade waste of some 70%.

Clearly to attempt to meet such a challenge in the face of the evidence available at that time would indeed have been a challenge and foolhardy. Some other solution was desirable.

9.12. AN OPPORTUNITY SEIZED

As suggested in the introduction, the community is wise to embrace industry—so is industry wise to be aware of the wider community environment in which it exists. Rather than concentrating on the local urban sewage works, a wider view was taken. The industrial site was on the edge of a city which had grown over the years, a city which had had the foresight to lay down a large and effective sewage works. Already the industrial undertaking had a small chemical synthesis unit operating in the city and connected to its works without any particular problems. The general picture is illustrated in Fig. 9.5.

One particular point in favour of the ultimately adopted solution was the recent closure of the city's town-gas works which had given rise to a

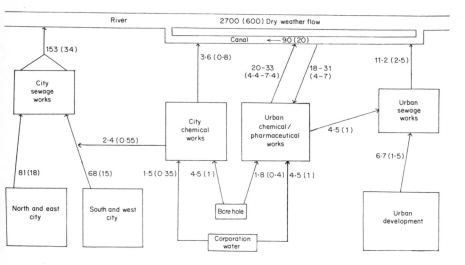

Fig. 9.5. Area water flows for 1968 in thousands of cubic metres per day. Numbers in parentheses are millions of gallons per day.

comparable treatment load. Advances were made to the city sewage works' management to explore the practicability of diverting the trade effluent from the urban works. Such diversion could not be regarded lightly—there were problems, not least of which was the city's treatment process itself. Also, in the event of serious interruption, the greater overall flow would give rise to greater consequences. However, the attraction of greater dilution and under-utilised potential merited serious study.

The city's sewage works used submerged oxidation followed by anaerobic digestion of bio-mass. It was well appreciated that receipt of trade effluent would demand much greater discipline than hitherto to ensure no adverse effects on the works. After much laboratory investigation, careful study and frank discussion the city sewage works' management agreed to accept a diversion of the whole trade effluent provided certain conditions were met. As part of this deal it was agreed that the industrial management should endeavour to understand the sewage works processing problems and to disclose production programmes beforehand in order to anticipate difficulties. This ultimate in co-operation continues today—to the benefit of all concerned.

It will be seen that the findings of the independent appraisal commissioned by the urban sewage works proved immensely valuable and that the larger city works was able to meet its several recommendations. Furthermore, the switch to the city works gave potential for future expansion without the need for further capital investment. In addition the load on the urban works was allowed to fall to well within existing treatment potential. This was, then, a good utilisation of community resource.

9.13. CONDITIONS OF ACCEPTANCE BY THE CITY

There was no need for a limitation on volumetric or oxidation loading (both in terms of quantity and concentration), but there was a need to be particular about other parameters, requiring:

(1) control of sulphate;
(2) control of Suspended Solids;

TABLE 9.3

UNDESIRABLE BACTERICIDES IN DISCHARGES TO CITY SEWAGE WORKS

Chemical	Solubility in cold water (mg/litre)	Recommended limit in effluent discharge (mg/litre)
Trichloroethylene	1 000	} 2.0
Perchloroethylene	200	
Trichlorotrifluoroethane	Relatively insoluble	
Carbon tetrachloride	800	} 0.1
Ethylene dichloride	9 000	
Methylene dichloride	20 000	
Dichlorophen	Slightly soluble	
Pentachlorophenol	Relatively insoluble	} 0.05
Trichlorofluoromethane	Relatively insoluble	
Chloroform	10 000	
1,1,-Trichloroethane	Relatively insoluble	} 0.025
Tris-dibromopropyl phosphate	Relatively insoluble	
Allyl isothiocyanate	2 000	} 3.0
2-Mercaptobenzothiazole	Relatively insoluble	
Methyl isothiocyanate	Slightly soluble	
Sodium methyldithiocarbamate	Very soluble	} 1.0
Dithio-oxamide	Soluble	
Thioacetamide	Very soluble	} 0.75
Sodium cyanide	Soluble	
Thiourea	90 000	} 0.15
Thiosemicarbazide	Soluble	

(3) elimination of certain reagents;

(4) virtual elimination of halogenated hydrocarbons by removal at source;

(5) process modification to eliminate high-volume relatively clean effluent; and

(6) process modification to eliminate or facilitate disposal.

The sulphate requirement was particularly pertinent at the time due to the very high soluble sulphate levels present — up to 50 000 mg/litre in some streams. As the industrial site is on the extremity of the city sewerage network, a limit of 300 mg/litre was sought. As the solubility of calcium sulphate in the trade effluent is considerably in excess of 1100 mg/litre, clearly neutralisation by lime would not provide a simple cure.

It was agreed that certain reagents would be totally eliminated by denying them access to the sewers. Typical examples are endosulfan, binapacryl and sumothion. The undesirable reagents included many of the common laboratory reagents, so that a change in long established practice was required. The agreed 'undesirables' are identified in Table 9.3.

9.14. ON SITE PROVISIONS

The flow-sheet for the pre-conditioning of the bulked effluent to meet pH, Suspended Solids and dissolved sulphate requirements is illustrated in Fig. 9.6. It is a very simple concept which, when respected, works well. The chemical processing effluents are separated into sulphate-rich and sulphate-lean streams. The sulphate-rich effluent is dosed with waste hydrochloric acid to increase calcium ion solubility and then neutralised with lime, precipitating as much sulphate as practicable. The clarified effluent is then combined with the sulphate-lean effluent, pH trimmed, skimmed and further clarified before admixture with the remainder of the site effluent. Only by attempting sulphate removal from the relatively small volume of sulphate-rich effluent could the city's Consent be respected and the sewers protected.

The chemical processing effluent was clarified to a far higher degree than required by the city's Consent in order to avoid the necessity of clarifying the remainder of the effluent and hence separating the process and foul drainage systems. The final mixed effluent readily complies with the Suspended Solids limit. Similarly, the pH of the ultimate outfall can be controlled by adjusting the pH of the pre-conditioned chemical effluent.

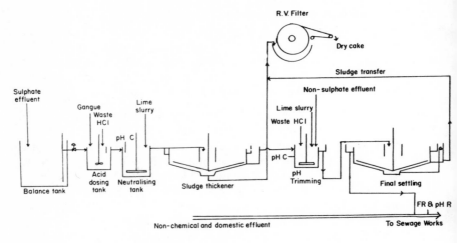

FIG. 9.6. Trade waste pre-conditioning flowsheet.

The 'gangue' shown being admixed with the sulphate-rich effluent was a low-pH residue of some significant oxidising potential. It was introduced here essentially to ease its disposal by taking advantage of calcium sulphate as a carrier. The hope that it would also effect useful COD removal did not materialise.

Halogenated solvents were dealt with at source either by steam stripping from process streams or separate collection of laboratory waste. The latter required extensive education and discipline of laboratory staff.

High-volume low-concentration streams were eliminated by water re-use and re-cycle. Advantage was taken of evaporating cooling towers. A particularly interesting example was water used on a barometric condenser of a vacuum soap drier. At first, frothing was anticipated as a major problem. This was avoided by employing a small purge of hard water. The difficulty actually experienced was one of biological growth on the packing, which was eventually resolved by controlled hypochlorite dosing.

Thus the ability of the site to operate and dispose of its effluent in a responsible manner was protected without the need for:

(1) capital investment for oxidation;
(2) separation of the existing mixed drain system;
(3) pre-treatment of all effluent; or
(4) pre-oxidation.

9.15. IMPLICATIONS OF CHARGES

At the outset and until 1975 the charges reflected the local authority's costs in operating the city sewage works. Since then the operation of the sewage works has become the responsibility of the Regional Water Authority — which, for reasons best known to itself, has decided to have a standard charge over the whole of the region. This has given rise to an escalation of 70% p.a. over the five years of equalisation of charges — 70% p.a., even in a time of general inflation, belies logic.

The principal criticism of the Regional Water Authority's charging philosophy is that it pays no respect to scale. In the case of the gas and electricity boards, industry is not expected to pay domestic tariffs. No such enlightened marginal costing concept has been applied by the Regional Water Authority.

A particular and unfortunate consequence of high and unrealistic charges is that industry may decide to totally or partially treat its own trade effluent. Thus, rather than taking the course of this case study, it may perhaps have shown better on the company's books in hindsight, to have solved the problems of total 'in-house' treatment. This may have been profitable in a narrow view, but from what has been said it is obvious that it would have been a loss to the community. In the opinion of the writer the Regional Water Authority was unwilling, or unable, to decide and act in the best interests of the community which it was set up to serve.

9.16. THE FUTURE

That which is let fall into a drain is not the only waste which arises. Greater attention is essential on the whole waste disposal front to permit the best utilisation of all resources. Some of what goes to drain today may best be dealt with differently tomorrow — especially those intractable materials if the river is to be regarded as a source of potable water. A possible future provision might be as shown in Fig. 9.7. Here, effluent streams of particularly high COD are separated and destroyed directly by incineration rather than biologically, so avoiding difficulties with the latter and massive production of biological sludge which can involve expensive disposal. Alternatively, a hybrid system involving direct sea dumping of such particular concentrated effluents may have economic advantages — this is already practised by some organisations involved in chemical synthesis.

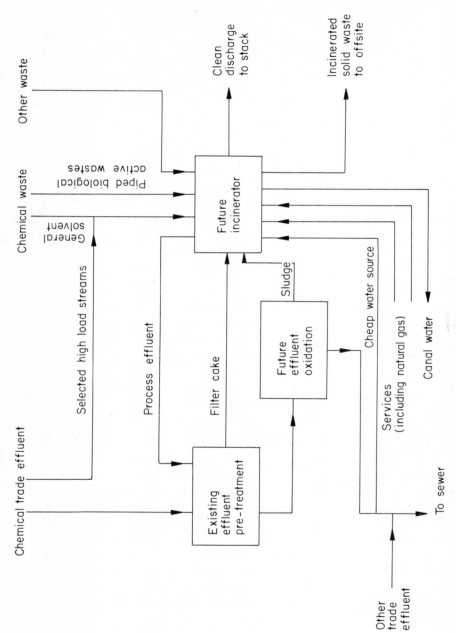

Fig. 9.7. The inter-relation of waste disposal facilities

10

The Disposal of Toxic Wastes

A. WINT

Lecturer in Chemical Engineering, University of Nottingham, UK

10.1. INTRODUCTION

10.1.1. General View of the Problem

The safe disposal of toxic waste materials is a problem of great importance, not only to industrial producers of such waste, but for the future well-being of the human race. The bulk of such material has been, and still is, treated by burial on land. There the vast majority of toxic substances are decomposed harmlessly by natural processes, provided that a suitable set of conditions for degradation is established. Cases where contamination of underground water supplies has arisen from this practice are very rare.

However, a few toxic materials are remarkably resistant to natural breakdown. Unless strict control is exercised over their disposal, they can build up to reach unacceptably high levels of concentration in various parts of the environment. These levels may have severely harmful effects on plant and animal species and even on man himself. This chapter includes brief case studies on some substances which have caused such events, for instance lead, mercury and various chlorinated organic compounds. It will become clear that the patterns of behaviour in the environment of these materials are dissimilar. An enormous amount of research effort has been necessary to determine the mechanisms by which they are transported and the ways in which they affect the balance of nature. Many parts of these puzzles are still incomplete. Thirty years ago it would have been impossible to predict the full effects that these substances would have. We must exercise great care to ensure that new examples do not occur, where inadequate control of disposal methods leads to serious disruption of natural processes. The chief lesson from the past is that it is very difficult to be certain how substances will behave in the environment if they do not occur naturally or occur only in substantially different forms or concentrations.

In spite of the concern expressed in the previous paragraph, it is important that a well-balanced view is taken of the problem of disposing of toxic materials. Often these substances arise unavoidably from processes manufacturing products of great benefit to mankind. In recent years manufacturers' disposal costs have risen very sharply, even when no substantial change has been made in an acknowledged safe and reasonable method of treatment. Part of the problem is an emotional attitude to the subject by the general public, resulting in its intrusion to an often unwarranted extent into local, national and international politics. Not many years ago the topic caused little concern. Hence little work had been done to investigate the performances of the different disposal methods which were available. In recent times, however, much progress has been made and a considerable amount of information on these methods now exists. The safe disposal of toxic materials is difficult. Although it used to be done very cheaply, without much thought, it can no longer be done so. Society at large must determine how much it is willing to pay to accommodate processes which produce these unpleasant wastes and it should do so on the basis of rational decisions, not emotional feelings.

The major and final part of this chapter is a description of the different disposal routes which are currently in use. However, neither toxic gases, released to atmosphere in dilute concentrations, nor the aqueous wastes treated as trade effluent in sewerage systems, will be considered in this chapter. Chiefly the substances dealt with are solid toxic wastes, but many liquids and slurries of a hazardous nature are also included, since they are generally treated by similar methods. Thousands of chemicals are of industrial significance. In a single chapter it is clearly impossible to give advice on treatment methods for each of these, other than general guidelines. No consideration will be given to the special problems of radioactive waste.

10.1.2. Historical Development
For perhaps obvious reasons public awareness of the problems of solid waste disposal lagged for many years far behind its appreciation of air and water purity protection. The quality of air has an immediate impact because we must continue breathing; supplies of drinking water too must obviously be protected from contamination. By comparison, the disposal of solids by the traditional method of tipping has only a limited impact on the general public. Up to the end of the 1960s little scientific research, either into the possible effects on the environment of inadequate disposal or on alternative forms of treatment, was carried out anywhere in the world.

In Britain the Government set up a Technical Committee in 1964 to investigate the disposal of solid toxic wastes and the findings were published in 1970.[23] The report highlighted the absence of knowledge in many parts of the subject at that time. It expressed concern over the lack of control over waste disposal practice and gave the opinion that widespread potential danger existed and would increase. By coincidence, shortly after the publication of the report, national feelings were aroused by some indiscriminate dumping of lorry loads of waste containing cyanide and by the deaths of some animals, poisoned by toxic waste. Shortly afterwards the Government introduced the Deposit of Poisonous Waste Act 1972, which was based on some of the main recommendations of the 1970 report.

The objectives of the 1972 Act were to curb indiscriminate dumping and to provide data on the waste disposal problem in the UK. It set up a system for producers of waste to notify both Local Authorities (since 1974 Waste Disposal Authorities) and Water Authorities with the quantity and composition of a load to be deposited. The Act was probably successful in its chief aims, but caused some controversy in other respects. For instance it has been alleged that the enormous volume of paper generated by the notification system has made it difficult to compile an overall view of the problem. Nevertheless the information recorded has enabled a far better understanding of the picture to be gradually built up than was possible before 1972.

The provisions of the Deposit of Poisonous Waste Act were gradually overtaken by the Control of Pollution Act 1974, different sections of which were implemented over a number of years. The effects of this Act have been and will be far-reaching in their impact on the practice of waste disposal. Hence it will be considered under a separate heading later.

10.1.3. Quantity and Nature of Toxic Waste

Annual production rates of all solid wastes in the UK were estimated in 1976 in a publication by the Department of the Environment.[3] Wastes 'controlled' under the 1974 Control of Pollution Act, and hence able to be deposited only at licensed sites, were thought to be generated at about the rates given in Table 10.1. Also included in the estimates, for the purpose of comparison, were mining waste at about 60 M tonnes per year and quarrying waste at about 50 M tonnes per year. The disposal of these wastes is not controlled under the 1974 Act since they are mostly innocuous. In fact part is used for roadmaking and in the production of building materials, the remainder being used as landfill.

The bulk of the industrial waste given in Table 10.1 probably comprises

TABLE 10.1
RATES OF PRODUCTION OF CONTROLLED WASTE[a]

Source of waste	Rate M tonnes/year
Household and commercial	18
General industrial	23
Building	3
Power Station	12

[a]Table compiled from data in DoE Waste Management
Paper No. 1, 1976[3]

relatively inert material, such as rubble, wood, paper and general rubbish. Nevertheless some of the included substances undoubtedly possess toxic, corrosive or carcinogenic properties and complex mixtures may be formed whose behaviour may be difficult to predict. In the limited survey of the Key Committee,[23] approximately 1% by weight of the industrial solid and semi-solid waste was classified as flammable process waste, approximately 4% as acid or caustic and approximately 2% as indisputably toxic. A list of parts of this waste included such diverse materials as tarry liquids, waste paint, arsenic waste, waste oil, residues from pesticide formulations, photographic waste, carbides, aromatic hydrocarbons and many others. More recent estimates of the total annual production in the UK of wastes that are toxic or otherwise dangerous fall in the range $2\frac{1}{2}$–3 M tonnes per year.[2,20,22] A figure quoted for the USA for 1973 was 10 M tonnes per year.[14]

10.2. THE CONTROL OF POLLUTION ACT 1974 AND ITS IMPLICATIONS

10.2.1. Provisions of the Act

As described earlier, the Deposit of Poisonous Waste Act 1972 was formulated and executed rapidly, as a short-term measure. By contrast, Part 1 of the 1974 Act, which relates to solid wastes, embodies a comprehensive set of controls, introduced over a period of several years. One of the most important features is that a disposal licence is necessary before a site can receive wastes, either for landfill or other forms of treatment. The licence is granted by the relevant Waste Disposal Authority who will take into account such factors as local amenities, health risks, nuisance, etc. Aspects such as quantities and types of wastes, methods of treatment, precautions to be taken, working hours and the recording of intake material may be specified in a licence. Clearly the operation of a licensed site must be monitored by the Waste Disposal Authority; the Regional Water Authority is required to do so too in order to protect water supplies.

Almost all types of solid wastes produced in the UK are controlled under the 1974 Act and thereby are able to be deposited only at licensed sites. Among the exceptions are mining and quarrying wastes, some building site materials, household wastes deposited within the grounds and small factory incinerators handling harmless materials. A licence is not required for waste disposed of by equipment or plant which is an integral part of the industrial process that produces the waste.

Other provisions of the Act include:

(i) Section 1 puts the responsibility on Waste Disposal Authorities for ensuring that all the waste generated in each county area is disposed of through authorised channels.
(ii) Section 2 calls on Waste Disposal Authorities to undertake surveys of the nature, type and quantity of the industrial wastes arising in their areas. In addition they should evaluate the total available disposal facilities within each county area, identify any areas of need and prepare an overall County Waste Disposal Plan.
(iii) Section 17 has powers for a notification procedure for certain dangerous wastes.

It is clear that the Control of Pollution Act embodies an attempt to establish a full and rational set of controls over the disposal of solid wastes. Some critics have suggested that its framework is too far-reaching, taking into account the short period of time elapsed since almost no control existed, therefore giving scientific and public opinion insufficient scope to reach a completely logical standpoint. Nevertheless it has already won approval in many quarters, but the full effects of the legislation will take time to become clear. Two major areas of uncertainty are discussed in the following sections.

10.2.2. The Relationship between Waste Disposal Authorities and Private Industry

In the list of production rates of controlled waste for the UK in Table 10.1 the 18 M tonnes per year of household and commercial waste was thought to be handled almost entirely by the Waste Disposal Authorities.[3] However, of the other 38 M tonnes per year, a considerable part was dealt with by the private waste disposal industry and by manufacturing firms treating their own wastes. Clearly there is some element of competition between the public and private sectors over waste disposal, yet the 1974 Act gives the former considerable powers over the latter by the site licensing procedure.

The delicacy of this position was recognised in another publication by the Department of the Environment,[4] part of a useful continuing series of papers on waste management. The publication said it would be absolutely essential for a spirit of good co-operation to be developed between the Waste Disposal Authorities and the various elements of the private sector, comprising industrial firms producing waste, waste disposal contractors, companies specialising in waste recovery and mineral operators. It stated that this co-operation should be aimed at:

(a) reclamation of materials, energy or land, wherever worthwhile;
(b) good planning, taking into account all available treatment and disposal facilities in each Waste Disposal Authority area;
(c) full effective use of the disposal capacity at each facility;
(d) the receipt of the kinds of waste for which sites have been licensed and are best able to handle; and
(e) the carrying out of disposal operations in a manner consistent with acceptable environmental and public health standards.

At a conference two years after the date of the above publication, it was said that the licensing system was working well, especially in reducing the number of landfill operations which had previously been run improperly.[10,22] Before the 1974 Act the public sector had been little concerned with the disposal problems of industrial wastes. Since then, however, there had been a marked change of outlook. Some Waste Disposal Authorities were accepting a wide variety of wastes at their own treatment facilities and were able to plan for all their area's needs. Examples of large-scale co-operation between the public and private sectors were beginning to emerge.[10] However, at the same conference it was alleged that long-term planning of disposal facilities was conspicuously lacking in some parts of the UK.[2] A case was made for overall planning by regions, each of which would include the areas of several Waste Disposal Authorities. Such regions would be more favourably placed than individual Authorities to decide the optimum sizes for treatment plants and the best sites for landfill operations with hazardous wastes.

With regard to the charging system for disposing of industrial wastes the Department of the Environment has encouraged Waste Disposal Authorities to impose the full economic cost for use of its disposal services or treatment facilities.[4] This cost should allow for such factors as depreciation, interest charges on capital, the market value of land and any resale of reclaimed material. With this system there would be no unfair advantage over private waste disposal firms and the full cost would be borne by the waste producers, not by the ratepayers in general. The further point was made that the charging structure should take into account the varying levels of cost incurred by a Waste Disposal Authority with different wastes, depending on the nature and relative difficulty in handling each material.

Compared with the situation existing prior to 1972, when the disposal of dangerous wastes was carried out with little systematic planning, the 1974 Act lays down a framework which should foster much better co-operation between public and private sectors of the disposal industry. The British methods of controlling pollution of both air and water have won acclaim by the way good relationships are normally established between all the parties concerned. If a similar pattern can be set up for the disposal of solid wastes, and early indications are promising, then much better planning to meet future disposal needs should result. Specific advantages gained could include possible sharing of large-scale facilities between the public and private sectors, co-operative measures during emergency shutdowns of a receiving plant, allowing redirection to an alternative place, and rational long-term planning for both new landfill sites and also other treatment plants.

10.2.3. The Rôle of the Water Authorities

Under the 1974 Act, before a waste disposal site can be licensed, approval must be obtained from both the local Waste Disposal Authority and the Regional Water Authority. In the event of a continuing disagreement between the two Authorities, a ruling has to be sought from the Secretary of State for the Environment. This rôle of the Water Authorities in the licensing procedure appears to be a particularly difficult one. They have a statutory duty to provide a wholesome supply of water for domestic purposes and are charged with securing the protection and proper use of all inland water, including water in the underground strata. However, they have no such direct responsibilities in respect of waste disposal. Consequently early critics of the 1974 Act expected the Water Authorities to play an entirely negative part over the licensing of disposal sites.

Waste disposal of toxic materials by burial in a landfill operation is discussed at some length later in this chapter. However, the following points are of major concern to Water Authorities when considering whether to give their approval to an application to start up a new landfill scheme:

(1) The prevention of groundwater pollution is of particular importance. Normally groundwater supplies are of naturally high quality and they are generally used for public consumption with little treatment. However, if any polluting material reaches such supplies, the effects are often serious. The rate of underground travel of pollutants may be slow and may be very difficult to detect. If such transport does occur and leads to the contamination of an aquifer, (a water-bearing stratum), then usually no emergency purification of that water can be carried out. Just as the onset of pollution is often slow to occur, so too is the reverse process. The recovery of an aquifer to its former purity generally takes a considerable time. Thus it is possible that an ill-considered decision to allow a particular disposal licence might cause contamination of a valuable groundwater supply for many years.

(2) While it is not easy to predict future demand for water, some forecasts indicate a progressively increasing rate of consumption. If these forecasts prove correct, Water Authorities will have to turn to new sources, including streams and rivers.Experience has shown that such surface waters are much more at risk to contamination from landfill waste disposal than groundwater supplies.

(3) Quite small concentrations of some pollutants render water unpalatable, by their effects on taste and smell. Additionally there is some anxiety about the effects of unnatural trace constituents in drinking water on the health of consumers and in the environment generally, as will be discussed in the next section.

To summarise their position, the Water Authorities are concerned to protect from possible contamination by pollutants all existing supplies of potable water and also other resources which may have to be called on if demand continues to increase. However, there is also a continuing demand for waste disposal sites. Although surplus space is often available in areas remote from industries producing waste, the use of such areas implies high transport and handling costs, often associated with intense public reaction against the road traffic which is generated.

There is evidence[21] that some Water Authorities in close consultation with Waste Disposal Authorities have been able to reach decisions based on good balancing of interests between waste disposal needs and the protection of water. This has meant accepting the arguments for a new landfill site to be licensed, as a service to local industry, even where there has been some risk of contamination to sources of water. Clearly some decisions of this type may not be easy to make, until more research has been carried out into the behaviour of potential pollutants after their burial in landfill schemes.

10.3. CASE STUDIES OF SOME PERSISTENT POLLUTANTS

10.3.1. Introduction

Some toxic substances, released into the environment by man's activities in greater amounts or higher local concentrations than occur naturally, can have a considerable impact in altering the balance of nature. Unlike most other materials, they may be biologically degraded only very slowly, or even not at all. Such persistent pollutants can accumulate in the soil or in species of living organisms at various stages of natural food chains. This may harm those species and may lead to upsets in the balance between adjacent species in the food chain. The well-being of man himself can be threatened, sometimes in small localities around the source emitting the pollutant, but also sometimes over a widespread population.

The problems posed by substances of this type are among the most serious in the entire field of pollution control. Since an appreciation of the possible impact of such materials is necessary to understand some of the measures and restrictions adopted in methods for waste disposal, four case studies are presented below. These describe persistent toxins which have already caused considerable alarm. They have been selected as examples because some knowledge now exists relating to their progress through, and their impact on, the environment. Following these case studies we will attempt to draw conclusions and recommendations which may be relevant to other persistent toxins, which have the potential to pose similar threats in the future.

10.3.2. Chlorinated Organic Pesticides

This class of compound came into the environmental spotlight in the late 1950s following some years of excessive use of substances such as DDT, dieldrin and aldrin. The general properties of these compounds include high stability, low vapour pressure, very low solubility in water although substantial solubility in oils and fats. Quite clearly these properties contribute enormously to their effectiveness as pesticides since they break down or evaporate into the atmosphere only slowly and are not washed away quickly by rainfall. In fact, with repeated heavy application, they accumulate both in soil and in the body fats of many animal species.

TABLE 10.2
DDT IN MAN[a]

Country	Average DDT in body fats in man, ppm
Canada	1.6
Czechoslovakia	5.5
France	1.7
Hungary	5.7
India	16
Israel	8.5
USA, California	5.3

[a]Modified from Sax[19]

Whilst the heavy agricultural dosings were aimed at insect pests, significant quantities passed steadily along the food chains into birds, rodents, fish, farm animals and eventually man. Over most of the world drinking water and milk were appreciably contaminated. Table 10.2[19] gives the following figures for the average concentration of DDT in the body fats in man in several countries of the world in the early 1960s, as determined by colorimetric analysis.

In the most heavily dosed regions some animal species were wiped out; smaller concentrations of pesticide affected the reproductive capacities of some species, in such matters as the fertility of parents, the survival of offspring and the shell thickness of birds' eggs. The body burdens of these pesticides in man have not been proved to cause ill-effects. In recent years, however, several of these compounds (aldrin, dieldrin, chlordane and heptachlor) have been shown to cause cancer in mice and rats; consequently they are now banned from use in the USA by the Environmental Protection Agency. Studies of their possible carcinogenic effects on man appear to have been inconclusive.

In the 1960s widespread public concern was voiced over the heavy use of persistent pesticides and their effects on the balance of nature. Since then their use in America and Europe has fallen sharply, only specialised agricultural applications being permitted. A corresponding decrease in the body burdens of man and of animals has been noted. Extensive use of these pesticides in tropical countries still continues.

Many other organic compounds containing halogen atoms exhibit similar toxic and persistent properties to those of the related pesticides. Consequently great care must be exercised to prevent their release to the environment, the treatment of waste residues containing such compounds is a difficult and expensive problem. They are listed in Annex I of the Oslo Convention which groups those materials banned from sea disposal except in trace quantities. This Convention was ratified by the UK by the Dumping at Sea Act 1974. In addition these compounds are often toxic to bacteria, even in small doses, so they must be precluded from microbiological treatment plants. Generally the only fully satisfactory method of disposal is incineration, with careful scrubbing of the off-gases to prevent atmospheric pollution, followed by chemical treatment of the liquor to yield a disposable solid.

10.3.3. Polychlorinated Biphenyls (PCBs)

This is a class of substances produced from the chlorination of diphenyl. In the past these substances were used extensively on account of their high stability, low volatility, non-flammability and dielectric properties; typical applications were as pesticides, heat transfer fluids, hydraulic fluids, lubricating oils and dielectric fluids for transformers.

It is thought probable that PCBs do not occur naturally. However, on account of their extremely high stability and persistence, they are now present over a wide area of the earth's surface, due to careless industrial use and waste disposal. It is estimated that the world cumulative production of PCBs has been of the order of 1 M tonnes; of this more than a half has entered dumps and landfills where it is likely to be stable and released only very slowly.[26] In animals these compounds are metabolised and excreted only very slowly and tend to accumulate in fatty tissues, especially those of aquatic species and predatory birds. Table 10.3[5] gives the levels of concentration which have been reported in some species. Marked toxic

TABLE 10.3
POLYCHLORINATED BIPHENYLS IN SOME SPECIES[a]

Species	Mean concentration of PCBs (ppm)
Lobsters	0.1
Mussels	0.5
Herring	2
A heron's liver	900

[a]Table compiled from data in DoE Waste Management Paper No. 6.[5]

effects on such species have been noted, as well as damage to the reproductive systems of birds. Regarding man, no widespread toxic effects have been noted, although in a region of Japan over 1000 people were seriously affected by an accidental contamination of rice with PCBs used as a heat-transfer fluid.

OECD Member countries have stated that[15] 'because of unacceptable levels of PCBs found in the environment and because of a number of incidents involving human health', they resolve to restrict the use of PCBs to:

(i) dielectric fluids for transformers of large power-factor correction capacitors,
(ii) heat-transfer fluids (other than in processing of foods, drugs, feeds and veterinary products),
(iii) hydraulic fluids in mining equipment, and
(iv) small capacitors (but working towards an elimination of this use).

A publication by the Department of the Environment has emphasised the need for good housekeeping where PCBs are concerned.[5] It strongly urges reclamation of PCBs from waste residues, wherever possible, otherwise they should undergo incineration at 1100°C for 2 s with 3% excess oxygen. Stack emissions should not exceed 1 mg PCB/m^3. Included in the incineration should be any contaminated equipment such as empty container drums, after use with PCBs. If neither recovery nor incineration is possible, wastes containing low concentrations of PCBs may be buried in containers in a landfill site posing no potential threat to water.

10.3.4. Mercury

Traditionally mercury was recognised as a threat to human health from its use in treating fabrics. However in the 1950s fishing communities living around Minamata Bay in Japan were stricken with a mysterious ailment, later shown to be a more insidious form of mercury poisoning. Many died while others suffered degrees of paralysis involving the limbs, speech and vision.

A significant difference between the effect on man of the 'Minamata disease' from that of elemental mercury lies in the speed with which the offending substance is eliminated from the body. Elemental mercury has a half-life in man of about 6 days whereas the Minamata form of mercury has a half-life of about 70 days and so tends to accumulate strongly in the body. Research has shown that in the latter form, mercury is combined with organic radicals to form stable compounds, all commonly referred to as 'alkyl mercury'. These compounds are apparently converted from inorganic forms of mercury in industrial effluents by a type of bacterium found in the bottom sediments of waterways and estuaries. (This is an unusual example of a bacterial process intensifying a disposal problem, rather than helping to abate it.)

Alkyl mercury accumulates in fish and shell fish and hence can present a severe hazard to humans whose diet is rich in seafood. Some lakes in Sweden, Canada and the USA are banned for fishing because of high mercury levels, the maximum limits being 1.0 ppm in Sweden and 0.5 ppm in Canada and the USA. Catches around Britain are monitored for mercury levels and some sea areas sometimes show levels above 0.5 ppm.[7]

A major unknown factor in this situation is the time taken for mercury in effluents to appear as methyl mercury in fish. The average time lag is probably several years. Many estuaries and sea areas around old discharge points have considerable residual mercury in sediments, so the position will need careful scrutiny for a long time. Attempts to reduce the formation of alkyl mercury, for instance by changing the pH of the water or by dredging up the sediments, have been unsuccessful. Hence the main remedy to be pursued is that in accordance with the following policy statement of OECD Member countries:[15]

'(a) To reduce all man-made emissions of mercury to the environment to the lowest possible levels, with particular attention to (i) the elimination of alkyl-mercury compounds from all uses that allow this material to reach the environment in any way; (ii) the maximum possible reduction of mercury in discharges from all industrial plants using or manufacturing products containing mercury chemicals;

(b) for which immediate targets should be: (i) the elimination of alkyl-mercury compounds in agriculture; (ii) the elimination of all mercury compounds from use in the pulp and paper industry; (iii) the maximum possible reduction in the discharges of mercury from mercury-cell chloralkali plants.'

For considering the disposal of waste streams containing mercury, the limit for acceptance as a trade effluent is only 1 mg mercury/litre. For possible disposal at sea, mercury is included in Annex I of the Oslo Convention, so that no more than trace quantities are allowed. Clearly therefore any mercury present in effluent water streams must be removed with a high degree of efficiency, for instance by precipitation as the sulphide.

10.3.5. Lead

It has been said that of all the poisons known to man, the general population is nearest to the limit with lead. However, lead is different from the persistent toxins already discussed, in that man is subject to its effects directly from his own activities, not through intermediate animal species. A vigorous research programme has been carried out to try and ascertain the effects of lead on humans. For instance studies have been made to monitor the rates of absorption of lead entering either the lungs or the stomach, the transport of lead within the body, its effects on the performances of the major organs and on health in general, and to measure rates of excretion. The movement of lead through the environment has also been studied to a great extent. Although some aspects of the situation have been greatly clarified, others are still subject to much uncertainty and controversy.

Lead poisoning has been known for hundreds of years, since the lead mining of the Roman era. Even now, however, it is very difficult to diagnose if no pointer to it exists. Most of the body burden lies as a relatively inert pool in the skeleton, generally increasing throughout life.[24] A much smaller, more mobile, portion lies in soft tissues and the blood. The concentration of lead in the blood is generally used as the most accessible indication of the threat to health.

In the past deaths have occurred through high exposure to lead, but it is probable that this risk is now small. There is greater concern currently over the subtler ways lead can damage health at moderate exposure levels. Especially is this true for young children. Some researchers believe that, at blood lead concentrations well below those thought dangerous for adults, children suffer brain damage and show serious behavioural problems of a hyperactive nature. Published results indicate significant decreases in the mental performances of groups with higher-than-average blood lead concentrations, even though these concentrations are well within the range normally found in children from industrial and urban communities. While the evidence is not yet conclusive, in its present form it is deeply disturbing.

It has been established reasonably accurately that about 35% of the lead inhaled by man is deposited in the lungs. However, even in air considerably polluted by lead particles, only a minor portion of the total intake of lead by the body enters this way. The major portion is taken in via the stomach, which absorbs approximately 10% of the lead content of food and drink. A dangerously high intake of lead can occur through airborne emissions from industrial smelters, any lead in toys or paints which might be chewed by children, and water supplies conveyed by lead piping, especially if these are soft and acidic.[1]

A particularly heated subject under debate is the danger arising from alkyl-lead additives in petrol, most of the lead content of which reaches the atmosphere in small particles. Calculations show that amounts inhaled will not normally constitute a major threat to health. Nevertheless these particles are distributed over wide areas, especially in highly populated towns. It is argued that this lead is dangerous to children of the vulnerable age range, for instance by ingestion via sweets or fingers dirty with dust. Almost all countries have now decided to reduce their usage of these additives to petrol.

Most plants do not take in substantial amounts of lead from the soil or via their leaves. However, cereals and root crops can absorb significant quantities and these can make high contributions to human daily lead intake. Therefore care needs to be exercised over the use as fertiliser of sewage sludge containing lead. Any lead in water effluent streams is concentrated into sewage sludge during microbiological treatment.

In practice now trade effluent is not permitted to contain more than 5 mg Pb/litre, so prior removal of lead is often needed to comply with this. With regard to disposal at sea, lead is included in the substances listed in Annex II of the Oslo Convention, which require special care owing to their bioaccumulative and toxic properties.

10.3.6. Conclusions from Case Studies

Four case studies have been described in which the well-being of man has been seriously threatened by the effects of chemicals in the environment. In each example the full severity of the hazards would have been almost impossible to predict. Even with lead many of whose toxic properties had been known for years, the particular vulnerability of children would not have been easy to forecast.

All of these case studies have been subject to an intense research effort devoted to establishing the means by which the toxins travel through the environment, the effects they have on plant and animal life, and more especially on man himself. It is clear that these four types of toxin have widely differing properties. Consequently it is difficult to draw conclusions which will be useful in counteracting other potential pollutants. Thus lead makes its impact on man largely in the forms in which it is discharged to the environment, whereas inorganic mercury is converted to a far more dangerous form by a bacterial process occurring in aquatic sediments. Links in the cases of this alkyl mercury and the chlorinated organic compounds are that the natural rates of breakdown in the environment are very slow, and that accumulation can take place in various stages of natural food chains. Future precautions to anticipate and avoid problems with such persistent toxins must include close monitoring of the environment to ensure that similar accumulations do not occur with new pollutants. The analytical work involved will be substantial. New chemicals of potential commercial significance are discovered at a surprisingly high rate. The OECD recommends that its Member countries should each keep statistics of rates of manufacturing and importing chemicals, and should develop procedures that may be used to assess these chemicals' potential effects on the environment. Also, before marketing any new products, their effects on both man and his environment should be determined.[15]

Apart from the well-documented impacts on natural processes made by the four types of pollutant described in the case studies there is concern about the possible public health risks associated with the presence of other trace organic compounds in water supplies. Perhaps the chief cause for worry is that some of these compounds are possible carcinogens, agents capable of causing cancer. With such agents the American Conference of Governmental Industrial Hygienists has traditionally held the view that the only safe concentration is zero. Certainly there is a great deal of controversy in attempting to relate the dosages used in animal tests to measure carcinogenicity and the results arising to the dangers facing man. In recent years additional valuable information on the properties of possible carcinogens has come from the development of mutagenic testing. However, taking into account the results of both mutagenic testing and tests on animals, considerable uncertainty remains.

Some opinions have been expressed that the majority of human cancers are caused by chemical carcinogens in the environment and are, therefore, ultimately preventable. However a Study Group of the Royal Society has said[18] that there is no firm evidence to suggest that industrial pollutants have had any major effect on the physical health and mortality of the general population, apart from the urban air pollutants implicated in chronic bronchitis. Nevertheless the same publication expressed concern over the use on a massive scale of a large number of substances, without adequate toxicological data. Also it said that systems for monitoring trends in human disease are inadequately developed.

In many countries regulations have been set up requiring the strict testing of chemicals to determine any toxic effects they may have on men or on the natural environment. From the past we can see that it is difficult to predict accurately the behaviour of substances new to the environment or present in higher local concentrations than occur naturally. Although the land, the atmosphere and the oceans are often regarded as the eventual sinks for many pollutants, these substances may return to man in his food and water. Great care will continue to be needed in disposing of wastes.

10.4. TOXIC WASTE TREATMENT METHODS

10.4.1. Reclamation

A process designer should look at this possibility before alternative methods of waste treatment, involving disposal. Certainly this aspect of solid waste treatment is given great emphasis in the 1974 Control of Pollution Act and Waste Disposal Authorities are expected to encourage recycling schemes. In recent years many successful projects have been reported, in which several materials are reclaimed, including metals, solvents, lubricating oils and plastics.[9] In the UK a Waste Materials Exchange has been set up[17] resulting in a considerable re-usage of process waste, with saving both to the two parties involved in each transaction, and to the country in reduced import costs for new materials.

Obviously the deciding factor in a potential reclamation scheme is financial. The cost of the treatment process, less the value of recovered material, must not be greater than the cost of disposing of the raw waste. It seems likely that, as time passes, the financial aspects will tend to move in favour of more reclamation. The cost of the most common method of solid waste disposal, to a landfill operation, will probably continue to rise (see Section 10.4.7). Furthermore the values of most mineral-based materials will probably tend to increase sharply, as the earth's resources become depleted. For instance, known reserves of lead and mercury will probably approach exhaustion in the period 1985–1990, with tin only slightly better placed. In such circumstances, research and development into new reclamation processes make good economic sense, as well as helping extend the life of natural resources and simultaneously reducing the risk of pollution.

10.4.2. Chemical Treatment of Wastes

Under this heading two different types of waste can be considered. Firstly, wastes of a mainly aqueous nature can undergo various forms of treatment to render them suitable for discharge to a sewer or to a river. Obviously the best sequence of treatment processes will depend on the toxic constituents of the waste, but may include such as the following:

   (i) alkaline oxidation of cyanide and nitrite solutions, to cyanates and nitrates respectively;

(ii) acidic reduction of chromates, to convert the hexa-valent chromium to the trivalent state, allowing later separation as the hydroxide;

(iii) neutralisation of any acidity or alkalinity;

(iv) precipitation of the hydroxides of iron, titanium, aluminium, zinc, tin, lead, nickel, manganese, copper, cadmium and chromium;

(v) removal of arsenic as ferric arsenate in alkaline solution; and

(vi) filtering of inorganic sludges, perhaps for disposal to landfill in the contained form described next.

A second type of disposal process which can be described as chemical treatment is one which achieves solid encapsulation of poisonous wastes. Several such processes have been put forward by proprietors in which the waste is mixed and sealed in a slow-setting material, such as a special polymer, or silicates and cement. The main advantage claimed is that wastes which would be dangerous to the environment in a conventional landfill operation, such as heavy metal residues, can be safely disposed of. Tests show that the rates of leaching of these toxins are cut by a very large factor, due to the presence of the encapsulating material. These processes have found considerable application for disposing of difficult wastes and simultaneously achieving reclamation of the land surface, after the encapsulating material has set hard.

10.4.3. Disposal of Wastes by Landfill

Most of the controlled waste referred to in Section 10.1.3 is disposed of in landfill operations. Frequently these schemes involve the refilling of a disused quarry or gravel pit, and they have the advantage that, with a suitable soil covering the land can be reclaimed for agricultural or leisure use. There are also operations to reclaim marshlands by the same process. In other parts of the world, although not normally so in Britain, the waste deposition is sometimes above the natural surface of the ground, resulting eventually in the creation of a landscaped hill. It is usually estimated that about 90% of the toxic, or otherwise dangerous, wastes described in Section 10.1.3 are disposed of in the UK by landfill.

As a method of waste disposal, landfill is cheap and reasonably straightforward in operation. Nevertheless there are some potential drawbacks. Public opinion is often opposed to landfill operations because of the nuisance caused by lorry transport and dust, smells and vermin from the sites. However, the effects of these last factors have been reduced over the recent decade by improved operational techniques, such as employing temporary surface coverings of soil or rubble over the waste. Nevertheless, there is a considerable hazard to the health of all the workers concerned, particularly from any toxic constituents of the waste. The complex nature of the mixtures of material being handled makes this a difficult problem to combat. A further disadvantage with landfill operations is that under certain conditions within the bulk of the waste, anaerobic decomposition of organic material occurs. Among the decomposition products are carbon dioxide and methane, possibly accompanied by hydrogen sulphide and ammonia. The gas seeping through the surface can be flammable and malodorous and a possible embarrassment in the use of the reclaimed land.

By far the most serious concern with waste disposal by landfill is that it may lead to contamination of either surface water or groundwater. However, remarkably few cases have occurred in the UK, even from sites formerly chosen more for their convenience and proximity to industrial areas, than from hydrogeological considerations. Recent research, which will be discussed later, indicates that with due attention paid to the selection of sites, landfill should be able to continue coping with the disposal of a high proportion of hazardous waste, without too high a risk of polluting water supplies.

Conditions Within a Landfill

It is probable that the bulk of household, commercial and general industrial waste remains relatively inert after burial. However, most of the organic material will be biodegraded gradually, sometimes in aerobic conditions leading to the production of carbon dioxide and water, sometimes in anaerobic conditions as referred to previously. The progress of these biochemical reactions will depend on the nature of the deposited waste, the age of the landfill, the moisture content and temperature within the waste, the availability of oxygen and the bacteriological conditions. Similarly other types of reaction and various transport processes can occur within a landfill in a complex overall situation. The properties of a waste material which may play a part in determining its behaviour are its solubility in water at various pH values, its own acidity or alkalinity, its solvent activity or chemical reactivity towards other constituents of the waste, its electrochemical potential and its action on the rock and soil containing the landfill.

Obviously the conditions within the waste in a landfill are complex and variable. The most significant result of the many varied happenings within such a mixture is that an aqueous liquor is produced, termed leachate. A typical leachate contains a wide variety of dissolved constituents, both organic in nature, such as fatty acids, aldehydes and ketones, and also inorganic, for instance the chlorides and sulphates of common metals. The flow of leachate, and hence to some extent the concentrations of the solutes it contains, will depend on a water balance taken over the whole landfill. The chief factors will be the rate of receipt of rainfall by the landfill, the rate of evaporation of moisture from the surface, the rates of surface run-in and run-off, the moisture content of the waste solids deposited, the rate of receipt of liquid waste and the rate of change of the moisture content of the waste in the landfill. The possibility of contamination of adjacent water supplies from a landfill operation depends on what happens to the leachate.

Classification of Landfill Sites

A rough classification of landfill sites based on geological factors has been suggested:[8]

(a) those providing a significant element of containment for wastes and leachates;
(b) those allowing slow leachate migration and significant attenuation (i.e. reduction in pollutant concentrations in the leachate); and
(c) those allowing rapid leachate migration and insignificant attenuation.

Landfill sites in practice may not be fitted easily into these categories, but nevertheless the classification is a useful framework for discussion purposes.

Obviously type (c) has no merit for toxic waste disposal. A site of type (a) places little reliance on natural attenuation processes which may occur in surrounding strata, but instead aims to prevent escape of leachate. Some sites are naturally of this type, as for instance disused clay pits, or they can be artificially created with an engineered lining. If leachate is successfully contained, there is clearly no chance of polluting water supplies. However, there are often operational difficulties with this type of landfill site, generally concerned with the possible build-up of liquid. The deposited waste may become saturated with water, leading to poor biodegradation conditions. Furthermore, leachate may overflow from the site causing surface water pollution. It may be necessary with such landfill operations,

(i) to restrict the disposal of liquid wastes,
(ii) to reduce the catchment of rain and other surface water, and
(iii) to collect and remove leachate for treatment elsewhere.

A possible alternative to the last measure is the use of a leachate recycling system, with redistribution over the entire landfill surface, partly to encourage evaporation losses and partly to accelerate stabilisation of the landfill.[20]

Most existing landfill sites in the UK probably fall into the classification of type (b), where the containing ground layers allow slow passage of leachate. In these layers, suspended solids are removed from the leachate by filtration, while natural processes of adsorption and biodegradation can bring about some reduction in pollutant concentrations. Further attenuation may then occur by the diluting effects of groundwater movements. Clearly, however, there is some risk of damage to the quality of this groundwater, originating from the waste deposited in such a landfill.

For some years a controversy has existed over the relative merits of landfills of types (a) and (b). The argument has been commonly referred to as 'concentrate and contain' versus 'dilute and disperse'. Little vigorous research had been carried out to help evaluate these opposing philosophies until recent years.

Research Findings
Near the end of 1973, the Department of the Environment set up a long-term research project, culminating in a report published in 1978 entitled *Co-operative Programme of Research on the Behaviour of Hazardous Wastes in Landfill Sites.*[6] Investigations were made into the behaviour of the wastes and the fates of the leachates at 19 existing landfill sites, especially selected to represent the main geological types found in the UK. The wastes comprised a wide variety of types and physical forms. Additionally a contaminated area in the region of an old gasworks was studied.

Chiefly the investigations entailed drilling boreholes into and around each of the sites. Thus samples of the landfill waste material and of the underlying strata were obtained, so that the composition of the waste and the quality of the groundwater could be monitored. Chemical analyses of the samples allowed the determination of the three-dimensional spread of contaminants from each landfill, while physical analyses of rock core gave an assessment of the major hydrogeological controls over the movement of these contaminants. Other work was done in taking water samples at regular intervals from boreholes outside the site, so that variations of groundwater quality with time could be measured. The research has thrown considerable light on such aspects of landfill disposal as the microbiological and chemical processes occurring within the waste, and the various factors affecting the transport of leachate from the landfill into groundwater. Interested readers should consult the report itself;[6] in this chapter there is space only to review the most significant findings.

The principal conclusion of the report is that the controlled disposal of wastes by landfill is acceptable; an ultra-cautious approach to the landfill of many hazardous wastes is not justified. The spread of pollutants around the landfill sites was often found to be restricted in extent. It was particularly noted that the presence of an unsaturated zone (in which pores and fissures are only partially filled with water, leaving space for a gas phase), was extremely beneficial at the base of a landfill. In such a zone the rate of transport of leachate was slowed, biodegradation of organic constituents was encouraged, and adsorption and precipitation often took place to reduce the concentrations of inorganic materials. Thus, provided the unsaturated zone was at least 2 m in thickness (preferably of mixed mineralogy, including clays) considerable attenuation of pollutants occurred. This took place at an ideal time in the overall leachate migration process, just prior to the stage of dispersion and dilution in any groundwater flows beneath the landfill. However it was also noted that, if the liquid loading of a landfill was excessive, no unsaturated zone existed at the base. Consequently leachate was able to pass relatively quickly from the landfill into the underlying strata, entirely through zones saturated with water, with little attenuation of pollutants other than by dilution.

The report points out that it is still not possible to categorise particular types of waste and assign them to particular classes of site. However, a table is presented in the report relating effective attenuation of pollutants with rate of leachate transport and site geology. This could be useful in practice for assessing a potential landfill site, taking into consideration the types and quantities of wastes, the proposed method of deposition and the use of any nearby ground or surface waters.

The 19 landfill sites under investigation included a large variety of wastes from both domestic and industrial sources. Within the latter category, particular attention was paid to heavy metals, polychlorinated biphenyls and other halogenated hydrocarbons, acid wastes, phenols, cyanide and oils. It was found that the presence of domestic refuse helped to retain heavy metals within the refuse, except where significant quantities of acid were deposited; these caused dissolution of the metals. There was evidence that in the normal conditions of a landfill, where anaerobic degradation of organic material was occurring, certain metals, such as mercury, were converted to their relatively insoluble sulphides and hence were retained in the waste. This finding was in agreement with work reported from Holland.[12] Domestic waste had some buffer capacity with respect to acid wastes, although to only a limited extent, as is evident from the example on metal dissolution cited above. Building wastes probably had a greater neutralisation capacity than domestic waste, although a smaller capacity for absorbing liquids. Domestic waste helped in adsorbing and retaining oil, polychlorinated biphenyls and other solvents in the landfill; however with phenol the process appeared to be reversible, leading to possible escape of phenol from the landfill over a lengthy period. Studies on cyanide showed that much of it disappeared harmlessly from a landfill in a variety of ways, leaving relatively small quantities which might contaminate groundwater.

In general, the co-disposal of domestic refuse with many industrial wastes appeared to reduce the potential threat of the latter regarding possible pollution of groundwater. This conclusion is also supported by work reported from a large privately-operated mixed disposal site.[20] Although the waste input included a considerable proportion of industrial waste, together with domestic refuse, the leachate had characteristics similar to those which would be expected to arise from domestic refuse alone.

10.4.4. Disposal to Tidal Waters

As with almost all possible methods of treating industrial wastes, disposal into tidal waters has controversial aspects. This part of the sea is extraordinarily rich in both plant and animal life; any disruption of the balance between species in this zone would have repercussions on natural activities in many other areas. Coastal regions are also important for leisure pursuits, such as bathing, boating and wild fowling, as well as for commercial ventures like harbours and shellfish farms.

However Britain is fortunate in possessing a coastline which is mostly well washed by swiftly moving water. There is high tidal flow, usually good mixing by wave action, and a relatively small temperature range through the seasons because of the Gulf Stream. The high rate of dispersion makes this an effective method of disposal for many aqueous industrial effluents. When discharge is by pipeline, considerable capital cost may be involved but the operating costs are low.[13] The design can be based either on a sparge pipe, with a high exit velocity through the orifices, or on a tidal discharge system requiring appreciable storage and control.

Under the 1974 Control of Pollution Act, Consent to discharge to any tidal water is needed, from the Water Authority in England and Wales and from the River Purification Boards in Scotland. Local Authorities are also involved in planning applications. Factors which need to be considered include the public amenity value of the area, both recreational and visual, existing commercial interests, conservation of the natural fauna and flora, and protection against possible damage to the discharge system by weather or shipping. Nevertheless the chief factors governing Consent will be the properties of the particular effluent and its probable effect on the tidal water area into which it is to be released. The principal properties to be considered have been listed as:[13]

(i) *Volume.* This should not be so large as to affect the local salinity of the sea. A particularly high rate of flow will require careful siting and an efficient discharge system.

(ii) *Temperature.* This should allow the tidal water to remain within its normal range of variation. It is unlikely to be problematical, unless a very large quantity of heat is involved.

(iii) *pH.* Seawater acts as a very effective buffer for both acids and alkalis. With good dispersion, values of effluent pH between 1 and 13 are acceptable, without toxic effects occurring.

(iv) *Oxygen demand.* The BOD load should not be so large as to reduce the dissolved oxygen level to the point where marine life is affected. However, most tidal waters around Britain move and splash sufficiently vigorously for this to be very unlikely. Quite high BOD loads can normally be tolerated.

(v) *Dissolved solids.* These have little effect provided they are not toxic.

(vi) *Flotable solids.* These should not be discharged unless they degrade extremely rapidly.

(vii) *Water-immiscible liquids.* These can be a severe nuisance in the locality of the discharge and should be carefully guarded against.

(viii) *Dense suspended solids.* These might accumulate on the sea bed so they are normally limited to levels below about 150 to 300 ppm.

(ix) *Pathogenic bacteria.* These are unlikely to create a hazard except through contamination of edible shellfish.

(x) *Persistent toxic materials.* As is evident from the examples discussed in Section 10.3, any substance of this nature which is present in the effluent will require very careful scrutiny. Neither its behaviour nor its effects will be easy to anticipate. Regular ecological monitoring, at least every two years and preferably once each year, is needed to note any toxic effects on individual species or any accumulation at points in natural food chains. The costs of this monitoring may represent a considerable proportion of the costs of the entire disposal scheme.

(xi) *Non-persistent toxic materials.* Usually dilution and degradation are sufficiently rapid for all species to be unaffected. However the degree of persistence needs to be checked by regular ecological monitoring.

(xii) *Nutrients.* Materials such as phosphates and nitrates may cause eutrophication, although this is unlikely in reasonably mobile waters.

Compared with land-based methods, disposal of wastes to tidal waters is attractive, especially for acid or alkaline liquors, or effluents having substantial BOD loads or a high content of dissolved salts. A necessary provision is the ecological monitoring scheme described above.

International opinion on the merits of this method of waste disposal is mixed. In the past there have been moves within the European Economic Community to standardise pipeline discharges within tight limits of purity, which would greatly restrict both existing and new pipeline discharges from the UK. A more logical position, strongly supported in British industry, is that criteria should be framed simply to conserve the quality of the water receiving the waste and the well-being of the natural species living therein. Turbulent tidal waters have a high capacity for dealing safely with many aqueous wastes.

10.4.5. Deep Sea Disposal of Wastes

Until a few years ago wastes containing dangerous materials were dumped into deep seas with little adverse comment. However increasing international concern was voiced, especially in relation to persistent toxins being able to accumulate in various species along food chains. Two international conventions were agreed in 1972:

(a) The Convention for the Prevention of Marine Pollution by Dumping from Ships and Aircraft — known as the Oslo Convention.
(b) Convention on the Prevention of Marine Pollution by Dumping of Wastes and Other Matters — known as the London Convention.

Whereas the former agreement covers only parts of the Atlantic and Arctic Oceans, the latter covers all sea areas of the world. The UK was a party to both agreements and has embodied them in the Dumping at Sea Act 1974. Now, before any sea disposal can be made of material originating in the United Kingdom a licence must be obtained from the Ministry of Agriculture, Fisheries and Food. Among the constraints are:

(i) Materials in Annex I of the Oslo Convention are banned from sea disposal except in trace quantities. These include most organohalogen compounds, most organosilicon compounds, carcinogenic substances, mercury and cadmium-containing materials and persistent plastics.

(ii) Materials in Annex II require special care because of their potential accumulative and toxic properties. These include arsenic, copper, lead, zinc, cyanides, fluorides and pesticides. The special provisions for such materials include a sea depth of not less than 2000 m and a distance from land of not less than 150 nautical miles.

(iii) Sea disposal should be considered as a solution only when other methods have been thoroughly examined.

(iv) Consideration needs to be given to the concentrations and effects in the sea which might result from the disposal.

(v) The material should not be in liquid form, but may be adsorbed on a solid.

(vi) Generally the material should be so packaged that it will not be released during descent, the container reaching the sea bed intact.

Clearly deep-sea dumping is now severely restricted in the composition of wastes that can be disposed of. Also the care needed to handle individual drums imposes a high cost on the operation. It has been estimated that in 1976 the quantity of wastes arising in the UK that was disposed of to deep sea was in excess of 2000 tonnes.[16]

Two other methods of disposing of hazardous wastes at sea have been described.[11] One utilises the excellent buffer action of seawater, referred to in the previous Section, by releasing waste acids directly above the propeller of the ship. Rapid dilution is reported to occur, of the order of 7000 to 1, with no damage to marine life. The other method disposes of halogenated hydrocarbons which are incinerated on specially designed ships. Whereas for a land-based incineration of these compounds, the elimination of hydrogen chloride from the tail gases poses a very difficult problem, at sea significant quantities of the hydrogen chloride are allowed to escape. It is claimed that these fumes are absorbed and rapidly neutralised by the seawater, with no ecological disturbance. A special control system has been developed for these incineration ships, with operating data from the most important stages of the disposal procedure recorded in a 'black box', for later scrutiny by government departments.

10.4.6. Incineration

This method of disposal of hazardous organic wastes has made tremendous advances in recent years. The installed capacity of plants for chemical waste incineration in the UK has been estimated to be now of the order of 100–200 thousand tonnes per annum.[2] The subject will be discussed in depth in the next chapter.

10.5. CONCLUSION

Since 1970 the subject of hazardous waste disposal has undergone considerable change. Whereas there was then little public interest and few controls existed, there are now elaborate systems for monitoring disposal methods and people are more vociferous. Clearly there have been some substantial benefits arising from these changes. The environment is better protected by this tighter control, and consequently there is a much smaller risk to the health of mankind from a build-up of toxins in food sources. A great deal of progress has been made from research into both traditional methods of disposal, such as landfill, and also newer methods such as incineration. It has been shown that landfill is an acceptable means of disposing of many hazardous wastes. Considerable expertise has been developed in the entire subject area, such as that possessed by the Hazardous Materials Service at Harwell.

On the other hand, the system built up for controlling disposal has led to a vast increase in paperwork and inevitably to sharply increased costs for manufacturers. No attempt is made in this chapter to estimate the costs associated with the various methods of treatment. Such costs are currently subject to a rapid rate of general inflation and also they vary considerably according to the form and composition of the particular waste mixture. Normally disposal by landfill or to tidal waters is much cheaper than an elaborate chemical treatment, or disposal to deep sea or by incineration. Looking to the future, it is generally anticipated that the amount of industrial waste will continue to increase markedly. Nevertheless its volume will still only be equivalent to about 20% of the void created by mineral extraction. In total availability of space therefore, disposal to land will not reach a limit in the foreseeable future. However, there will probably be a marked shortage of such sites close to many urban and industrial areas. Unless permission is given to develop above-ground mounds of waste, to be landscaped later, more distant landfill sites will have to be used, with a consequent sharp increase in costs.

It is more difficult to predict any other changes which may occur. The major uncertainties are the effects of any future international agreements on pollution control measures and also the actions of public pressure groups demonstrating a dislike for the transport of dangerous wastes or for the local effects of waste treatment sites.

Within the entire subject of hazardous wastes, the most serious worry is that of persistent toxins. The examples described in Section 10.3 indicate how they are able to disrupt the balance of nature and also to threaten the well-being of mankind. Recently elaborate testing procedures have been set up to predict the effects of all chemicals within the environment and on health. This system will be a good safeguard against the re-occurrence of similar events caused by other toxins, but vigilance will still be needed by all concerned.

REFERENCES

1. Cook, J., Environmental pollution by heavy metals, *Intern. J. Environmental Studies*, **10** (1977), 253.
2. Davies, D.R., In *Conference Transcript; Treatment and Disposal of Hazardous Wastes*. Oyez, London, 1978.
3. Department of the Environment, *Waste Management Paper No. 1. Reclamation, Treatment and Disposal of Wastes*. HMSO, London, 1976.
4. Department of the Environment, *Waste Management Paper No. 5. The Relationship Between Waste Disposal Authorities and Private Industry*. HMSO, London, 1976.
5. Department of the Environment, *Waste Management Paper No. 6. Polychlorinated Biphenyl Wastes*. HMSO, London, 1976.
6. Department of the Environment *Co-operative Programme of Research on the Behaviour of Hazardous Waste in Landfill Sites*. Final Report of the Policy Review Committee. HMSO, London, 1978.
7. Gardner, D., Mercury in fish and waters of the Irish Sea and other United Kingdom fishing grounds, *Nature*, **272** (5648) (1978), 49.
8. Gray, D.A., Mather, J.D. and Harrison, I.B., *Hydrogeological Guidelines for the Selection of Landfill Sites*. Institute of Geological Sciences, London, 1974.
9. I. Mech.E. Conference publications, *Waste in the Process Industries*. Mechanical Engineering Publications Ltd., London, 1977.
10. Jackson, D.W., In *Conference Transcript; Treatment and Disposal of Hazardous Wastes*. Oyez Ltd, London, 1978.
11. Kuntze, E., Location, control and disposal of liquid wastes from trade and industry in the Federal Republic of Germany, *Prog. Wat. Tech.*, **10** (1978), 399.
12. Mather, J.D. and Bromley, J., Research into leachate generation and attenuation at landfill sites, Land Reclamation Conference, 1976, Thurrock, Essex.
13. Moss, A., The disposal of effluent to tidal waters by pipeline, Eurochem. Conference, Paper 31, 1977, Birmingham.
14. Office of Solid Waste Management Programs, *Report to Congress: Disposal of Hazardous Wastes*, US EPA, No. SW-115. Washington, DC, 1974.
15. Organisation for Economic Co-operation and Development, *OECD and the Environment*. OECD, Paris, 1976.
16. Pearce, K., Deep sea disposal of wastes, Eurochem. Conference, Paper 32, 1977, Birmingham.
17. Poll, A. and Allen, J., The working of the UK waste materials exchange, In *Waste in the Process Industries*, I. Mech. E. Conference. Mechanical Engineering Publications, London, 1977.

18. Royal Society Study Group, *Long-term Toxic Effects; Final Report.* The Royal Society, London, 1978.
19. Sax, N.I., *Industrial Pollution.* Van Nostrand Reinhold Co., London, 1974.
20. Scott, M.P., Strategies for land disposal of hazardous wastés, *Publ. Health Engr.,* **6** (1978), 94.
21. Selby, K.H., In *Conference Transcript; Treatment and Disposal of Hazardous Wastes.* Oyez Ltd, London, 1978.
22. Singleton, K.G., In *Conference Transcript; Treatment and Disposal of Hazardous Wastes.* Oyez Ltd, London, 1978.
23. Technical Committee Report, Ministry of Housing and Local Government *Disposal of Solid Toxic Wastes.* HMSO, London, 1970.
24. World Health Organisation, *Environmental Health Criteria; Lead.* WHO, Geneva, 1977.
25. World Health Organisation, *Environmental Health Criteria; Mercury.* WHO, Geneva, 1976.
26. World Health Organisation, *Environmental Health Criteriá; Polychlorinated Biphenyls and Terphenyls.* WHO, Geneva, 1976.

11

Incineration

G.D. KELSEY

Chief Engineer, Process Engineering, NEI International Combustion Ltd, Derby, UK

11.1. THE WASTE PROBLEM

Waste materials arise from our everyday activities both at home and at work. The dust bin is a familiar sight at every household and is used as that receptacle into which all domestic discard is placed.

Industry follows a similar pattern in that there is some reject material from virtually every production process, be it packaging material from incoming goods, general process waste in the form of 'off cut' material, off specification raw materials or pollution debris together with all the domestic quality waste materials which originate from normal establishment operations. Until the realities of waste disposal confront the plant management, the magnitude of the problem is frequently not appreciated. Waste may be in the form of solids, sludges, pastes or liquids, so that the method of disposal must be selected which is compatible with the physical conditions.

Incineration is the disposal process which converts combustible material to gaseous oxides, leaving incombustible material as residues. This operation converts waste into a reasonably consistent, innocuous mass suitable for landfill and a gaseous product as is generally expected of a normal combustion process. Also the total bulk is reduced to manageable proportions.

11.2. SYSTEMS AVAILABLE FOR WASTE DISPOSAL

11.2.1. Tipping

Tipping is the accepted method for the disposal of bulky waste of the domestic type. This class of waste is generally free of toxic materials and as such is not expected to present the accepted problems associated with toxic materials.

Tipping, however, does demand sufficient space for acceptance of bulky waste. It also demands that such space will not be used for load bearing structures for a number of decades.

The land strata in the tipping area must also be such that leachate from rainfall will not percolate through to underground water supplies, nor should it drain away to pollute natural waterways. Waste material may be in the 'as collected' form or compressed into bales for disposal. Industry does not generally have such space available but it may use Local Authority facilities if permission is granted.

Disposal of this class of waste takes place firstly by burying, but over the years biodegradation sets in to give methane, carbon dioxide and water vapour as principal products. The final product is a humus which requires absorption by the soil for total disposal.

11.2.2. Composting

Making compost from the domestic type of waste is a highly attractive technical outlet and can be used for joint disposal with sewage sludge, although the economics and commercial absorption of the product are sometimes questionable. In the UK the humus content of the soil is generally of an acceptable level and, as an ongoing soil additive, compost generally satisfies only the domestic outlet. Commercially, manures, peat, etc., are used to satisfy humus conditions. In other countries the problem is different in that many have soils which are of minimum fertility due in part to shortcomings in the humus content.

The process of making compost from domestic-type waste material does specifically require that waste selection or waste preparation should be carried out to remove those materials which are non-biodegradable, i.e. glass, plastic, metals, ceramics, etc. Not all will be removed and a small content of 'hard' material is bound to be beneficial in the handling characteristics of the product. The reject material must be disposed of, for example by tipping. Composting does give a route whereby highly organic cellulosic waste and vegetable matter can be disposed of, the process producing a large volume reduction in the waste.

11.2.3. Pyrolysis

Pyrolysis is a thermal treatment process whereby waste is subjected to heating in an atmosphere with a deficiency of oxygen below stoichiometric combustion levels. Under such conditions thermal degradation of organic materials takes place to give gases, liquids and a solid char. The gases and liquids may be considered as fuels for subsequent use either in the actual pyrolysis process, or transported off-site where they may be used as refined fuels. The char is the 'coke' ingredient and contains mineral matter, free carbon and inert material present in the waste. It is innocuous and may be further processed as required to give resource recovery. Pyrolysis dictates that some sorting of the waste is carried out, together with size reduction of the desired ingredients which are to be subjected to heating.

11.2.4. Incineration

Incineration is a combustion process and for combustion to be effectively achieved, the waste must be considered as a fuel whose use requires some degree of quantitative assessment to be made. Incineration breaks down waste to release organic constituents in the gaseous form and the inerts and residuals in the form of ash. By such a process the bulk volume of waste is reduced to a low level, the ash being suitable for landfill for all purposes. Incineration will take waste in a variety of forms, be it solid, paste, sludge, slurry, liquid or gas, with specialist devices being applied to achieve the same objectives, i.e. innocuous gases and inert solids.

11.3. WASTE PROBLEM DEFINITION

Before a disposal route can be defined there are certain basic requirements to be met. Initially these will be a knowledge of:

(i) the amount of waste for disposal;
(ii) the outlets of all waste production;
(iii) the qualitative make-up of wastes at each of these outlets, i.e. the constituent items; and
(iv) the periodicity of collection from each outlet.

This analysis of the problem gives a qualitative appreciation from which the disposal route may be easily defined.

Selection of incineration as the disposal route requires that further analysis of the problem be made to define:

(i) the chemical analysis of each specified waste;
(ii) the storage requirements for each waste;
(iii) the blending of constituents; and
(iv) the methods of feeding the constituents to the combustion process.

Once the problem has been defined and all the above pertinent data collected the mechanism of the combustion process must be considered.

The quantitative/qualitative analyses on a constituent basis will give a picture of the physical nature of the waste which is to be regarded as a fuel for combustion purposes. This approach is similar to the screening analysis of coal which indicates to the fuel technologist the physical nature of the fuel from which he can prescribe the handling equipment and type of combustion equipment necessary to burn it. Similarly, oil may be defined in terms of viscosity which again will define the approach to combustion.

11.3.1. Waste Analysis

Constituent Analysis
Having defined the physical appearance of the waste, the next stage is to build up an analytical picture. It has already been stated that a knowledge of the qualitative make-up of waste at each waste outlet is a basic requirement. To proceed to the next stage of analysis requires that the quantitative make-up of waste in constituent form shall be undertaken. This is done by hand sorting in the case of solid waste to define the proportions of, for example, paper, plastics, rubber, wood, glass, vegetable, etc. Workers[1] in this field have given values for analyses of these components and these values when applied to constituent analyses will give a computed analysis for the waste. Care should be taken in using the analyses, since moisture variations in particular may be quite wide.

Whilst this approach is the simple one, actual analysis of the composite refuse is the ideal approach or actual analysis of each component as it arises in an establishment may be more accurate for day-by-day computing. Sampling can be applied to the waste constituents to give representative samples on which the basic fuel analysis can be made.

Proximate Analysis[2]
This type of analysis is a more detailed form of constituent analysis in that it defines the moisture, ash, volatile matter and fixed carbon of an organic material. A calorific value determination completes this analysis.

Moisture is usually determined by loss in weight when a sample is heated to 105°C. It may however be determined by other methods for any materials which are unstable at this temperature. For example, Dean and Stark and vacuum drying are two methods which are frequently used.

Volatile matter is the loss in weight when a sample is heated to 925°C in the absence of air for a defined time period. This is usually done in a crucible with a close fitting lid to allow gas outflow and prevent oxygen ingress. The loss in weight is actually volatile matter plus moisture, but since the moisture content is separately determined the volatile matter is readily calculated. The residual matter is a char which comprises the ash together with what is frequently referred to as 'fixed carbon'.

Ash is separately determined by ignition of a sample of the waste to constant weight in a fully oxidising atmosphere. Subtraction of the ash value from the residue of the volatile matter determination gives the fixed carbon content.

Calorific value is determined by the bomb calorimeter method, which is described in detail in most physics text books.

The proximate analysis gives an indication of how the residue will break down when heat is applied. Consider the case of a solid waste which is being burnt in the form of a bed of material. Waste is fed into a hot combustion zone and radiant heat drives off the volatile material. The amount of volatile matter indicated by analysis identifies the degree of burning in the form of flame. The fixed carbon content indicates that, if it is to be burnt, air must pass through the bed of char. The ratio of air required to burn volatile matter, and that to burn fixed carbon gives an appreciation of the anticipated primary and secondary air requirements.

Ultimate Analysis

In order to calculate the true quantities of air for combustion it is necessary to carry analysis a stage further to determine the elemental composition of the organic waste. In this aspect ash and moisture do not play a very significant part. The elements that are significant are carbon, hydrogen and oxygen and it is of importance to analyse for these elements using methods as outlined in most practical organic chemistry text books.[4] Calculations from this analysis will give the proportions of combustion products and will enable design and operating parameters to be laid down.

Interpretation of Analyses

From the results of the analysis calculations can be readily carried out to assess:

(a) the theoretical amount of air required for combustion;
(b) the gas analysis of combustion products for variations in excess air supply;
(c) gas temperature in relation to excess air requirements; and
(d) the amount of residual ash which will arise from the combustion process.

Basic chemistry indicates reactions as follows:

$$C + O_2 \rightarrow CO_2 \tag{1}$$

$$H_2 + \tfrac{1}{2}O_2 \rightarrow H_2O \tag{2}$$

$$S + O_2 \rightarrow SO_2 \tag{3}$$

For reaction (1)   one unit by weight of carbon requires 2.67 units by weight of oxygen to give 3.67 units by weight of carbon dioxide.

For reaction (2)   one unit by weight of hydrogen requires 8 units by weight of oxygen to give 9 units by weight of water vapour.

For reaction (3)   one unit by weight of sulphur requires one unit by weight of oxygen to give 2 units by weight of sulphur dioxide.

Air contains   75.5% by weight and 78.06% by volume nitrogen.
                     23.2% by weight and 21.00% by volume oxygen.
                     1.3% by weight and 0.94% by volume of inerts.

From this data air mass requirements for stoichiometric combustion for unit mass of each principal combustible element will be:

	Oxygen	Nitrogen	Inerts	Total (Air)
Carbon	2.67	8.69	0.15	11.51
Hydrogen	8.00	26.03	0.45	34.48
Sulphur	1.00	3.25	0.06	4.31

To give flue gas products as follows:

	SO_2	CO_2	H_2O	N_2	Inerts	Total
Carbon	-	3.67	-	8.69	0.15	12.51
Hydrogen	-	-	9.00	26.03	0.45	35.48
Sulphur	2.00	-	-	3.25	0.06	5.31

If this data is applied to the combustion of cellulose, which is one of the principal ingredients of waste, being present in paper, rags, vegetables, timber, etc., then on the dry basis, air requirements and products of combustion may be readily calculated. The basic chemical formula for cellulose is $(C_6H_{10}O_5)_x$ which gives the following mass % analysis by the ultimate analysis approach

Carbon	44.45%
Hydrogen	6.17%
Oxygen	49.38%

Thus 1 kg of cellulose will require 1.680 kg of oxygen for complete combustion. Available in the cellulose is 0.494 kg of oxygen which leaves 1.186 kg to be supplied by the combustion air. The air requirement is thus 5.11 kg dry air/kg dry cellulose. The combustion products resulting are:

	kg	%
Carbon dioxide	1.630	26.66
Water vapour	0.556	9.09
Nitrogen	3.862	63.17
Inerts	0.066	1.08

Since it is not practical to operate a combustion system under stoichiometric conditions, some measure of excess air is necessary to enable good combustion to take place and to give satisfactory temperature control. Figure 11.1 shows the relationship between excess air and analysis of products of combustion.

Whilst this approach is ideally suited to a single waste ingredient, a similar approach may be made whenever a waste analysis can be given.

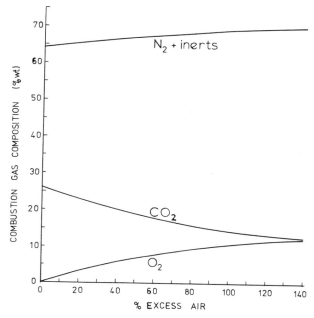

FIG. 11.1 Relationship between excess air and analysis of products of combustion.

From the known calorific value of the fuel the specific heats and specific volumes of the gases, the gas temperature is easily calculated.

11.4. TERMINAL CONDITIONS OF INCINERATION

The combustion of waste material will result in the conversion of solid waste into gases and inert residue of low bulk. Before gases from such a process are released to the atmosphere any particulate solids present must be removed. Legislation calls for different solids loadings in different parts of the world and suppliers and users of incineration equipment should make themselves aware of the legislation for their own class of establishment.

11.4.1. Gases

The particulate matter will cover a wide range of particle size from what may be loosely termed grit down to colloidal smoke. To remove such material there are several systems available which will be discussed in more detail in Volume 2. Those most widely used in incineration systems are: wet scrubbers, cyclone collectors, electrostatic precipitators and bag filters.

Wet Scrubbers

Since there are many types of wet scrubber available, only the principles of wet scrubbing need be considered. For wet scrubbing to be effective it is essential that there should be maximum contact between gas and water during transport through the scrubber. This is achieved in a number of ways such as, cascade, water droplets, foams and venturi throats. For high efficiency the latter appears to be most acceptable. For wet scrubbing to be effective there must always be available a ready supply of fresh or clean water, and a suitable means of effluent treatment for the pass-out water to ensure its quality is suitable for either disposal to drain or for re-use.

Wet scrubbing promotes the suspension of solids in water which require separation to give environmentally sound conditions but at the same time it will absorb certain products of combustion, e.g., SO_x from materials containing sulphur, NO_x from materials containing nitrogen and HCl from certain plastics, e.g. PVC. The resultant scrubber liquor is acidic and requires neutralisation in keeping with either re-use or disposal.

Cyclone Collectors

All cyclone separations, whether wet or dry, are based on differences of centrifugal force between the solid and fluid phases, removal effectiveness being proportional to the square of the diameter of the particle and the difference in specific gravity between the solids and the fluid medium in which the solids are suspended. There is also a degree of turbulence, interference by wall effects and flow patterns which show problems in fine particle removal. As such, cyclone collectors are in effect *centrifugal classifiers* and will only collect solids according to their particle size. They are applicable to particle sizes down to $10\,\mu m$, but not to fine emissions. Multi-cyclones are also frequently used. The collected solids are dry and require conditioning by moisture to allow disposal by open tipping.

Electrostatic Precipitators

On all major installations electrostatic precipitators are most frequently used to meet emission standards. Operating performance has been very good and most installations throughout the world meet the legislation laid down.

The electrostatic precipitator utilises the general principle known for many years, that if a gas conveying solid or liquid particle is caused to flow between two electrodes, one of which is charged to high potential and the other earthed, then the gas and its burden are ionised and the particulate matter driven to the earthed electrode and thus removed from the gas stream.

The charged electrodes may be in the form of wires, rods or plates, but for gas cleaning and heavy industrial use the earthed receiving electrodes are generally tubes with a discharge electrode suspended down the centre of each. They may also be plates hung vertically and suitably spaced so that the discharge electrodes may be suspended at frequent intervals between them.

Ionisation occurs at $30\text{--}50\,kV$ between electrodes. This potential gives a corona which provides the ionisation. The earthed electrode holds the solid particles which are removed by a rapping device. The solids drop into a hopper beneath and are conveyed out by screw conveyor.

Design of electrostatic precipitators for a specific gas flow is quite critical and separation efficiencies of 99% are achievable. The collected solids require conditioning as do those from cyclone separations.

Bag Filters

These are filters in the true sense of the word in that gases pass through a filter medium in the shape of a bag or stocking, made from textile fabrics, e.g. polypropylene. The solids adhere to the bag whilst gas is passing through and after a predetermined time the solids are removed from the bag by reverse air, rapping or any other mechanical means.

By virtue of the fact that the bag materials are synthetic, the operating temperature becomes very critical. In addition water quench may lead to dewpoint problems and must be avoided. Bag filters, although able to meet environmental standards, are not generally used with incineration units because of temperature control risks. Again the dry solids need conditioning.

Temperature Control

In order that gas cleaning equipment can be effective, the gases must be presented at a temperature which the equipment can tolerate. With sufficient excess air, gas exit temperatures are normally limited to 1000°C, but most gas cleaning equipment must have a temperature of no more than 350°C and in the bag filter a considerably lower temperature, in keeping with bag materials.

To achieve this temperature reduction water in the form of a fine spray is introduced into the gas stream. Evaporation of the water gives rapid cooling because of its large latent heat of vaporisation. Figure 11.2 illustrates the water requirement to quench the gases. Since this water passes directly to atmosphere, an essential part of the operation is available source of water of adequate quality for gas quenching.

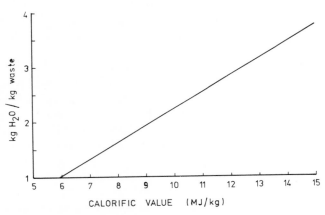

FIG. 11.2 Relationship between quench water requirement and calorific value of the waste material.

11.4.2. Ash Residues

Ash residues leave the combustion chamber at a temperature determined by the incineration equipment design. In broad terms it will be discharged at 600–900°C and for transport should be cooled to a temperature compatible with the handling equipment for removing the ash to disposal.

Low-ash waste incinerated on a static grate deposits ash into zones under the grate or just away from the grate where primary air can give cooling. When the ash is removed, it is in relatively small quantity and is cooled sufficiently for normal discharge arrangements.

On large units, where the ash content may be appreciable, the ash is discharged into a trough of water from where it is continuously removed by a dewatering conveyor into a transport vehicle. In such a form the ash is damp and cool and will meet all disposal requirements.

11.5. APPLICATION OF INCINERATORS TO VARIOUS TYPES OF WASTE

11.5.1. Waste Specification

In assessing a class of waste it is frequently difficult to label the waste as being in a certain category. Table 11.1 is a basic classification which is reasonably descriptive in that it gives much of the basic information discussed earlier in Section 11.3.1.

Garbage and animal wastes have high water contents and low calorific values. Such materials are not autothermic, i.e. they do not burn unassisted, and an auxiliary fuel is applied through two or more burners, one to promote the actual combustion of the residues and the second for overfire to destroy smoke and odours.

Many small industrial incinerators operate on a batch-loaded basis and during combustion there is variation in the combustion operation. Charging the incinerator with material containing a proportion of highly combustible material gives unstable conditions. An example of this type of residue is hospital waste which today contains plastics of high calorific value (CV) and swabbings of low calorific value due to moisture content. Initially, that material which is of high CV ignites a high proportion of the volatile matter, which if there is insufficient secondary air present gives heavy black smoke. Overfire connection with auxiliary burner and air ingress gives the necessary conditions for completion of combustion at a temperature of at least 725°C. The second stage of combustion is then centred around burning the residual carbonaceous mass and high-moisture residues; for

G.D. Kelsey

TABLE 11.1

INDUSTRIAL WASTE CLASSIFICATION

Class	Description	Main components	Approx. composition % by wt	Moisture content %	Incombustible solids %	CV (as fired) kJ/kg
0	Plastics	100% plastics	100	0	0	35 000
	Trash	Highly combustible waste—paper, wood, cardboard. Up to 10% treated papers, plastic or rubber scraps.	100	10	5	20 000
1	Rubbish	Combustible paper, cartons, etc., floor sweepings, domestic, commercial and industrial sources.	Rubbish 80% Garbage 20%	25	10	15 000
2	Refuse	Dometic type	Rubbish 50% Garbage 50%	50	7	11 000
3	Garbage	Animal and vegetable waste, hotel, markets, clubs, etc.	Garbage 65% Rubbish 35%	70	5	5 800
4	Animal waste	Carcasses, hospital waste, surgical residues	up to 100%	85	5	2 300

this to go to completion the ignition burner is brought into use as appropriate.

Automatic feeding of such devices is possible but expensive. However, most units work on a batch feeding basis and, providing care is taken not to overcharge due to large batch accumulation of waste, the design normally looks after the total combustion operation. Ash residues are not automatically rejected and at convenient times these are raked out. On many industrial wastes a low CV is generally due to high moisture and not to high ash content, hence there is no need for excessive time involvement in de-ashing.

11.5.2. Chemical Wastes

It has already been emphasised that in considering any waste disposal problem it is essential to know the composition of the waste. Incineration of certain materials can lead to difficulties with gaseous products. In particular, for example, attention should be drawn to halogenated hydrocarbons, nitrates, etc., which in turn may produce irritant, corrosive gases, the emission of which to the atmosphere is forbidden by legislation. Gas washing through conventional systems will contain these offensive materials putting them into solution. In addition to corrosive conditions, the high solubilities of chlorides, nitrates, etc., can lead to problems with the disposal of concentrated scrubbing liquors. Regeneration of water for re-use from such liquors is an expensive operation. Before incineration of any wastes, considered as chemical wastes, is undertaken, all aspects of the overall problem should be carefully investigated.

Whilst incineration of chemical waste appears easy, to meet legislation requirements the plant may become complex. In the examples just mentioned only carbon and hydrogen may be considered as being disposed of. Other elements will only be transformed in compound form. From chlorides one may be left with hydrochloric acid recovery, or calcium or sodium chloride if neutralisation is practised. For nitrogenous compounds an equivalent condition exists. Disposal of such solid compounds or saturated solutions then becomes a problem.

11.5.3. Specific Industrial Problems

Incineration can lead to economies in the form of material and energy recovery in certain industries. It is not always what appears to be as indicated above and considerations will now be given to certain process systems which show economies. These are examples, and others exist:

(a) disposal of black liquor from paper pulp manufacturing processes;
(b) heat recovery from wood waste; and
(c) regeneration of hydrochloric acid from spent steel pickling liquor.

These examples of waste are consistent in quality.

Black Liquor Disposal

A classic example of a byproduct waste which can be incinerated is that arising from the manufacture of paper pulp from feedstocks of timber or agricultural residues (straw, bagasse, etc.). The paper pulp manufacturing process consists basically of digesting the raw material with a reagent containing sodium hydroxide and sodium sulphide. Other reagents may be used but this one serves as a good example for a pulp making process called the KRAFT process. The alkaline digestion dissolves the non-fibrous portions of the wood and leaves the pulp as a fibrous residue. Separation of the fibre from the liquor results in a liquor referred to as 'black liquor'.

The black liquor contains much organic material as well as alkali salts. Something like 45–55% of the wood is in the liquor. The total solids content of the black liquor after separation from the pulp is 15–20% and the disposal process starts by concentrating the liquor, using a multiple-effect evaporator, to 50% solids and then by direct gas-contact evaporation to around 63% solids. In this form it is suitable for direct spray injection into a furnace. The calorific value of the liquor solids is around 15 MJ/kg so it can be directly ignited giving heat which can be recovered for power generation. The combustion results in the formation of an alkali residue in the form of sodium carbonate, which by subsequent treatment in solution form by slaked lime will give sodium hydroxide for re-use:

$$Na_2CO_3 + Ca(OH)_2 \rightarrow 2NaOH + \downarrow CaCO_3.$$

There is, therefore, both recovery of heat and recovery of chemicals by this incineration process. Whilst this is accepted as part of the pulp process, it is also an example of byproduct waste, since on small units it may actually be a waste product. It is given as an example of effective incineration with economic benefits. Figure 11.3 shows diagrammatically the basic resource recovery from black liquor.

Wood Waste

Another classic example of utilising process waste is in the furniture manufacturing industry, which produces large amounts of sawdust and wood chips. Burning of these wood wastes gives sufficient hot air, after heat exchange, to support space heating.

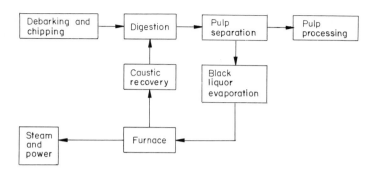

FIG. 11.3 Diagram of basic resource recovery from black liquor.

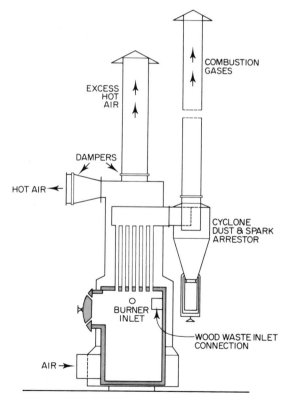

FIG. 11.4 Plant arrangement of Nihot Wood Waste Incinerator (Courtesy of NEI International Combustion Ltd).

By a system of in-house collection, sawdust and shavings can be segregated from larger items such as 'off-cuts', collected, stored and fed pneumatically to a combustion chamber for burning in suspension. It will be seen from Fig. 11.4 that clean air is fed to the heat exchanger above the furnace and heated air passed through to the factory workshop for space heating. This is an ideal system of incineration, utilising waste as a fuel for factory services.

Many other examples of this type could be cited, but there are also many examples of factory waste incineration which do not utilise the waste heat.

Steel Pickle Liquor

Steel sheet, wire, bar, etc., is pickled in hydrochloric acid to remove the oxide film produced in manufacture. This oxide film passes into solution as ferrous chloride. Disposal of ferrous chloride must take place otherwise the process is not environmentally sound.

Disposal on major plants is achieved by evaporation to a concentrated liquor and incinerating the solid residue to give the following reaction:

$$2FeCl_2 + 2H_2O + \tfrac{1}{2}O_2 \rightarrow Fe_2O_3 + 4HCl$$

The incineration is carried out in a fluid bed at 850°C using the granules of iron oxide produced as heat exchange medium. Gaseous products of combustion pass to a venturi scrubber fed with spent pickle liquor as scrubber medium. Evaporation of liquor in the venturi throat gives

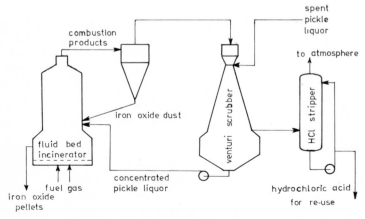

FIG. 11.5 Schematic diagram of pickle–liquor disposal plant.

hydrogen chloride and water vapour as the passout gases, the concentrated liquor passing to the fluid bed. The hydrogen chloride is scrubbed from the gases with water to give hydrochloric acid back to the process at a suitable concentration. Figure 11.5 shows a schematic diagram of a pickle-liquor disposal plant.

This is a good example of utilising heat to 'incinerate' a difficult material and to give usable products for re-use. This type of 'regenerative in-cineration' process will become more widely used in the foreseeable future.

Incineration of other industrial wastes in liquid form and gaseous form should be considered to give a more complete description of solutions to problems since such wastes do arise in abundance.

11.6. FORMS OF INDUSTRIAL WASTE

As indicated in Sections 11.3.1 and 11.5.1, a description of the waste leads to an understanding of the problem being tackled. However, such descriptions are generally applicable only to solid waste of Class 0 to Class 3. The description goes much deeper when one considers a Class 4 type of waste which covers carcasses and surgical residues. It goes deeper still when the waste is presented to an incinerator. It gets really complex when the various sludges and slurries are considered.

11.6.1. Physical Condition of Industrial Solid Wastes

Dry Solids
These are relatively simple to incinerate because they will burn in much the same way as a conventional solid fuel of the bituminous type. The spectrum of particle size and the shape of constituent pieces gives a mass with maximum surface exposure to combustion conditions. It also means that it is not necessary to produce any movement of the bed to maintain combustion. With static-bed systems, any bed agitation is achieved by manual rodding from outside the unit.

Filter Cakes
This is a general term for those products resulting from liquid/solids separation process. Organic sludges, the result of filtration of process wastes or the processing of organic sludges resulting from biological treatment of waste, are produced in a form which is generally of fine particle size, with all voidage filled with water. The voidage will depend on the

dewatering process, e.g., the filter press will give a high degree of compaction to the solids and, if they are of a compressible nature, some water will be squeezed out as the voidage is reduced. This results in a hard compact mass with minimum surface exposure for combustion. The rotary vacuum filter cake will be formed under low pressure and as such full advantage of the compressibility will not have been taken in the dewatering part of the filtration cycle, with the result that the cake will be produced in a thin sheet of a drained form. It will, however, stick to itself and tend to give a semi-gelatinous mass with minimum exposure of surface. Centrifuge cakes will fall into similar categories.

Sludges

These arise as complex masses which are neither liquid nor solid. Their handling requires special consideration, but the fact remains that surface exposure for combustion is a prime requisite. Also such materials may not be autothermic and will require assisted combustion from some auxiliary fuel.

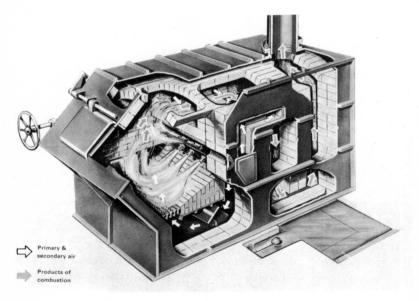

FIG. 11.6 Typical system for burning of hospital waste (Riley Gaserator) (Courtesy of NEI International Combustion Ltd).

11.7. TYPES OF INCINERATION EQUIPMENT

11.7.1. Static-grate Incinerator for Solids

The static-grate incinerator is ideally suited to the combustion of industrial waste which is produced in nominal quantities. Such units are readily brought on stream from cold using auxiliary burner systems and can be used where incineration is required as the need arises, without the need for 24 h/day supervision. The static-grate type of unit is low in capital cost and operating cost and requires manual attendance for charging the combustion chamber and discharging the ash produced.

During operation of this type of unit the air-to-solids ratio for combustion to give clean stack conditions, changes from the beginning to the end of a combustion cycle. Good operation can control this and frequently 'after burners' to burn smoke produced during combustion are

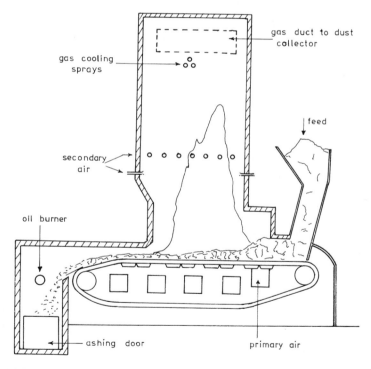

FIG. 11.7 Continuous system for burning mixed factory waste (Courtesy of NEI International Combustion Ltd).

brought into use; smoke is associated with sub-stoichiometric combustion and after-burning offers the correction.

Hospital waste falls into that category which is most suited to a static-grate unit, because waste which comprises plastics, paper, surgical residues and high moisture-content swabbings is collected and presented to the combustion unit in sealed plastic bags. Gas outlet conditions must be clean in all respects. For such applications the use of auxiliary burners within the incinerator body give the desired conditions.

For higher capacities and for continuous rated systems the use of a travelling grate or rocking grate is found to be more acceptable than mechanical rodding to obtain movement of solids during combustion. Also the feeding arrangements may be carried out in a more continuous form from a feed hopper or from a programmed batch charging device. Figure 11.6 shows a typical system for the burning of hospital waste, and Fig. 11.7 shows a continuous system for burning mixed factory waste.

11.7.2. Multi-hearth Unit for Filter Cakes and Sludges
On the large scale for applications such as sewage sludge which has been dewatered, the multi-hearth kiln is widely used. The unit is basically a development of the Parkes furnace originally patented in the UK in 1850, further modified by McDougall in 1873 and later revised in the USA by Herreschoff for the roasting of pyrites for sulphuric acid manufacture.

In effect the unit consists of a number of horizontal circular hearths each mounted above the other. A central tube carrying a set of radial arms for each hearth rotates at low speed. Conditioned feed drops onto the uppermost hearth and is raked to the next hearth, and then progressively downwards with hot gases moving countercurrently. Ignition occurs after some drying has taken place, and the action of the sweep of the arms against the hearths breaks the material down to give exposed surface for the combustion to take place. The centre column and arms are air cooled to protect the metal parts. Ash residues are discharged at the base and gases taken off from the top. Figure 11.8 shows a diagram of a multi-hearth unit.

11.7.3. The Rotary Incinerator for Multi-phase Waste
For more widespread application to industrial sludges rotary incinerators are gaining popularity since they are available for small capacity duties and have the capability of accepting multi-phase wastes. Basically the plant consists of a refractory-lined cylinder slightly inclined to the horizontal. The unit is rotated at low speed to lift and tumble the ignited mass. This

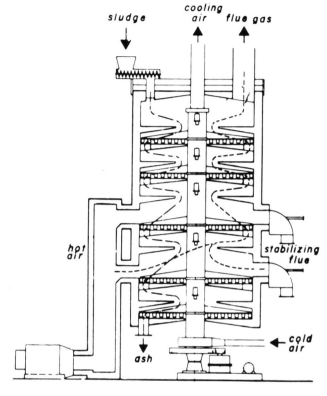

FIG. 11.8 Diagram of multi-hearth unit.

lifting and tumbling action continuously exposes fresh surface to the combustion environment and increases the rate of combustion. With variable speed of rotation and some degree of adjustment to the slope of the cylinder, process settings can be adjusted to suit. This mode of operation enables solid waste, sludges and liquid waste to be introduced into the same combustion chamber at positions suitable for each. The turbulent movement of the solids will increase the quantities of particulates present in the gaseous product and will also tend to cause some degree of attrition to the refractory brickwork. Accepting these facts, rotary systems can show some definite advantages for multi-phase wastes. Figure 11.9 shows the arrangement of a rotary incinerator.

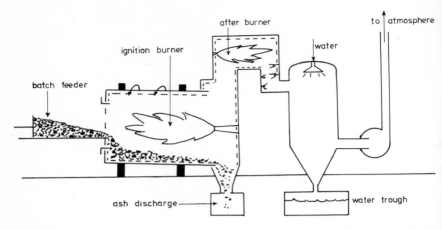

FIG. 11.9 Rotary incinerator arrangement (After Combustion Engineering Inc).

11.7.4. The Fluid-bed Incinerator

The use of the fluid-bed incinerator is attracting considerable interest for the disposal of organic waste materials of defined physical characteristics. The description of the disposal of steel pickle liquor in Section 11.5.3 illustrates its use for a specific problem related to an endothermic reaction and indicates a total process plant concept for incineration and recovery of resources.

The fluid-bed system consists essentially of three distinct operating zones. The fluid bed itself is made up of distinct particulate material supported on a distribution plate underneath which is a windbox which allows air to pass through the bed to fluidise the bed solids. The zone above the bed where solids from fluidising drop back to the bed is known as the freeboard. The bed material may be particulate, high-quality sand generally of size around 250 microns and contained within a narrow size spectrum, or other dense material which has a high resistance to attrition as the particles collide with each other during fluidisation.

Initially the bed is heated by an auxiliary fuel to bring the whole combustion chamber up to that temperature at which ignition commences and combustion takes place. Any requirement for additional heat input e.g. for non-autothermic waste, is accommodated by top-up heat applied to selected areas of the bed. The feed to this type of incinerator should be of a certain physical quality such that inerts of a coarse nature are not present. The residues from incineration should be such that they can be removed via

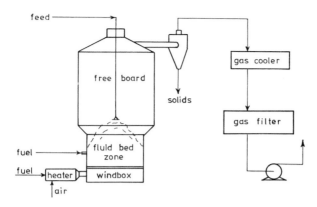

FIG. 11.10 Basic layout of a fluid-bed system.

the gas off-take by conventional means. The feed solids should be conditioned to give as uniform physical conditions as possible to optimise contact with the particulate heat-exchange medium.

Control of temperature by spray systems or other acceptable devices will ensure that incineration residues will not be heated above the softening temperature. If this were allowed to happen, slagging problems would occur with subsequent loss of fluidity in the bed. Exhaust gas clean up is the direct application of conventional techniques, i.e. wet scrubber or reduction in gas temperatures followed by filtration.

The fluid-bed incinerator is ideally suited to those materials which can be applied in a well conditioned form, e.g., liquids, slurries and sludges which can be fed at a controlled rate. Multi-phase wastes can give problems in operation and require special consideration. Figure 11.10 shows the basic layout of a fluid bed system.

11.7.5. Liquid Waste Incinerator

Liquid wastes fall into two basic classes: those which are autothermic and generally organic in chemical character and those which are of an aqueous character.

Organic waste materials do not present any major problems in disposal, since the heats of combustion can generally be harnessed and used for steam raising. Suppliers of combustion equipment offer a range of designs from which a selection can be made to cover such physical aspects as viscosity, air requirements, etc. The incineration of those organic liquids containing halogens, nitrogen compounds, sulphur compounds, etc., should be carefully considered, since such materials lead to exhaust problems which require special attention, as discussed in Section 11.5.2.

Aqueous liquid wastes may be treated in a number of ways. Basically these are of low calorific value and contain insufficient combustible matter to enable them to support combustion, thus requiring the use of a support fuel. Such wastes arise from a variety of processes and commonly occur in the chemical industry. To calculate the back-up heat requirement certain factors must be taken into account. First of all the total heat required to convert the aqueous fraction to a vapour at the incinerator temperature, allowing for any combustible organic input which may be present, is considered. In practice the latter may be ignored and compensated as necessary by adjustment of the input fuel using a temperature control system. Burning of such streams requires that optimum atomisation takes place and that the finely atomised droplets are mixed with air before introduction into the combustion zone of the support fuel.

Providing that there is appropriate combustion volume, retention in the high-temperature environment will ensure complete combustion.

11.7.6. Multi-phase Waste Incinerators

The rotary incinerator of Section 11.7.3 is a single unit incinerator capable of handling multi-phase waste materials which have been conditioned to a form suitable for feeding into it.

The availability of waste may be such that the conditioning operation may be very difficult to achieve, particularly if the solids are of a bulky nature. The 'bulky nature' problem is present with municipal waste disposal establishments and incineration both in the bulk and disintegrated form is practised. However, the latter is not favoured by industry because its bulky waste is generally in the form of containers. For those industries where such containers may be contaminated with chemicals, disintegration will create problems which may be unacceptable and direct bulk incineration is the satisfactory solution. The requirement, therefore, is to handle bulky waste in a separate chamber.

In dealing with multi-phase waste segregation must be practised with the incineration process arranged in a sequence of operations. This sequence will be based on the burning characteristics of each segregated phase. The material having the highest calorific value and possessing good burning characteristics would be selected as the primary feedstock for ignition and the products of combustion which are at a high temperature would be used to promote the combustion of each of the other constituent phases. For a multi-phase waste containing dry solids of good combustion characteristics, bulky waste, slurries, sludges and liquids the combustion sequence would be in the form of a number of units in series.

Unit 1 would comprise a static-hearth unit designed to handle loose solid waste fed on a batch basis. This unit would give clean combustion with hot gases passing through to a second unit. Unit 2 would be a chamber into which bulky refuse is fed, the preferable practice being to charge this chamber on start-up and clean out on shut-down. This unit may also be charged with carcasses and similar waste which would require a long combustion time. Gases from Unit 2 would then pass into Unit 3 where sludges may be fed, preferably by a positive displacement system. Such sludges would have low calorific value and would require a long residence time to render residues innocuous. Consequently it is necessary to have a controlled rate of feed so that the heat loads from units 1 and 2 are able to sustain combustion of these sludges. Finally, in a fourth unit aqueous liquids may be injected, again at a rate in keeping with heat available. Finally, to ensure that the exit gases are free from organic odours, after-burners operating on temperature control, using waste organic liquids, gases or auxiliary fuels would be brought on stream. Pass-out gases would then go via a gas cleaning system to the atmosphere.

This sequence of units may be built into a complete module with operation being controlled by the feed rate of the various phases and the use of auxiliary fuels as necessary. Figure 11.11 shows a diagrammatic arrangement of a multi-phase waste incinerator. In the design of such a unit note must be taken of the actual combustion environment in the specification of refractories at each unit stage. Figure 11.12 shows a typical arrangement of a multi-phase waste incinerator.

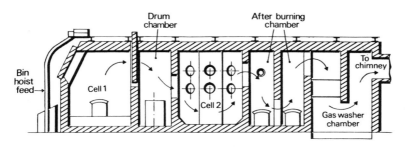

FIG. 11.11 Diagrammatic arrangement of a multi-phase waste incinerator (reproduced by kind permission of the Incinerator Co. Ltd).

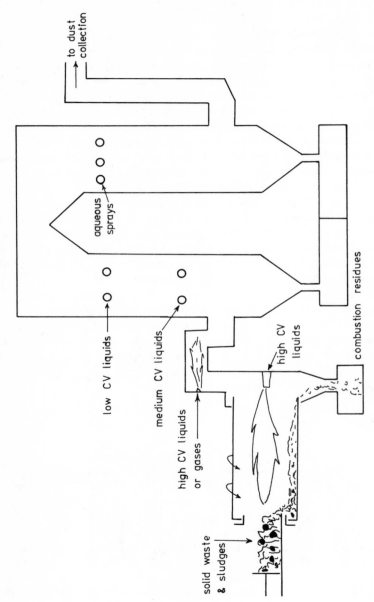

FIG. 11.12 Typical arrangement of a multi-phase waste incinerator.

11.8. PYROLYSIS

11.8.1. Fundamentals of Pyrolysis

In Section 11.3.1 under *Proximate Analysis* the method for the determination of volatile matter was described. The normal treatment of organic wastes in the absence of oxygen gives breakdown of organic molecules without any primary combustion taking place. Those molecules which are purely hydrocarbons will give a breakdown into lower molecular-weight hydrocarbons with carbonaceous residues, whereas those molecules containing oxygen will breakdown to include carbon monoxide and carbon dioxide. The thermal breakdown of coal which contains oxygen is a classic example of this, the oxygen appearing as carbon monoxide in the gas, hence its poisonous quality.

The breakdown of organic molecules present in waste is unpredictable in that various factors can affect the total spectrum of products produced, all of which contribute to product quality, e.g., the rate of heating, the maximum temperature achieved and catalysis by constituents within the waste. The effects of catalysis are unknown, but the effects of the other two factors may be determined by basic test work.

11.8.2. Benefits of Pyrolysis

There are definite advantages from pyrolysis as a system of thermal disposal of solid waste materials —

  (i) Pyrolysis is generally accepted as a resource recovery process in that there is no major release of heat and all phases produced are easily handled.

 (ii) Since no air is used in a pyrolysis operation, the volume of gases from the process is considerably reduced, showing large savings in fan power and reduction in the gas cleaning requirements. Air pollution by particulate material is virtually totally eliminated.

(iii) There are no problems associated with gas cooling, hence economies in the utilisation of water.

(iv) The process char, i.e. that residue remaining after evolution of liquid and gas components at the pyrolysis temperature, is sterile. It is also in a friable form and as such is amenable to resource recovery, e.g., glass, metal, etc. Also, it is totally innocuous. After removal of innocuous material, the char from low-residue waste may find a use as a fuel, or as a source of activated carbon.

 (v) The gas and oil products lend themselves to ease of transport to other sites for use as energy sources. Thus the pyrolysis operation converts waste into an easily handled form of energy. Such material can be used in conventional boiler plants without the problem of fouling which is generally associated with the burning of solid waste materials.

(vi) It is anticipated that such plants, for the stated reasons above, will be more compact than incinerators and lower in capital and operating costs.

11.8.3. Characteristics of Waste for Pyrolysis

In an age of organic products it is inevitable that as a result of manufacture of these products appreciable waste material is produced. This waste may arise from faulty formulations of compounds, off-cuts, etc. Also, when the products cease to have any functional value, they are discarded as waste. Since the raw materials generally have petro-chemical origins, the waste material has a high thermal value. When it is considered that high energy-content materials are being used to undertake purely physical functions, e.g., plastics containers, motor car tyres, etc., then conversion of such materials back for utilisation as an energy source makes sound economic sense. However, those waste materials which are of low calorific value, although having reasonable combustion characteristics, are generally not economically suitable for pyrolysis operations due to the amount of moisture and carbon dioxide produced.

From a chemical point of view the waste should be of a high carbon-to-hydrogen ratio with other constituent elements of minimal proportion. Residual char should be of a form such that its caking index[5] and swelling numbers are low, the char having minimal tendency to form agglomerates.

11.8.4. Preconditioning of Waste

Broad-spectrum waste presents problems in pyrolysis in that it will contain such constituents as metal, wood, glass, plastics, paper, board, etc. All these may be of differing sizes and to effect gas movement as it is evolved in pyrolysis the size should be such that gas will flow evenly through the bed and also that heat transfer rates can be maintained nearly uniform in all areas.

Achievement of this objective requires the use of pulverising equipment to reduce the waste to pieces of handleable size and at the same time to give the best conditions for the pyrolysis operation. This in turn is followed by a classifying operation to remove heavy material such as metal, glass, etc., and give an enriched waste.

Pre-drying to remove excess water from certain classes of waste helps to

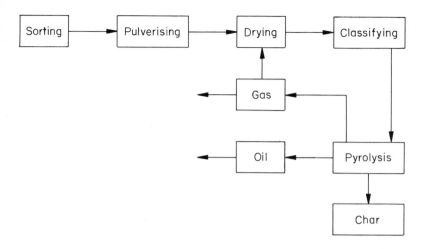

FIG. 11.13 Diagram of a pyrolysis system.

minimise the quantity of aqueous liquid products. It is possible to have the preconditioning stages above linked with pyrolysis as shown in Fig. 11.13, perhaps with some of the gas used for heat input to the dryer.

11.8.5. Process Development

The attractions of resource and energy recovery by pyrolysis are leading to high outlays in research investment in certain countries. Reports 7302 *Destructive Distillation of Scrap Tyres* 1969 and 7428 *Conservation of Municipal and Industrial Refuse into useful Materials by Pyrolysis* 1970 issued by the US Bureau of Mines give certain valuable conclusions.

Destructive Distillation of Scrap Tyres gives the following findings:

   (i) the highest yield of liquid products at 500°C;
  (ii) the highest yield of solid and gas products at 900°C; and
 (iii) liquid and gas composition was dependent on temperature.

Similar conclusions are drawn for refuse of the municipal type:

   (i) increase in pyrolysis temperature favours gas production with decrease in solid and liquid yields;
  (ii) rapid rate of heating favours gas production; and
 (iii) optimum temperature for the production of hydrocarbon gases is 600–700°C.

Full-scale operating data for commercial units are now awaited to confirm the anticipated economies of a pyrolysis operation.

11.8.6. Utilisation of By-products of Pyrolysis

Pyrolysis produces solid, liquid and gaseous by-products.

The solid material is referred to as char and contains fixed carbon, debris and mineral matter. It has been postulated that the char may be refined further to give two separate density fractions from a medium flotation system, the floats being the char which can be separated by thickening and filtration to give material which may be further processed to activated carbon. The sinks on the other hand may be separated into ferrous and non-ferrous by means of a magnetic separator and used for recycling.

The liquid by-product is separated from the gas stream in a condenser and further separated into 'oil' and 'water' by conventional phase separation devices. The water is contaminated and its treatment to discharge standards is essential. The oil is a very complex mixture dependent for its composition on the actual pyrolysis reaction, but it is a fuel oil which is easily transportable off-site for use as required.

The gas may also be used off-site, but since the pyrolysis reaction is endothermic as opposed to exothermic for incineration, the gas may be used as the prime fuel for raising the temperature of the feedstock to that for pyrolysis.

11.9. STATUS OF THERMAL DISPOSAL PROCESS

11.9.1. Incineration

Incineration of organic waste materials and those materials exhibiting exothermic reactions on disposal has reached a stage of development where art and science can be successfully applied to disposal problems both on the small and large scale. Auxiliary processes attached to incineration such as heat recovery have reached commercial viability on many applications but each process must be considered in detail before final decisions are made. Incineration of normal wastes does give environmentally sound terminal conditions and in this respect it is fully acceptable as a waste disposal process.

11.9.2. Pyrolysis

Pyrolysis is rapidly developing and is favoured for rubber and plastics. In the near future it is expected that commercially viable plants will come on stream. A number of units to operate on domestic waste have been built in various parts of the world and operating data from such systems will indicate the economic and technical standing of the process as an alternative to incineration.

REFERENCES

1. Higginson A.E., *Institute of Public Cleaning Conference*, 1966.
2. *British Standard Specification* 1016 *Pt* 3, BSI, London.
3. *British Standard Specification* 1016 *Pt* 6, BSI, London.
4. Partington, J.R., *General and Inorganic Chemistry*, 4th edition. MacMillan, London, 1966.
5. *British Standard Specification* 1016 *Pt* 12, BSI, London.

Appendix

INLAND WATER POLLUTION AND DISPOSAL OF SOLID WASTE: LEGAL PROVISIONS

V.J. SHRUBSALL

Lecturer in Law, University of Nottingham, UK

A.1. WATER POLLUTION

The industrialist discharging trade effluent to inland waterways may incur liability under the *civil* as well as the *criminal* law. If he does an act which is made a criminal offence by statute, the state initiates and prosecutes the charge against him. In order to establish civil liability it is left to an individual to proceed with litigation. That person will normally be the property owner whose property interests have been infringed by the action of the industrialist.

A.2. CIVIL LIABILITY

The polluter may incur civil liability in the tort of nuisance or according to the rule in *Rylands v. Fletcher*[1]. A nuisance is an interference with a person's use or enjoyment of land. The general principle is that a landowner may do as he wishes on his own property but only for so long as he does not thereby unreasonably interfere with his neighbour's reciprocal right. The law is concerned with the balancing of conflicting interests. Where interference is unreasonable, the holder of a proprietary interest who suffers damage by that interference can invoke the civil law of nuisance and obtain redress. What amounts to unreasonable interference depends on variable factors such as the nature of the locality, the degree of inconvenience and the level of infringement which might reasonably be expected to be tolerated.

'Whether anything is a nuisance or not is a question to be determined, not merely by an abstract consideration of the thing itself, but in reference to its circumstances: what would be a nuisance in Belgrave Square would not necessarily be so in Bermondsey'—Thesiger L.J. in *Sturgess* v. *Bridgman* (1879).[2]

Illustrations of the tort of nuisance are as follows:

In *Young* v. *Bankier Distillery* (1893)[3] the appellant and the Bankier Distillery Co. owned neighbouring land by the side of a stream. The Distillery Co. used the water in the stream in their process of distilling whisky. They and their predecessors in title had done so for 60 years past. The appellant then began mining operations on his property and pumped waste water into the stream thereby rendering it unfit for use in the distillation process. The Distillery Co. brought an action for nuisance and sought an injunction restraining the appellant from discharging his waste water to the stream. The action succeeded and the award of the injunction was confirmed when the appellant appealed contending that since the water was still fit for its primary purposes, i.e. drinking, washing, etc., there was no actionable infringement.

Lord Macnaghten imposed a high standard—'Every riparian proprietor is entitled to the water of his stream in its natural flow, without sensible diminution or increase and without sensible alteration in its character or quality. Any invasion of this right entitles the injured party to the court's intervention.'[4]

This principle that natural waters of a stream must not be affected by any sensible alteration in quantity or quality applies also to wells supplied by water percolating through underground strata. So in *Ballard* v. *Tomlinson* (1882)[5] the plaintiff was successful in a nuisance action when underground water which supplied his well was polluted by sewage.[6]

Not every interference will amount to a nuisance: pollution must be continuous or recurrent and not too minute or trivial. Since the law is concerned with balancing conflicting property interests parties are not permitted to stand on their extreme rights. It has been held, for example, in *Bradford Corporation* v. *Pickles* (1895)[7] that discoloration of water is not actionable provided that the discoloration is innocuous.

If the plaintiff is able to prove nuisance, his remedy is an injunction against the defendant requiring the cessation of the action complained of and/or monetary damages compensating loss already suffered. It is not easy to make out a nuisance claim. The nuisance action is used only in the occasional case where a plaintiff can show serious harm caused by a particular defendant. He must trace the source of the effluent complained of to a particular person or undertaking. However, if that can be shown, the absence of negligence on the part of the defendant is no defence,[8] nor is it an answer that the plaintiff came to the nuisance, i.e. the discharge of effluent was continuing before the plaintiff took possession of his property and he must therefore be held to have accepted an existing state of affairs. The only exception is if the defendant can be said to have acquired a prescriptive right to discharge effluent, if he has done so as of right for upwards of 20 years.

The alternative civil action which may be brought by a property owner who suffers by the discharge of trade effluent to water is under the rule in *Rylands* v. *Fletcher*. Under that rule a person who collects and keeps on his land anything likely to do mischief if it escapes is answerable for all the damage which is the natural consequence of its escape. The principle has been applied to polluting matter passing from A's land to that of B.[9]

A.2.1. Statutory Nuisance

Bridging the gap between the common law of nuisance and statutes creating criminal liability is the concept of the statutory nuisance. This concept gives statutory status to the tort of nuisance but provides a summary procedure to deal with acts of pollution and, ultimately, attaches criminal sanctions. The previous nuisance liability continues but the Public Health Act 1936 Section 259 adds the following statutory nuisances:

'(a) any pond, pool, ditch, gutter or water course which is so foul or in such a state as to be prejudicial to health or a nuisance;
(b) any part of a water course, not being a part ordinarily navigated by vessels employed in the carriage of goods by water, which is so choked or silted up as to obstruct or impede the proper flow of water and thereby to cause nuisance, or give rise to conditions prejudicial to health.'

Where a statutory nuisance exists, the relevant local authority is given power to invoke the procedure established by Part III of the Public Health Act 1936. It serves an abatement notice on the person by whose act, default or sufferance the nuisance occurs. The abatement notice requires the cessation of the nuisance and the execution of steps necessary to effect that end. Where the person responsible for the nuisance cannot be found, the local authority has power to take the necessary abatement action and charge expenses to the owner of the property. If the abatement notice is not complied with, the local authority may cause a complaint to be made to a magistrates' court. The magistrates can back up the abatement notice with an enforcement order and can also impose a fine. The Control of Pollution Act 1974 raised the maximum limit of that fine to £200. If the enforcement order itself is not complied with, after a further complaint to the court, there is provision for a further fine together with a daily penalty for each day on which the action continues. The maximum limits of those fines were increased by the Control of Pollution Act 1974 to £400 and £50 respectively. Additionally, if the enforcement order is not complied with, the local authority has power to take the steps necessary to stop the nuisance and may claim expenses from the person responsible for the nuisance.

A.3. CRIMINAL LIABILITY AND STATUTORY PROVISIONS

A.3.1. Discharge to Sewers

The effluent producer may discharge directly to inland waters (see *post*) or may discharge to sewers whose contents are treated before being discharged to inland waters. Under the Public Health Act 1936 a duty was imposed on local authorities to provide public sewers as necessary to drain effectually their districts and to deal effectually with the contents of sewers by means of sewage disposal works. These duties were transferred to the Water Authorities by the Water Act 1973.

The Water Authority is bound to accept into its sewers foul water drainage and surface water drainage. It is *not* obliged to accept trade effluent. The discharge of trade effluent to sewers is governed by the Public Health (Drainage of Trade Premises) Act 1937 as amended by the Public Health Act 1961. The Control of Pollution Act 1974 further amended the legislation.

Under the 1937 Act the general rule is that the occupier of trade premises may discharge trade effluent into a Water Authority's sewers *only* with the consent of that Water Authority. 'Trade effluent' is defined as: 'any liquid, either with or without particles of matter in suspension therein, which is wholly or in part produced in the course of any trade or industry carried on at trade premises. . . but does not include domestic sewage.'[10]

The procedure for obtaining a Consent is that the occupier of trade premises serves a trade effluent notice on the Water Authority stating the nature and composition of the trade effluent, the maximum quantity to be discharged on any one day and the highest rate of the proposed discharge. The Water Authority may then refuse to accept the effluent or Consent to the discharge conditionally or unconditionally. The action taken by the Water Authority will depend on the existing discharges to the relevant sewers, the capacity of the sewage disposal works, etc. The conditions which the Water Authority is competent to impose are contained in Section 2(3) of the 1937 Act and Section 59 of the Public Health Act 1961. These conditions may specify the particular sewers to which discharge may be made, the composition of the effluent (which may involve some treatment of it before discharge to the sewers), the temperature of the discharge and the elimination of a specified constituent. In nearly every case the Water Authority will impose a charge for accepting the effluent (see Chapter 2). The conditions imposed by the Water Authority can be varied under the Public Health Act 1961 but not within two years of a previous variation, i.e. charges and other conditions may be increased or changed every two years. There are rights of appeal against the refusal of a Consent and against the imposition of unreasonable conditions.

It is a criminal offence to discharge trade effluent into sewers without the Consent of the appropriate Water Authority or without compliance with the conditions attached to a Consent.[11] The Control of Pollution Act 1974 raised the penalty for this offence to a fine of up to £200 and a further daily fine of up to £50.

A.3.2. Exemption from the Consent Requirements

An exemption originally contained in Section 4(4) of the 1937 Act for liquid produced solely in the course of laundering articles was repealed by the Water Act 1973.

Discharges made before the commencement of the 1937 Act did not require Consent provided they continued at the same nature and composition after the commencement of the Act. However the Public Health Act 1961 brought these discharges into line to the extent of allowing the appropriate Authority to charge for accepting them. The Control of Pollution Act 1974 removed the exemption from the Consent requirement for these discharges. After 19th July 1976* these discharges were to be treated in the same way as post-1937 discharges, i.e. no right to discharge to sewers except with a Water Authority Consent. For a transitional period of six months from 19th July 1976 Consent was deemed given on the application of the occupier of premises from which the discharge was made.

A.3.3. Discharge to Rivers

If the effluent producer discharges directly to a river, he is subject to different legal controls. These provisions also apply to discharge by Water Authorities from sewers or sewage disposal works to rivers or inland waters. The principal statutes controlling discharge of effluent or other matter to rivers are

* Made the 'appointed day' by the Control of Pollution Act (Appointed Day) Order 1976 Statutory Instrument 957.

The Rivers (Prevention of Pollution) Act 1951
The Rivers (Prevention of Pollution) Act 1961
The Control of Pollution Act 1974, which contains provisions for rationalising and replacing those statutes.

The 1951 and 1961 Acts deal primarily with pollution of streams. A 'stream' is defined so as to include 'any river, stream, watercourse or inland water'.[12] The definition does not include any lake or pond unless it discharges to a stream. Nor does it include tidal water.

A.3.4. The Provisions of the 1951 and 1961 Acts

(i) *The offence of causing or knowingly permitting to enter a stream any poisonous, noxious or polluting matter.*
Section 2(1) of the 1951 Act states —
'A person commits an offence under this section:
(a) if he causes or knowingly permits to enter a stream any poisonous, noxious or polluting matter; or
(b) if he causes or knowingly permits to enter a stream any matter so as to tend either directly or in combination with similar acts (whether his own or another's) to impede the proper flow of the water of the stream in a manner leading or likely to lead to a substantial aggravation of pollution due to other causes or of its consequences;
and for the purposes of paragraph (a) of this subsection a Water Authority shall be deemed to cause or knowingly permit to enter a stream any poisonous, noxious or polluting matter, which passes into a stream from any sewer or sewage disposal works vested in them, in any case where either the Water Authority were bound to receive the matter into the sewer or sewage disposal works, or they consented to do so unconditionally, or they consented to do so subject to conditions and those conditions were observed.'

'Poisonous, noxious or polluting matter'. There is no statutory definition of these words. Section 5 of the 1951 Act did give the river boards (then responsible for controlling discharges to rivers) powers to prescribe standards for their areas to determine what matter should be treated as poisonous, noxious or polluting. That power was taken away by the 1961 Act. The reason that there is no remaining statutory aid to the interpretation of the phrase is presumably to give the Water Authorities maximum flexibility and to discourage litigation on the meaning of words employed in any definition. The only assistance, albeit negative, is given by Section 11(3) of the 1951 Act: 'matter shall not be deemed to be poisonous, noxious or polluting by reason of any effect it may have in discoloring a stream, if the discoloration is innocuous.' Save for that provision, the words must be given their ordinary meaning.

'Causes or knowingly permits'. The element of fault, motive or intention which the Crown has to prove in order to achieve a successful prosecution was uncertain. Because the provision says 'causes or knowingly permits' rather than 'knowingly causes or knowingly permits', it was argued that the offence was one of strict liability and all that had to be 'shown by the prosecution was commission of the act itself. The point was considered in *Impress (Worcester) Ltd.* v. *Rees* (1971).[13] The appellants kept a fuel oil storage tank on their property which was open to and visible from the highway. There were two outlets in a wall enclosing the tank, only one of which was kept closed, and a gate valve in the bottom of the tank was not kept locked. The appellants did not employ a night-watchman. A trespasser entered the premises at night and opened the gate valve. Fuel oil escaped through the open outlet in the enclosing wall and into the river. The appellants were convicted of the offence under Section 2(1) (a) of the 1951 Act of unlawfully causing to enter a stream poisonous, noxious or polluting matter. Their appeal to the High Court was successful. The finding was that the appellants had not 'caused' oil to enter the river. Although they were at fault in failing to lock the gate valve at night and in leaving the outlet open there was 'an intervening cause of so powerful a nature that the conduct of the appellants was not a cause at all but was merely part of the surrounding circumstances.'[14]

This decision does not mean that the prosecution must show fault but it is necessary for it to show a chain of causation down to the defendant. Given that the defendant can be said to have 'caused' the act, is absence of neglect, or lack of intention, a defence?

Let us now consider the case of *Alphacell Ltd.* v. *Woodward* (1972).[15] The appellants prepared manilla fibres, the raw material for paper making, at their works on the bank of the River Irwell. Part of the process involved the washing of fibres and the water which was thereby polluted was piped down to two settling tanks on the river bank. There were two pumps in each settling tank whose purpose was to prevent water overflowing into the river. One pump was automatically switched on when the water in the tank reached a certain level and the other was manually operated. The inlet valve to each pump was protected by a rose filter. The pumps were maintained by a fitter who was supposed to inspect them weekly. On one occasion leaves and ferns built up around the rose filters with the result that the pumps failed to prevent the overflow of polluted water into the river.

The appellants were convicted of the offence under Section 2(1) (a) of the 1951 Act. They appealed to the Court of Appeal and to the House of Lords but the appeals were unsuccessful. All five Law Lords took the view that it was not necessary for the prosecution to show fault or negligence in order to make out the offence. Here there was no escape from the conclusion that the company's acts 'caused' the polluting matter to enter the river. It was no defence that the pollution was unforeseeable and that the defendant took all reasonable care.

Lord Salmon said, 'If this appeal succeeded and it were held to be the law that no conviction could be obtained under the 1951 Act unless the prosecution could discharge the often impossible onus of proving that the pollution was caused intentionally or negligently, a great deal of pollution would go unpunished and undeterred to the relief of many riparian factory owners. As a result, many rivers which are now filthy would become filthier still and many rivers which are now clean would lose their cleanliness. The legislature no doubt recognised that as a matter of public policy this would be most unfortunate. Hence Section 2(1) (a) encourages riparian factory owners not only to take reasonable steps to prevent pollution but to do everything possible to ensure that they do not cause it.'

The House of Lords might have upheld the conviction on the grounds of the appellants' negligence since there was a failure to maintain the equipment properly. There was, however, no finding of negligence so the offence is held to be one of strict liability. However, the implication from the judgements is that had there been an intervening act of a trespasser or an act of God, such as freak weather conditions, which caused the overflow the decision might have been different.[16]

The essential elements of the offence were again considered in *Price* v. *Cromack* (1975).[17] The appellant entered into an agreement to allow effluent created by an industrial company to pass on to his land and be dispersed. The amount of effluent increased and, with the consent of the appellant, two lagoons were built by the company on the appellant's land to contain the effluent. Cracks developed in the walls of the lagoons and effluent escaped through them into a nearby river. The appellant was convicted of causing poisonous, noxious or polluting matter to enter the river. On appeal the conviction was quashed. The High Court held that the offence required some positive act on the part of the accused and not merely a passive looking-on. The effluent had come on to his land and passed from there into the river by natural forces and without any positive act of the appellant. It could not therefore be said that he had 'caused' the polluting matter to enter the river.

The industrial company which created the effluent and built the lagoons was probably the proper defendant and, by analogy with *Alphacell* v. *Woodward* a prosecution would probably have succeeded.

The penalties for commission of an offence under Section 2(1) of the Rivers (Prevention of Pollution) Act 1951 are a fine of up to £200 for conviction on indictment and a fine of up to £50 on a summary conviction. But there are greater penalties available against the polluter who is convicted, pays the fine, and then continues to commit the offence. Here there is a possibility of a daily fine and, ultimately, of imprisonment.

There is also a provision under which if the offence is committed by a company, a director, manager, secretary or similar officer of the company may be personally liable as well if the offence was committed with the consent, connivance or because of the neglect of that person.[18] So, for example, if a company's Environment Protection Officer is responsible for the maintenance of equipment preventing overflow of polluted water to a river and he neglects his responsibilities, he and the company may be charged with the offence.

The Control of Pollution Act 1974 re-enacts this offence but with the following changes:

(1) a third limb of the offence is created; that of causing or knowingly permitting any solid waste to enter a stream or restricted waters;

(2) the offence of causing or knowingly permitting poisonous, noxious or polluting matter to enter a stream is extended to all 'relevant waters', this phrase includes the sea within three nautical miles of the coastline and all estuarine waters;

(3) no offence is committed if the entry is in an emergency and to avoid danger to the public and the relevant Water Authority is informed as soon as is reasonably practicable;

(4) regulations may be made requiring precautionary measures to be taken by persons having control of poisonous, noxious or polluting matter to prevent that matter from entering any relevant waters;

(5) where the Secretary of State considers that the carrying on in a particular area of a certain activity is likely to result in poisonous, noxious or polluting matter entering relevant waters, he may control that activity by regulations;

(6) the penalties are increased to imprisonment of up to three months and/or a fine of up to £400 on summary conviction; and imprisonment of up to two years and/or an unlimited fine on conviction or indictment.

(ii) The treatment of trade and sewage effluent.
The Rivers (Prevention of Pollution) Acts of 1951 and 1961 contain provisions under which the discharge of trade and sewage effluent to streams is controlled by a Consent procedure similar to that outlined above which governs discharge to sewers.

Section 7 of the 1951 Act enables Water Authorities to control *new* discharges of trade or sewage effluent to streams, i.e. discharges which began after the commencement of the Act on 1st October 1951. This Act also brings within their control use of new or altered outlets for discharges, i.e. outlets constructed or substantially altered after 1st October 1951.

The 1961 Act Sections 1–3 establish a system of control over *old* discharges of trade and sewage effluent to streams, those not already covered by the 1951 Act.

A.3.5. Control of New Discharges and New Outlets
Section 7 provides that no person shall, without the Consent of the appropriate Water Authority, bring into use any new or altered outlet for the discharge of trade or sewage effluent to a stream or begin to make any new discharge of trade or sewage effluent to a stream.

'New discharge' is defined as a discharge which is not, as respects the nature and composition, temperature, volume and rate of discharge, substantially a continuation of a previous discharge made within the preceding twelve months.

'Trade effluent' includes any liquid which is discharged from premises used for the carrying on of any trade or industry, other than surface water and domestic sewage.

Land or premises used wholly or mainly for agricultural or horticultural purposes or for scientific research or experiment are deemed to be trade premises.

On an application for Consent the Water Authority may grant Consent subject to conditions:

  (i) in the case of a new or altered outlet the conditions may specify the point of discharge into the stream or the construction and use of the outlet or of any other outlet on the same premises;
  (ii) in the case of a new discharge conditions can specify the nature, composition, temperature, volume or rate of discharge.

The Consent of the Water Authority to the discharge must not be unreasonably withheld and the conditions attached to the Consent must be reasonable. Appeal lies to the Minister. Each Water Authority is required to maintain a register of Consents and conditions imposed on the discharge of effluent from land and premises in its area. That register, however, is not open for public inspection.

If a person acts in contravention of Section 7 of the 1951 Act, e.g., by beginning a new discharge without Consent or without complying with the conditions attached thereto, he commits an offence. The penalties are a fine of up to £200 for conviction on indictment and a fine of up to £100 on summary conviction.

A.3.6. Control of Pre-1951 Discharges to Rivers

Section 1 of the Rivers (Prevention of Pollution) Act 1961 makes it unlawful after the commencement of the Act to make any discharge of trade or sewage effluent which is not already controlled under the 1951 Act without the Consent of the appropriate Water Authority.

When applying for Consent the applicant must state:

  (i) the nature and composition of the effluent;
 (ii) the maximum temperature at time of discharge;
(iii) the maximum quantity which it is proposed shall be discharged in any one day;
(iv) the highest rate at which it is proposed to discharge the effluent.

In giving Consent the Water Authority may again specify conditions as to nature and composition, temperature, partial treatment, etc. Consent must not be unreasonably withheld and the conditions imposed must be reasonable.

The penalties for contravention of Section 1 of the 1961 Act are somewhat harsher than the equivalent penalties under the 1951 Act. The fine on summary conviction is the same, £100, but there is no maximum limit to the fine which may be imposed after conviction on indictment.

The Water Resources Act 1963 contains similar provisions controlling discharge of trade or sewage effluent to underground strata. The Consent of the appropriate Water Authority is made a pre-requisite to the lawful discharge of such effluent and a similar procedure for obtaining Consent is established.

The Control of Pollution Act 1974[19] purports to unify the above provisions relating to the discharge of trade and sewage effluent. It is believed that the provisions will be operative by the end of 1979. When the new Act becomes operative there will be no distinction continuing between pre- and post-1951 discharges; there is one offence of causing or knowingly permitting* trade or sewage effluent to be discharged:

* The phrase is that used under Section 2(1) (*a*) of the 1951 Act so discussion *re* mental element is applicable here too.

  (i) into any relevant waters, or
 (ii) from land in Great Britain through a pipe into the sea outside
      controlled waters, (i.e. the sea within three nautical miles from the
      coastline) or
(iii) from a building or from plant on to or into any land or into any lake,
      loch or pond which does not discharge into a stream. . . unless the
      discharge is made with the Consent. . . of the Water Authority in
      whose area the discharge occurs. . . and is in accordance with the
      conditions, if any, to which the Consent is subject.[20]

The penalties for committing the offence of discharging trade or
sewage effluent without Consent or without complying with conditions attached to a Consent notice are: imprisonment for up to three
months and/or a fine of up to £400 on summary conviction; and
imprisonment for up to two years and/or an unlimited fine after conviction
on indictment.

There is a similar procedure under the 1974 Act as already exists for
obtaining Consent to a discharge from the Water Authority. The main
changes will be as follows.

(i) Much greater publicity will be given to applications for Consent and
to the grant of Consents. On receiving an application for Consent the Water
Authority, before determining the issue, is given a duty to publish the
application in a local newspaper and in the London Gazette, to send copies
to the Secretary of State, the Minister of Agriculture and each local
authority in whose area the discharge is proposed to be made. The Water
Authority is also obliged to consider written representations relating to the
application made by any person within six weeks of the publication of the
application. This gives local pressure groups and individuals who may
object to the discharge an opportunity to air those objections. Further
publicity is achieved by requiring Water Authorities to maintain a register
of Consents and conditions which shall be open to inspection by the public
free of charge. It will even be possible for members of the public to obtain
copies of entries in the register on payment of reasonable charges. However,
the Secretary of State can grant exemption from the publicity if he is
satisfied that it would prejudice to an unreasonable degree some private
interest by disclosing information about a trade secret.[21]

(ii) Under the Control of Pollution Act 1974 the Water Authority will
have a duty to review from time to time the conditions attached to a Consent
and will have power to revoke it or vary the attached conditions. There is a
similar provision to that now existing under the 1961 Act that conditions
must not be varied within two years of a previous grant or variation.

It is not provided in the present legislation, nor is it contained in the Control of Pollution Act 1974, that discharge to a sewer or to inland waters in compliance with conditions attached to a Consent from the relevant Water Authority is a valid defence to a civil action in nuisance. So it remains possible that an industrialist discharging trade effluent in strict accordance with the requirements of the Water Authority, may still be held liable in damages for any substantial harm he causes to the property interests of his neighbour.

A.4. APPLICATION OF THE ACTS

The Public Health (Drainage of Trade Premises) Act 1937 and the Rivers (Prevention of Pollution) Acts 1951 and 1961 do not extent to Scotland nor to Northern Ireland.

The river purification boards have control over discharges to inland waters in Scotland and under the Rivers (Prevention of Pollution) (Scotland) Acts of 1951 and 1965 there is established a similar Consent procedure to that which applies in England and Wales. The river purification boards are given no powers of prosecution; that is the prerogative of the Procurator Fiscal. Under the Water (Scotland) Act 1967 regional water authorities have responsibility for water supply. The Control of Pollution Act 1974 does extend to Scotland to bring discharges of trade and sewage effluent to relevant waters under control. The offence of causing or knowingly permitting poisonous, noxious or polluting matter or solid waste to enter a stream or restricted waters also will apply in Scotland. The provisions controlling discharges of trade effluent to sewers do not extend to Scotland.

Control of pollution of inland waters in Northern Ireland is vested in the Department of the Environment by the Water Act (Northern Ireland) 1972. That Act establishes a control over discharges direct to inland waters similar to that which applies in England and Wales. The water provisions of the Control of Pollution Act 1974 do not extend to Northern Ireland.

A.5. CONTROL OF INLAND WATER POLLUTION IN EUROPEAN COMMUNITIES

Unlike the UK, the other member states of the European Community have no inflexible statutory limits on discharges of trade and sewage effluent or quality standards. Planning laws are widely employed to restrict the concentration of undertakings producing effluent in given areas and to control discharges from industrial concerns who do obtain planning permission. Control over water pollution appears to have developed in a haphazard fashion, being contained in a variety of laws relating to public health, agriculture, fishing, etc. Belgium introduced a licensing system similar to the UK Consent procedure in May 1974. Under that provision no effluent may be discharged to underground waters, surface waters or sewers except in accordance with a licence and the conditions attached thereto. The Federal Republic of Germany has a similar Consent control procedure but there all discharges may be prohibited within designated 'protection areas'.

In France, the six River Basin Financial Agencies fix standards of purity and impose charges for accepting effluent and for allowing abstraction of water. In Italy the regional presidents administer Ministry of Health Urban and Industrial effluent limits given in terms of acidity, colour, odour, temperature, BOD, COD, etc.

In Denmark, the Environmental Protection Law requires permission for any new discharge to surface waters or for the discharge of any polluting matter to underground water. The standards of purity and limits appear to be fixed, as in other member states, on a local basis, having regard to the requirements of a particular area.[22]

A.6. DISPOSAL OF SOLID WASTE

Civil liability may arise as a result of an industrialist depositing waste on his own land under the general principles of nuisance[23] or occupier's liability, if the waste creates a hazard to persons visiting the premises. The deposit of solid waste on land belonging to another is a trespass[24] unless the permission of the landowner is obtained and the person depositing the waste may be liable in damages.

Until comparatively recently there was little criminal liability to be risked by a person dumping waste. Apart from the specific offence of abandoning a motor vehicle 'or other thing' under Section 19 of the Civic Amenities Act 1967 and the provisions governing the deposit of alkali waste,[25] dumping of unwanted material was regulated only by the application for, and grant of, planning permission. It was common practice for the waste producer to pay and pass the headache of disposal on to commercial tip operators. The result was that there existed little central or authoritative control over the type of waste deposited on any given site. The dangers of cyanide waste dumping attracted public attention in 1971/2 and the Deposit of Poisonous Wastes Act 1972 was hurried through Parliament as an interim measure pending the enactment of more comprehensive legislation on waste disposal. That comprehensive legislation is now contained in Part 1 of the Control of Pollution Act 1974, most of the provisions of which are now operative.

A.6.1. The Control of Pollution Act—Solid Waste

The 1974 Act contains a reformulation of the law on the collection and disposal of waste by local authorities. It requires them to make comprehensive plans for the disposal of waste and to ensure satisfactory standards of disposal. The provisions cover 'controlled waste', i.e. household, industrial and commercial waste[26] but power is given to the Secretary of State to make regulations to extend the Act's provisions to other waste.

Control over the dumping of waste is achieved by imposing a system of licences. Section 3 provides—

'Except in prescribed cases a person shall not—
(a) deposit controlled waste on any land or cause or knowingly permit* controlled waste to be deposited on any land; or
(b) use any plant or equipment, or cause or knowingly permit any plant or equipment to be used for the purpose of disposing of controlled waste or of dealing in a prescribed manner with controlled waste, unless the land on which the waste is deposited or, as the case may be, which forms the site of the plant or equipment is occupied by the holder of a licence . . . which authorises the deposit or use in question and the deposit or use is in accordance with the conditions, if any, specified in the licence.'

The 'prescribed cases' are those excepted by the Secretary of State because the deposits are sufficiently small to be excluded or adequate controls already exist.

Sections 5–8 contain the procedure for the issue, variation and transfer of licences for waste disposal. A licence does not displace the requirement for planning permission. Both must be obtained. When considering an application for a licence, the disposal authority must take into account representations from a relevant Water Authority. A register of licences must be maintained which is open to inspection by members of the public. The

---

* The phrase is that used under Section 2(1) (a) of the 1951 Act so discussion *re* mental element is applicable here too.

authority can stipulate the kinds and quantities of waste to be deposited on any given site. the precautions to be taken and how the waste should be dealt with.

It is an offence to do any act in contravention of Section 3 which is punishable by a fine of up to £400 on summary conviction or by a term of imprisonment of up to two years and/or an unlimited fine on conviction on indictment. Higher penalties are provided if the deposit constitutes an abandonment of poisonous, noxious or polluting waste, the presence of which is likely to give rise to an environmental hazard. In these circumstances the penalties are imprisonment for up to six months and/or a fine of up to £400 on summary conviction or imprisonment for up to five years and/or an unlimited fine for conviction on indictment.

It is a defence to a charge under Section 3 that the defendant —

(a) relied on information from others that there was no contravention; or
(b) acted under instructions from his employer and was not aware of the contravention; or
(c) acted in an emergency to avoid danger to the public; or
(d) took all reasonable steps to ensure that the conditions specified in a disposal licence were complied with.

Apart from the licensing of controlled waste, the Secretary of State is given wide powers to regulate the handling and disposal of dangerous or intractable waste. He can require the giving of notice and the keeping of records concerning such special waste. He can take steps to prevent the accumulation of large quantities of such waste awaiting disposal and, where there is a risk of damage to persons, animals or vegetation, his Department can undertake the disposal.

REFERENCES

1. (1868) Law Reports 3 House of Lords Cases 330.
2. (1879) 11 Chancery Division 856.
3. (1893) Appeal Cases 691.
4. *Ibid.*, 698.
5. (1885) 29 Chancery Division 115.
6. See also *Tipping* v. *Eckersley* (1855) 69 English Reports 779; *Oldaker* v. *Hunt* 52 English Reports 439.
7. [1895] Appeal Cases 587.
8. *Pwllbach Colliery* v. *Woodman* (1915) Appeal Cases 634.
9. *Jones* v. *Llanwrst* UDC (1911) 1 Chancery 393.

10. Section 14 of the Public Health (Drainage of Trade Premises) Act 1937.
11. Section 2(5) of the Public Health (Drainage of Trade Premises) Act 1937.
12. Section 11(1) of the Rivers (Prevention of Pollution) Act 1951.
13. [1971] 2 All England Reports 357.
14. *per* Cooke J. at p. 358.
15. [1972] 2 All England Reports 475.
16. See commentary 1973 *Criminal Law Review* p. 41
17. [1975] 2 All England Reports 113.
18. Section 2(8) Rivers (Prevention of Pollution) Act 1951.
19. Part II Sections 31–56 of the Control of Pollution Act 1974.
20. Section 32(1) of the Control of Pollution Act 1974.
21. Section 42(I) (b) of the Control of Pollution Act 1974.
22. See J. McLoughlin, '*The Law and Practice Relating to Pollution Control in the Member States of the European Communities: A Comparative Survey*' Graham and Trotman Ltd, 1976.
23. See, e.g., *Maberley* v. *Henry Peabody & Co. Ltd.* (1946) 2 All E.R. 192.
24. See, e.g., *Kynoch Ltd* v. *Rowlands* [1912] 1 Chancery.
25. Under the Alkali Etc. Works Regulations Act (1906).
26. Section 30 of the Control of Pollution Act (1974).

Index